INTERNATIONAL TRACTS IN

**COMPUTER SCIENCE AND TECHNOLOGY
AND THEIR APPLICATION**

General Editors ; N. METROPOLIS—Chicago

E. PIORE—New York

S. ULAM—Los Alamos

assisted by an International Honorary Editorial Advisory Board

VOLUME 4

COMPUTING METHODS

CONFERENCE ON COMPUTING METHODS AND THE PHASE PROBLEM IN X-RAY CRYSTAL ANALYSIS, Glasgow, August 10-12, 1960

CONFERENCE PHOTOGRAPH

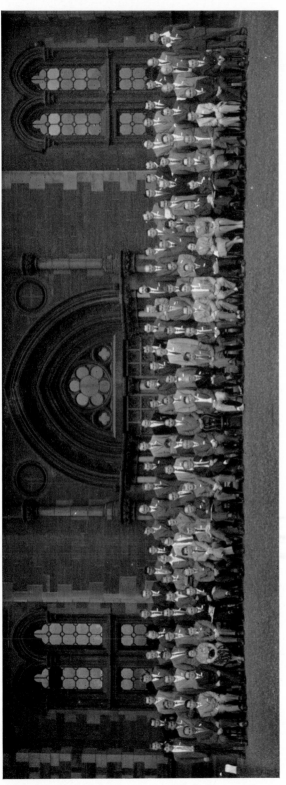

FRONT ROW (*left to right*)—H. Schemmel, Y. Iitaka, R. Sadanaga, K. Dornberger-Schiff, G. Walker, C. H. Carlisle, T. Hamor, G. A. Sim. P. Pauling, J. D. Dunitz, S. McGavin, J. Iball, V. Vand, I. Nitta, (J. M. Robertson). R. Pepinsky, J. C Speakman, D. W. J. Cruickshank, W. Cochran, W. N. Lipscomb, H. Hauptman, E. F. Bertaut, O. Kennard, J. M. Rowe, P. G. Owston, B. Richards, D. Rogers, W. A. Pillow, R. A. Sparks, H. A. Levy, A. Dennery.

MIDDLE ROW (*left to right*)—J. S. Wood, E. Hoehne, I. Olovsson, B. Matkovic, R. Dickerson, H. Jaggi, R. E. Rundle, D. P. Shoemaker, D. van der Helm. A. Åkeson, G. S. D. King, H. Muirhead, J. Ladell. F. H. Herbstein, M. G. Rossmann, G. Kartha, F. R. Ahmed, G. A. Jeffrey, H. Sörum, R. K. McMullan, I. Murray, M. Wells, A. Zalkin, P. Sutton, P. Tollin, J. Leech, J. S. Rollett, O. S. Mills, S. Ščavničar, A. Niggli, T. Löfgren, C. J. Brown, M. Woolfson.

BACK ROW (*left to right*)—A. T. McPhail, I. C. Paul, S. Bähr, W. Hoppe, R. Liminga, D. Feil, L. H. Jensen, E. C. Lingafelter, H. N. Shrivastava, C. L. Coulter, D. M. Blow, T. S. Wylie, B. Strandberg, S. Westman, S. Åsbrink, J. G. Sime, D. G. Watson, S. Sutherland, J. Trotter, G. Ferguson, W. Fuller, S. Arnott, J. L. Katz, D. A. Marvin, D. F. Grant, F. A. Kanda, H. Brumberger, J. S. Clunie, A. W. Davie, E. L. Drever, J. M. Cowley, B. Dawson, J. Wunderlich. G. Will, S. C. Abrahams. Y. Okaya.

COMPUTING METHODS
AND THE PHASE PROBLEM
IN X-RAY CRYSTAL ANALYSIS

REPORT OF A CONFERENCE
HELD AT GLASGOW
AUGUST, 1960

Conference on Computing methods ---

edited by

RAY PEPINSKY, J. M. ROBERTSON
AND J. C. SPEAKMAN

SYMPOSIUM PUBLICATIONS DIVISION

PERGAMON PRESS

NEW YORK · OXFORD · LONDON · PARIS

1961

PERGAMON PRESS INC.
122 East 55th Street, New York 22, N.Y.
P.O. Box 47715, Los Angeles, California

PERGAMON PRESS LTD.
Headington Hill Hall, Oxford
4 & 5 Fitzroy Square, London, W.1

PERGAMON PRESS S.A.R.L.
24 Rue des Écoles, Paris Vᵉ

PERGAMON PRESS G.M.B.H.
Kaiserstrasse 75, Frankfurt am Main

Library of Congress Card Number 60–53576

PRINTED IN GREAT BRITAIN BY BELL AND BAIN, LTD, GLASGOW

PREFACE

IN April, 1950, there was held at Pennsylvania State College a conference on "Computing Methods and the Phase Problem in X-Ray Crystal Analysis." Under this title the proceedings were issued in 1952 as a volume edited by Ray Pepinsky. In her introductory remarks, Mina Rees is there recorded as saying that, though one analogue computer (X–RAC) had already done—and was continuing to do—important work, the high-speed digital computer was "still just over the horizon." At that date, it was hard to predict exactly what part such computers were likely to play in crystal-structure work; and it was against this background that the 1950 conference was held.

The lapse of ten years has now seen revolutionary developments in electronic, digital computers and in their applications to crystallography. 1960 is therefore an appropriate year in which to have arranged a second conference on the same subjects. It was held in the Chemistry Department of the University of Glasgow during the three days, August 10–12, being timed immediately to precede the Fifth General Assembly of the International Union of Crystallography at Cambridge.

The present book, which bears the same title as its predecessor of 1950, contains the papers delivered at Glasgow and, in an Appendix, an edited version of the discussions that followed the reading of those papers. Inevitably some of this material is of a kind that quickly becomes out-of-date; but the book fairly reflects these problems as they appear in 1960. Should a third decennial conference be held in 1970, "volume III" of the series will certainly chronicle hopes and achievements that still lie far over our present horizon.

Our conference was supported by grants received from the University of Glasgow, from Imperial Chemical Industries Limited, and from Research and Control Instruments Limited. We wish to record our thanks to these organizations, as well as to the numerous individuals who helped us in many other ways—notably Dr. J. G. Sime for assistance in correcting the page-proofs of this Report.

RAY PEPINSKY
J. M. ROBERTSON
J. C. SPEAKMAN

Chemistry Department,
The University,
Glasgow, W.2
September 9th, 1960

v

NOTE

Because of circumstances beyond the control of the authors of Papers 15 and 28 of this volume, those papers were submitted in preliminary form and too late for pre-printing for the Conference, and could not be completed or corrected in time for publication. Paper 15 is printed in part only. The authors concerned offer their deep apologies for this. Complete, corrected copies of these two papers are available without cost from Prof. R. Pepinsky, Crystal Research Laboratory, Department of Physics, The Pennsylvania State University, University Park, Pennsylvania, U.S.A.

CONTENTS

vii

Paper 1

ZEBRA AND THE CRYSTALLOGRAPHER

by D. ROGERS

Physics Department, University College,
Cathays Park, Cardiff

ABSTRACT

The features of the Stantec Zebra Mark I are discussed and a review is offered of the state of its crystallographic repertoire in May, 1960. It is shown that although on paper Zebra appears to be handicapped by the smallness of its immediate-access store, yet this is satisfactorily offset by other machine features, and that it is able to hold its own very well with other apparently more powerful medium-sized machines. Some remarks are also included on the suitability of the new Mark II for crystallography.

ZEBRA is a medium-sized computer engineered by Standard Telephones and Cables Ltd. to a novel logical design due to Dr. L. van der Poel of the Netherlands P.T.T., and there are now 30 of them in operation. It was specifically designed for mathematical and scientific work, and for convenience has been designed to operate in two distinct modes, Normal or Machine Code and Simple Code, both of which have been used for the crystallographic programs discussed later.

Normal code is a flexible, fixed-point method of programming which allows of a high effective speed of operation provided optimization is carried out. In this mode approximately 7350 drum locations are available.

Simple code is a versatile interpretive 1-address code in which optimization is neither needed nor possible. In this code all arithmetic operations are in floating point (33-bit accuracy in the mantissa) and average 35 msec. Approximately 2500 " simple-code locations " are available, each comprising two drum locations. Programming in this code is extremely easy.

Sample times for each code are:

	N-code	S-code
Addition	312 μsec	40 msec
Multiplication	11 msec	35 msec

Input and output are normally by 5-hole paper tape; input being in a special code, and output in International teleprinter code.

ZEBRA is a serial machine, having a word length of 32 + 1 bits with an

1

extra 7-bits gap between words, making a total word time of 312 μsec. The machine incorporates 2 accumulators, 12 immediate-access registers (in the form of regenerative 1-word drum loops), 12 functional registers (associated with constants, logical operations and input and output organs), and a main drum store of 8192 words and mean access time of 5 msec. The machine is constructed to make access to the drum efficient. All switching of trackheads (256 of them) is effected by transistors in the 7-bit gap between words, and there is no paralysis time. Thus the same head can be used for reading and writing operations in consecutive word times if necessary.

In Normal-code operation the functional part of the instruction comprises 15 independent digits each having a distinct logical function and any or all of the fifteen can be used together. Each instruction controls the simultaneous movement of several items of information, and it is thus possible to compress within a single instruction what would take several orders on other medium-sized machines. The normal rate of execution is one instruction in every word time (312 μsec), and by reason of the distinctive logic of the machine it is possible to arrange for longish spells of " underwater programming," i.e. strings of instructions which are synthesized within the machine and executed at maximum speed—but are initiated by only a few orders.

In order to reduce the complexity and cost of the machine multiplication and division are carried out programwise, and the sub-routines for these are good examples of underwater programming. Both operations can, however, be interrupted at any point along the multiplicand (or dividend) and this has been put to frequent use in the crystallographic programs.

Fifty char/sec punches are the standard means of output, and there is an on-line teleprinter which can be used for output of calculated results or critical results, but is usually reserved in the crystallographic programs for comments, progress indications and notification of errors.

A valuable accessory is a telephone dial which allows the rapid insertion of occasional data in decimal form, and rapid access to dialled addresses.

The crystallographic users of ZEBRA are linked by a special subsection of the ZEBRA club of which the author is Secretary, and it has been our aim to develop the crystallographic repertoire as efficiently as we can and according to a common scheme of interchangeability wherever possible. We have aimed too to " clothe " the programs with comments and safeguards and to provide such detail as to the program and emergency procedures that they can be run efficiently by non-crystallographers. This is certainly true at present of all programs that have reached status A—except for the least squares refinement program, with which we are still experimenting to see how far we can build crystallographic judgment into the program. Bureau work is therefore perfectly possible and is rapid especially if the hirer can supply ready-made data tapes.

ZEBRAS are available on a bureau basis at the following S.T.C. centres and at the hourly rates mentioned.

Newport
Southgate (London) } £20 (special rates to academic users).
Johannesburg
Sydney
Montreal

Some private ZEBRA installations are also occasionally able to accept this work.

The principal contributors to the ZEBRA crystallographic club are

Dr. J. C. Schoone	Utrecht
Dr. D. W. Smits	Groningen
Professor P. de Wolff *et al.*	Delft
Drs. J. D. Neethling and van Niekirk	Pretoria
Dr. D. Rogers *et al.*	Cardiff

There are also several others who use the programs, but who are not yet in a position to contribute new programs.

THE CRYSTALLOGRAPHIC REPERTOIRE OF ZEBRA
(May 1960)
1. Fourier summation and allied programs

ZK1   (Written by J. C. Schoone and D. W. Smits in Normal code.) This is a general 2- or 3-dimensional program for either centro- or non-centrosymmetric space groups. All problems are treated as if they were $P1$ or $P\bar{1}$, i.e. data for half a zone or hemisphere must be stored.

The maximum number of terms that can be accommodated is about 2650 and they must be stored in a certain optimum order if the full speed of the program is to be realized. The first, second and third summations are taken in turn over the indices H_1, H_2, H_3 and whatever the relation between these and the indices h, k, l the program will annotate the output correctly and fully. The magnitudes of H_1 and H_2 must be less than 128 and H_3, which is never negative, must be less than 64. The F's are input as integers (< 512), but there is nothing to prevent a term being entered several times to make up an extra large F.

The coordinate mesh is in 256ths, the interval, starting and finishing points all being specifiable.

The output rate (if terms are in optimum order) is about 1 point per second, and on large jobs the time taken for the first and second summations are dwarfed by the third summation and output. For the job specified (30 sections, each 30×60 points and 1000 independent reflections in a monoclinic space group) the time taken would be 15 hours.

ZK2 (Written by D. W. Smits in Normal code.) This is similar in every respect to **ZK1**, except that it is written for centrosymmetric data only and can accept about 5500 terms with amplitudes not exceeding 32,767. The speed is similar to that of **ZK1**.

Both programs make thorough checks on the input data and the output format is fully annotated. Several auxiliary programs (**ZK3, 4, 5, 6**) (some in Normal code and some in Simple code) exist for preparing the data tapes for **ZK1** and **2**, making use of data punched in a very brief fashion, but it has not been thought advisable to incorporate this simplified input into the main programs as it does not offer the thorough safeguards on the input that we insist on.

Non-integral Miller plane sections are possible only if parallel to one axis and only by special tricks.

Fourier programs designed specifically for special symmetries are planned. These programs are likely to gain considerably in speed and capacity when used in the new Mark II machine.

ZK10 (Written by J. C. Schoone in Normal code.) This is a 2-dimensional Buerger-minimum program which utilizes the output from **ZK1** or **2** if the latter has been computed for half the cell area. If the cell subdivisions are $2^m \times 2^n$ the maximum size of Patterson that can be handled has $m + n = 13$.

2. Structure factor and least squares programs

ZK20 (Written by M. Shimshoni and D. Rogers in Normal code.) This makes use of stored tables of trigonometric functions (sine and cosine packed together in one word and covering $0 \to 2\pi$), exponentials and f's. It is currently available for $P2_12_12_1$, $P2_1/c$, $P1$ and $P\bar{1}$, but others can be readily prepared by replacing a short space group insert. At present it caters only for isotropic thermal motions. There is no limit to the number of reflections it can handle. It can accommodate about 150 atoms of the asymmetric unit (depending on the number of f tables to be stored).

The program is designed for rapid work in the initial stages of refinement, so the output has been limited to:

$$h, k, l, A, B, |F_c| \text{ (or } F_c \text{ only if centrosymmetric).}$$

No attempt is made to interpolate when reading from the tables, so these have been quoted at fairly fine intervals—sufficiently small to keep errors in R to about 1 or 2%.

As an example of its speed, 17 atoms per asymmetric unit in $P2_12_12_1$, 2 f tables and 3 sorts of B's, calculation and output took 1·0 sec per reflection. 1000 independent F's for 10 atoms in $P2_1/c$ would take between 15 and 20 minutes.

A modified version, sacrificing some speed in order to cover all space groups in the triclinic, monoclinic and orthorhombic systems, is in preparation.

ZK21 (Written by D. W. Smits in Normal code.) This also makes use of stored tables but at finer intervals than **ZK20**, and values of the exponentials and f's are interpolated. This is rather slower than **ZK20**, and we often loosely distinguish them as the " accurate " and " fast " programs respectively. There is again no limit to the number of terms, and this time the F_o data are read as each term is tackled.

Output includes:

$$h \ k \ l \ \sin^2\theta/4\lambda^2 \ A_c \ B_c \mid F_c \mid A_o \ B_o \mid F_o \mid$$

and at the end, $\Sigma \mid F_c \mid$, $\Sigma \mid F_o \mid$, $\Sigma\Delta F$, R and a new scaling factor.

As an example, 8×3 atoms/cell in $P42_1c$ took less than 3 seconds per F. 1000 independent F's for 10 atoms in $P2_1/c$ would take about 90 minutes.

ZK22 (Written by J. C. Schoone in Normal code.) This is a least squares refinement program which is running, but is possibly still not in its final form. At present it caters for $P1$ and $P\bar{1}$; Pc, $P2/c$, $P2_1/c$, Cc, $C2/c$; and $P2$ and $P2_1/m$ for both b and c axes unique. It normally handles about 2100 terms and 81 atoms, but for every atom less or more, add or subtract 32 extra terms.

It uses the diagonal terms only and refines the scale of F_o, the atomic coordinates, and mean or individual isotropic B's. It does not tackle anisotropic B's and at present no E.S.D.'s are computed.

The machine time for one cycle of 1000 reflections and 10 atoms in an asymmetric unit of $P2_1/c$, and for refinement of both coordinates and B's would be about 75 minutes.

3. Programs for molecular geometry and related topics

These were all written by D. Rogers in Simple code.

ZK30 Bond scan. Provides a scan of all interatomic distances within a specified list of atoms in any unit cell, and outputs the " bond " length if it is less than a specified length together with the reference numbers of the atoms concerned. For a molecule of 17 atoms, 18 bonds ($\leqslant 2$ Å) were found and output in 3 minutes. The program can also output the coordinates referred to axes parallel to

$$\mathbf{a}^*, \mathbf{c} \times \mathbf{a}^*, \mathbf{c},$$

and scaled in Å, but this output was suppressed in the above example.

ZK31 Contacts scan. Similar to **ZK30**, but searches for and outputs all intermolecular contacts less than a specified distance.

Neighbouring molecules are specified by a simple code related to the standard notation of symmetry relations. This consists of six signed integers. The first, third and fifth are 24 times the translation components parallel to a, b, c; while the others are code numbers as under:

$$\pm 0 \quad \pm x \quad \pm y \quad \pm z \quad \pm (x - y)$$
$$\pm 0 \quad \pm 1 \quad \pm 2 \quad \pm 3 \quad \pm 4$$

Thus $1 - y$, $\frac{1}{4}$, $\frac{1}{2} - z$ would appear as

$$+ 24 - 2 + 6 + 0 + 12 - 3.$$

ZK32 Molecular geometry. This is a comprehensive program for measuring up molecules and structures. It converts all coordinates to orthogonal axes scaled in Å (as mentioned for the bond scan), determines the bond lengths and direction cosines of all bonds in a list (each being specified by a pair of atom reference numbers), outputs the valence angles between specified pairs of bonds, and finally will evaluate the direction cosines and intercept of the normal to a specified plane—as well as the distances of specified atoms from this plane. The planes can be specified either by 3 atoms, 2 atoms and a best fit to 2 or more others, 1 atom and a best fit to 3 or more others—or a best fit to 4 or more atoms. There are no restrictions on the specification of these atoms, and in consequence there is complete flexibility in specifying a series of such planes. Example of speed: For a 17-atom structure, 32 " bonds," 23 angles, 5 planes; the time required was 11 minutes.

ZK35 A program tabulating for the triclinic lattice of nylon all the amide dipole–dipole interactions out to a specified radial distance from one dipole taken as origin. Output consisted of the lattice and polar coordinates of each dipole together with the interaction energy. For a radial limit of 40 Å, 1750 dipoles were found in a total of $3\frac{1}{2}$ hours.

ZK36 (Author D. W. Smits.) A program for evaluation of Madelung constants. In preparation.

4. Programs for powder work

ZK50 (Written by B. W. Delf in Simple code.) Evaluates d's from given unit-cell data. Separate versions have been written for each of the crystallographic systems. All d's out to a specified limit are output, but there is no provision for the suppression of systematic absences. Output at about 0·8 to 1·0 sec per spacing.

ZK51 (Written by P. de Wolff *et al.* in Normal code.) A program based on de Wolff's scheme for recognizing zones of reflections in powder data from substances with unknown unit cells.

ZK52 (Written by P. de Wolff *et al.* in Simple code.) A program for evaluating Q values from lattice constants.

ZK53 (Written by P. de Wolff *et al.* in Simple code.) A program for calculating reciprocal lattice constants from indexed Q values by least squares analysis. (No details are available for the last three programs, but all are complete.)

ZK54 (Written by J. D. Neethling in Normal code.) A program for the Stokes correction of line profiles for instrumental broadening. It takes both the observed profile and the instrumental broadening function at regular intervals (not exceeding 500 ordinates for each). $F(t)$ is evaluated for $t = 0 - (0.2) - 2 - (1)$—specifiable limit of t. The speed is approximately $70n$ msec for each value of t, where n is the number of entries in each list of ordinates.

5. Sundry programs

Tables of $4\sin^2\theta$ (to 5 decimal places) and their differences have been evaluated for $\theta = 0° - (0.01) - 90°$. (B. W. Delf and D. Rogers in Simple code.)

Other programs have been written for odd points in precision X-ray diffractometry and the design of a precision diffractometer. (D. Rogers, Simple code.)

A program (by D. W. Smits in Simple code) exists for the calculation of single-crystal 2-circle settings for crystals in $C2/c$ and provides other geometrical data for each setting.

A program for one-dimensional Fourier transformation is being written by D. Rogers in Normal code.

At present our biggest weakness is in the absence of any programs for processing the raw intensity data, but we hope to have one for Lorentz-polarization correction, another for absorption corrections, and a third for Wilson's method of scaling written this autumn. A program for direct structure analysis using triple sign relations is also planned for late this year.

ZEBRA MARK II

The first model was exhibited at Olympia in May, 1960, and although no crystallographer has so far used it, some comments can be made as to its bearing on crystallographic work.

It does not differ from the Mark I in basic logic and indeed all programs written for Mark I will run on the Mark II (though the reverse is not necessarily true).

It is transistorized throughout and is equipped with more comprehensive checking facilities. It has a new self-checking 7-channel paper tape code which is common to input and output.

It is designed to function as the nucleus of a flexible system that can be built up to suit individual needs and these supplementary facilities make it a very formidable system indeed. Thus, magnetic tape stores, ferrite stores, and card or tape readers can be added. The Creed 3000 punch can also be used with it.

But the most important developments within the computer itself are:

(1) the optional provision of a multiplier capable of generating a full double-length product in 3 word times (936 μsec instead of 11 msec), and also of normalization in 3 word times, and can be used as two independent accumulators,

(2) blocks of ferrite buffer store for input and output channels, and for drum transfers,

and (3) up to 8192 words of ferrite computing storage in blocks of 512.

The increases in speed and capacity, and the stiffer checking are all likely to benefit crystallographers considerably. In particular, the greatly increased immediate-access storage will relieve us almost entirely of the need to optimize our Normal code programs, with a consequent reduction in programming effort and time.

In conclusion I should add that almost all the above programs were written during the last two years and as more machines are installed we expect the number of contributors and their combined output to increase.

There are some difficulties in the writing of Normal code programs, it is true, but they have been much exaggerated (the present list is testimony to this) and it is evident from the speeds recorded above that where the labour of optimization is justifiable it pays handsomely.

The Simple code is especially useful in general scientific work for the ease, flexibility and speed of its code, and has proved invaluable for checking the logic of some intricate flow diagrams which are later to be written in Normal code, and convenient too in view of the ease with which sections of old programs can be transferred to new ones. It should be added that both Normal and Simple codes can be interwoven within the one program.

Thus ZEBRA in both its codes has shown itself to be well suited to serious crystallographic work and to compare very favourably with machines twice its price or more.

As a machine it is compact, trouble-free and economical to run, and, by reason of its simple logic, very easy to service. Both its purchase price and its rental are modest, and either should commend itself to the crystallographer. The Mark II looks a particularly promising development as it can be extended to match the growth of our needs in the next decade.

Paper 2

SOME EXPERIENCES WITH THE
BULL GAMMA 3B-AET COMPUTER

by HERMANN JAGGI

University of Berne, Switzerland

The Gamma 3B–AET computer, made by Compagnie des machines Bull à Paris, belongs to the group of medium-size machines as, for example, IBM 650. It has a storage capacity of 8192 words on a magnetic drum (divided into 64 channels with 8 blocks of 16 words each) making 2750 r.p.m. The average access time is 10 msec. It is used to store information which it receives from and transmits to the small high-speed memory (4 groups of 16 magneto-striction memories with an average access time of 85 μsec for each memory). The arithmetic unit provides additional 6 high-speed memories (the so-called " normal memories ") for computing purposes.

Each of the 12 decimal places of a word are separately represented in the normal binary manner (4 bits for a decimal digit, i.e. 48 bits for a word). For program purposes, however, the unused binary digits from 10 to 15 are used, too. In direct programming a word may be split and it is possible to work with single decimal or even binary digits (variable word length). Calculations in the arithmetic unit are normally performed on a decimal basis, but the machine may be switched over to pure binary calculating for modifications of addresses and instructions. Additions and subtractions take 0·5 msec, multiplications and divisions 10 msec on the average.

For our crystallographic work we do not use the direct programming method, but we make use of AP–2, an automatic programming system with the choice of symbolic or pseudosymbolic address-indication. Here the numbers are represented in floating decimal with sign. The 12 decimal places of a word are split up into a sign, 9 significant decimal digits, and two decimal digits to indicate the position of the decimal point (exponent). In AP–2 a lot of sub-routines are built in and may be called up with a single instruction, e.g. the trigonometric functions, square roots, e-functions and logarithms, etc. If plans are made a little bit in advance, it is possible to use a block of instructions without modification in many different calculations, e.g. Lorentz and polarization factor, multiplicity factor, etc.

9

Though the AP–2 programming system is very easy to use it has the big disadvantage of being quite slow, and furthermore it does not make best use of the high-speed memory. There exists, therefore, another programming system PAM for matrix operations which does make better use of the high-speed memories and is very easy to program. The formulas used for Fourier syntheses in crystallographic work can be expressed as a series of matrix operations. This method was suggested to us by Prof. W. Nef, Head of the Department of Applied Mathematics at the University of Berne. Each section through the three-dimensional electron density is then represented by a matrix. The dimensions of this matrix depend on the symmetry and the subdivision of the cell. A division into 60 parts each yields in the asymmetric case a matrix of 61×61. The handling of such big matrices might be near the capacity of our machine or even exceed it, but it is pretty easy to " get by " with 31×61. The necessary matrices have to be set up in advance. This is best done by an AP–2 program. In three dimensions the procedure is as follows: First the $F_{hkl}.\cos \alpha$'s and $F_{hkl}.\sin \alpha$'s have to be arranged in as many matrices as there are different indices in the direction perpendicular to the plane of section. In the two other directions the trigonometric functions have to be computed and arranged as matrices of the respective indices and axes. The trigonometric functions for the first summation are introduced with the PAM program. This has to be done anew for each section. If a different treatment of some classes of indices hkl (e.g. $l = 2n$ and $l = 2n + 1$) is called for, different matrices have to be set up. Later the resulting matrices have to be added algebraically.

To illustrate the procedure I shall give some data on a calculation we did recently for copper hydroxide, space group $D_2^5—C222_1$.

The formula is:

$$\rho xyz = \frac{8}{V} \left\{ \sum_{l=0}^{6} \sum_{h=0}^{13} \sum_{k=0}^{3} \left(\overset{l=2n}{F_{hkl}} \cos \alpha \cos 2\pi ky \cos 2\pi hx \cos 2\pi lz \right.\right.$$

$$\left. - \overset{l=2n}{F_{hkl}} \sin \alpha \sin 2\pi ky \sin 2\pi hx \sin 2\pi lz \right)$$

$$\pm \left(\overset{l=2n+1}{F_{hkl}} \sin \alpha \cos 2\pi ky \sin 2\pi hx \cos 2\pi lz \right.$$

$$\left.\left. - \overset{l=2n+1}{F_{hkl}} \cos \alpha \sin 2\pi ky \cos 2\pi hx \sin 2\pi lz \right) \right\}$$

The first part

$$\sum_{l=0}^{6} \sum_{h=0}^{13} \sum_{k=0}^{3} \overset{l=2n}{F_{hkl}} \cos \alpha \cos 2\pi ky \cos 2\pi hx \cos 2\pi lz$$

looks as follows in matrix notation:

$$L'(A.H)$$

where L' is a z by l matrix of cos $2\pi lz$ for l even only

          H is an h by x matrix of cos $2\pi hx$

          A is an l by h matrix which is the result of $\sum\limits_{k=0}^{3} C_k F_k$

with $C_k = $ cos $2\pi ky$ (scalar) and F_k are l by h matrices of F_{hkl} cos α
           for $k = 0, 1, 2, 3$ and l even only.

In the x-direction points were calculated in intervals of $1/60$ up to $1/2$, in the y-direction in intervals of $1/20$ up to $1/4$ and in the z-direction in intervals of $1/30$ with the plus sign in the formula above to $1/2$ and with the minus sign from there on to unity.

    Because of a systematic extinction (*hkl* with $h + k = 2n$ only) there are only 128 observable reflections with Cu$_{K\alpha}$ radiation. There were 16 starting matrices, 4 each for l even F cos α, l even F sin α, l odd F cos α and l odd F sin α respectively. Starting with h, k, l, observed intensity and assumed positions of the 3 kinds of atoms $\frac{1}{2}$ hour was used to compute these F-matrices. The time to get the necessary 6 trigonometric matrices (one each with cosine and sine terms for h and x, l even and z, l odd and z) was 10 minutes. After the first summation 4 matrices are left. Eight matrix multiplications, some rearrangements and 4 additions or subtractions lead to one section of the electron density in about 15 minutes. Another 10 minutes were used to extract the final matrix in a form suitable to easy drawing of contour maps. So it was possible to calculate and print an additional section of the electron density every half hour, since trigonometric and F-matrices could be used again.

Acknowledgments
    Thanks are due to Prof. W. Nef and Dr. R. Hüsser who helped with this work.

Paper 3

SMALL-SCALE COMPUTERS IN X-RAY CRYSTALLOGRAPHY

by Alfred Niggli

Crystallography Dept., Swiss Federal Institute of Technology,
Zurich, Switzerland

1. GENERAL CONSIDERATIONS

1.1. Small-scale computers vs. large-scale ones

In our age of large electronic digital computers a discussion of small-scale computing devices may seem obsolete. An X-ray crystallographic laboratory may for various reasons, however, want to have some computing equipment of its own; as in such cases the cost usually imposes severe limitations, small-scale computers still have got a chance to be a valuable help. Furthermore, they become more and more important as a didactic tool for training students who, otherwise, often do not know what they really are calculating on a large-scale computer. So their discussion is justified even now, whereas the overwhelming and still growing importance of large-scale computers is stressed by the relative number of papers covering their field at this conference.

Of course, the relation between size and efficiency does not favour small all-purpose computers. The most interesting small devices are therefore designed for one special task, and it will be seen that they are found mainly in the family of analog computers.

1.2. Criteria for choosing a suitable computer

For purely economical reasons the amounts of work and expense should be reasonably balanced. Although this principle may roughly determine the over-all size of a computer, there are still many interacting and often mutually excluding qualities for which a compromise has to be found. The discussion will be simplified, if the main qualities by which a computer might be judged are summarized under three categories, viz. reliability, convenience and availability.

The *reliability* states how far the results of a calculation can be trusted.

In what follows, this concept will be taken so as to include the amount of information yielded; therefore the criteria coming under it are

accuracy of results;

density of points at which the resulting function is evaluated;

possibility of mistakes.

The *convenience* expresses the amount of time and effort saved. It is composed of qualities such as

speed of calculation;

work required for preparing input data and representing output data (scaling, maps, etc.);

versatility as to related problems (e.g. necessity of breaking down a problem in several parts for higher number of dimensions, higher number of terms in a series, higher density of points at which a function is to be evaluated, or different symmetry);

simplicity in operating (e.g. automation);

technical simplicity and reliability (need of trained personnel to keep the computer running).

The *availability* has a somewhat different meaning for a computer to be owned or to be rented by a laboratory. The following criteria come under it:

price for buying or renting, respectively;

if to be owned, possibility of construction in the laboratory or commercial availability;

if not owned, accessibility (location, waiting times).

Because of the complexity of these three categories, criteria often have to be specified in more detail: e.g. there are computers which make mistakes highly improbable but give only low accuracy, and vice versa. Furthermore, the individual qualities may interact in different ways; e.g. a fast computer may make up for lacking reliability, if the calculations are subdivided in parts of a length corresponding to the average time between two mistakes and repeated until two results are in agreement.

1.3. Comparison of some typical computers

For a given task, computing aids and computers may be plotted against the three categories of qualities mentioned in §1.2, in a manner analogous to a ternary phase diagram. This has been done in Fig. 1 for the case of Fourier summations.

As the three qualities under consideration do not add up to unity, a fourth variable should be required for the over-all scale. However, if only one property at a time is considered, the main features of the relationship are clearly shown, at arbitrary scales, in the qualitatively normalized diagram of Fig. 1. Three families of computers gather along different curves: calculation by hand (I), digital devices (II) and analog devices (III).

Because of the complexity of the three categories, the relative position of the computers may be open to discussion, according to the weight attributed to different qualities, e.g. the IBM 407 operated with Beevers–Lipson cards is much faster in summing Fourier series than the IBM 604; on the other hand, it is more sensitive to mistakes made by the operator in selecting the cards, and the IBM 604 is more versatile (it may be used for structure factor

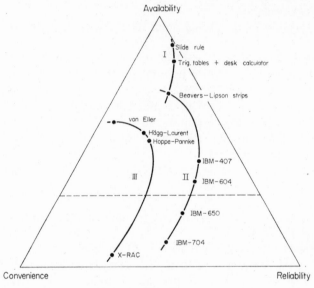

FIG. 1

calculations as well, and even for refinement calculations). Furthermore, some computers may be operated with different peripheral equipments, such as the IBM 704 which with cathode-ray tube display becomes more convenient, though less accurate, than X–RAC.

At present the large-scale digital computers have a strong tendency of increasing their availability; this is due to their more and more widespread use as well as to the growing variety of programs prepared. However, the following survey is restricted to the field above the broken line in Fig. 1.

2. COMPUTING AIDS AND SMALL-SCALE COMPUTERS

As has been pointed out in §1.1, the most efficient small-scale devices are specially suitable to one type of problems only, with the possible exception of small digital computers, such as IBM 407 or IBM 604. Therefore, in the following survey some typical computers are mentioned under different headings, corresponding to different computing problems in X-ray crystallography.

2.1. Fourier summations

Fourier (or Patterson) syntheses in two or three dimensions can be developed in one-dimensional summations; this has to be done in most cases, as already a device that would perform a complete one-dimensional summation instantly must provide for two arrays of variables, viz. the coefficients of the terms in the series and the values of the resulting function along a line. The basic difficulty of reconciling different qualities, such as accuracy, range of series terms and density of points at which the function is evaluated, at reasonable expense, is apparent already in the various modifications of the strip method.

Lipson and Beevers (1936) gave the cosine and sine terms at an interval of 6°, for indices up to 20 and amplitudes ranging from 1 to 99, on about 4000 strips; later, Beevers (1952) reduced the interval to 3°. On the other hand, Robertson (1936a, 1948a, 1948b) extended the range of the amplitudes to 1–999, at the same time restricting the index to the value 1; other indices had to be obtained by shifting the strips in a sorting board. Finally, the stencils described by Patterson and Tunell (1942) facilitated the reading of strips. Although the strips, combined with a desk calculator, are a big help for doing summations by hand, even the simplest analog devices are much more convenient; the accuracy of the Robertson strips, however, is surpassed only by digital computers, such as the IBM 407 mentioned in §1.3.

A one-dimensional digital mechanical device has been designed by Robertson (1954); it is remarkable for combining high accuracy (to 5 digits) with low cost, as only complete revolutions are counted and the backlash of its gears is neglected. As to *mechanical analog computers*, Vand (1952a) has described a two-dimensional " Fourier electron-density balance " consisting largely of Meccano parts, in which 140 terms are summed as torques and weighed. The one-dimensional " Fourier synthesizer " of Hoppe and Pannke (1956) is commercially available; the function is built up by adding one term after another and is represented by the position of markers on endless tapes at 25 points which may be taken as subdividing one whole, one half or one quarter cell edge. If the machine is well adjusted, its accuracy is superior to most electrical analog computers.

The most common one of the *electric analog computers* is the one-dimensional machine designed by Hägg and Laurent (1946). Adding up alternating potentials, the original model covered a range of indices up to 16 and after setting potentiometers and switches according to the amplitudes and signs of the sine and cosine terms evaluated the function at 60 points along the cell edge, selected by means of a multiple switch. Frank (1957) replaced the selector switch by more reliable telephone uniselectors, and Weber (1958) described a model in which direct potentials are added. Hägg machines for extended indices range and finer subdivision of the cell edge have been built in several laboratories. A different approach consists in generating the alternating potentials representing trigonometric functions by resolvers (selsyns). Shimizu, Elsey and McLachlan (1950) used a two-dimensional array of resolvers in the " Utah computer " to perform double Fourier summations; the one-dimensional resolver device " ODFAC " designed by Azaroff (1954) is commercially available, and later Azaroff (1958) has shown how two of his machines may be combined for two-dimensional calculations. A common feature of electric analog computers is the facility of automatizing the representation of output data, e.g. Pepinsky's large-scale analog computer X–RAC displays an undistorted two-dimensional contour map of the function on the screen of a cathode-ray tube.

The *optical analog devices* are particularly suitable for two-dimensional work; their limited accuracy is somewhat compensated for by high speed and convenience as well as by the fact that the two-dimensional function is evaluated qualitatively at the whole continuum of points. They are based on the idea of superposing the sinusoidal light-dark band pattern of masks as designed by Bragg (1929) and Huggins (1941, 1944); Howell, Christensen and McLachlan (1951) have shown a technically easier way of obtaining these patterns by out-of-focus projection of a master mask containing black-and-white fringes. The different masks representing the terms of a double series may be projected either in succession by a normal enlarger, or simultaneously by a multiple projector such as the one designed by McLachlan and Woolley (1951), where the array of point light sources, the masks and the image are arranged on three parallel planes. The most convenient device, however, seems to be the commercially available " photosummator " designed by von Eller (1955). One mask only, mounted on an optical bench, is used; by shifting it longitudinally, different projection scales and hence the various wave numbers are obtained, whereas lateral shifts allow for arbitrary phase angles. Moreover, a mark indicating the combined mask shift and film-holder orientation describes the position in two-dimensional reciprocal space. Therefore, by plotting a reciprocal net, placing the mark on the net points in succession and exposing according to the amplitudes, an undistorted picture of the function is obtained very quickly (a double summation with both indices ranging up to 20 takes about an hour). A different optical device, based on the " X-ray microscope " by Bragg (1939), has been described by Buerger (1950); it controls the phase angles by means of mica sheets. In the pictures yielded by any optical analog methods, the positions of even weak maxima of the function can be seen readily, and by superposing several copies of a picture with appropriate shifts with respect to each other, image-seeking product functions are obtained in a most convenient way. On the other hand, attempts to use the optical analog methods quantitatively, e.g. by densitometry of the films, do not seem to be promising in view of the many sources of errors inherent to the photographic method.

As has been pointed out, even small-scale *digital computers* such as the IBM 407 may be used for Fourier summations; for performing two-dimensional syntheses or blocks of three-dimensional ones in one step, however, the necessary memory capacity is provided only by medium or large-size electronic computers. As to small-scale computing equipment to be owned by a laboratory, the combination of a one-dimensional mechanical or electric analog computer (e.g. the Hoppe–Pannke or the Hägg machine) and a two-dimensional optical analog computer (e.g. the von Eller machine) seems to be very useful: in three-dimensional work, for a fast survey the first summation is performed mechanically or electrically, and the two-dimensional sections are evaluated optically, whereas when quantitative results are required, the whole synthesis is calculated on the one-dimensional computer.

2.2. Structure-factor calculations

In calculating structure factors, the usual approach consists in first evaluating the geometrical structure factors corresponding to point atoms and then modifying by scattering factor curves. The sum form (e.g. $\cos 2\pi(hx + ky + lz)$) and the product form (e.g. $\cos 2\pi hx . \cos 2\pi ky . \cos 2\pi lz$) are more suitable for lower and higher symmetries, respectively, the limit being about orthorhombic symmetry. Robertson (1936*b*) and Beevers and Lipson (1952) have shown how the strip method mentioned in §2.1 may be used for structure-factor calculations as well, and Alexander (1953) has designed special structure-factor strips suitable to the product form.

Of the more convenient *computing aids*, two typical ones will be mentioned. For sum-form calculations, the device by Radoslovich and Megaw (1955) is commercially available; it consists in a trigonometric table (2 digits, interval $2\pi/100$), the argument part of which may be shifted with respect of the function part. Similar devices with higher accuracy (e.g. 3 digits, interval $\pi/100$) are easily constructed, and Radoslovich (1955) has described a somewhat larger device called " SUMCOS," handling ten atoms at a time. For product-form calculations, the structure-factor slide rule by Fischmeister and Niggli (1960) is useful; it includes the multiplication by scattering factors.

Some of the *analog computers* mentioned in §2.1 may be used for structure-factor calculations as well: the Hoppe–Pannke machine evaluates a one-dimensional series of structure-factors for spherical or circular atoms with a constant electron density inside the atom boundary, and the von Eller machine with some auxiliary equipment yields a two-dimensional array of structure-factor signs at a time. Furthermore, several analog computers have been designed specially for structure-factor calculations. Vand (1950) described a mechanical analog computer of the tide-predictor type (24 atoms, 8 structure-factors per minute), and (1952b) a simpler device with gears, simultaneously evaluating 11 structure-factors for one atom. An electric analog computer using resolvers has been described by van der Walt (1956); it calculates two-dimensional structure-factors in the sum as well as in the product form. A larger machine built by Hellner (1956) handles ten atoms at a time and, by means of symmetrically coiled resolvers, avoids the necessity of using amplifiers. An optical analog device, the " photoelectric analyzer," has been described by Lipson and Taylor (1949); it superposes Bragg–Huggins masks (cf. §2.1) to a card with holes punched in according to the two-dimensional structure, similar to the ones used in the " optical diffracto-meter " (cf. §2.3), and performs the summation over the unit cell by focusing the transmitted light on a photocell. Finally, the optical analog devices performing Fourier transformations (cf. §2.3) may be used for structure-factor calculations, if the Fourier transform is sampled at reciprocal lattice points; the results are only qualitative, but a whole zone is covered at a time.

If small-scale *digital computers* are to be used for structure-factor calcula-tions, they must be able to do multiplications. E.g., this is the case for the IBM 604, but not for the IBM 407.

2.3. Fourier transformations and convolutions

As calculating *Fourier transforms* corresponds to the evaluation of structure-factors at points between the reciprocal lattice points, it can in principle be done on any one of the computers mentioned in §2.2, if a hypothetical crystal with large unit cell is assumed. The Hoppe–Pannke machine (cf. §2.1) may be used as well, for with minor changes it allows for non-integral wave numbers, at least for a discontinuous set of amplitudes. An optical analog device designed specially for calculating Fourier transforms in two dimensions is the " optical diffractometer " by Hughes and Taylor (1953). It combines features of the " X-ray microscope " and the " fly's eye " by Bragg (1939, 1944) and is commercially available, together with a pantograph punch for preparing the cards with holes representing the structure; its applications have been described by Taylor, Hanson and Lipson (1953).

The " versatile projector " designed by Philips and McLachlan (1954) is based on a device by Robertson (1943) and performs *convolutions*: by pro-jecting two images (holes punched in cards or photographs) of a structure at different scales from two parallel planes, the two-dimensional " theoretical Patterson function " is obtained in a third parallel plane.

2.4. Other computing problems

There are numerous other computing problems in X-ray crystallography, but as they are either less frequent (e.g. calculation of interatomic distances and bond angles) or very large (e.g. refinement calculations), no special computers have been designed for them. Many small computing aids, especially graphs, have been described for minor tasks, such as intensity correction for Lorentz-polarization-factors or for absorption. Although some refinement calculations can be done on small scale digital computers (e.g. the IBM 604), the modern tendency is to program larger electronic computers for all such purposes.

3. CONCLUSION

If computer time is to be rented, large electronic computers generally are more economical for two reasons:

Comparing a large computer (with magnetic core memory, such as the IBM 704) to a medium-size one (with magnetic drum memory, such as the IBM 650), the increases in cost and speed are of the orders of magnitude 10 and 100, respectively.

For reducing waiting times and avoiding interruption by other customers, a job should not take more than, say, one hour. This requirement tends to place the optimal size of a hired computer into the field of large-scale ones.

Furthermore, as has been pointed out in §1.3, the larger computers are becoming more and more available.

If on the other hand a laboratory is to have some computing equipment of its own, in most cases its limited resources will prevent it from buying a large-scale computer; besides, a large computer could never be fully employed even by a big crystallographic laboratory. Then the buying or building of small-scale computers is justified.

In choosing a suitable computer, the immediate need for calculations should not be the only guide: according to " Parkinson's law," the amount of work to be done will grow with the facility to do it. And as to designing new computing devices, it is to be hoped that the stream of ingenuity that crystallographers have put into this task, will not stop abruptly.

REFERENCES

ALEXANDER, L. (1953). *Acta Cryst.* **6,** 727.
AZAROFF, L. V. (1954). *Rev. Sci. Instr.* **25,** 471.
AZAROFF, L. V. (1958). *Rev. Sci. Instr.* **29,** 317.
BEEVERS, A. C. (1952). *Acta Cryst.* **5,** 670.
BEEVERS, A. C. and LIPSON, H. (1952). *Acta Cryst.* **5,** 673.
BRAGG, W. L. (1929). *Z. Krist.* **70,** 475.
BRAGG, W. L. (1939). *Nature* **143,** 678.

BRAGG, W. L. (1944). *Nature* **154**, 69.
BUERGER, M. J. (1950). *Proc. Nat. Acad. Sci. U.S.* **36**, 330.
VON ELLER, G. (1955). *Bull. Soc. Franc. Min. Crist.* **78**, 157.
FISCHMEISTER, H. and NIGGLI, A. (1960). *Acta Cryst.* **13**, 508.
FRANK, V. (1957). *J. Sci. Instr.* **34**, 210.
HÄGG, G. and LAURENT, T. (1946). *J. Sci. Instr.* **23**, 155.
HELLNER, E. (1956). *Fortschr. Mineral.* **34**, 56.
HOPPE, W. and PANNKE, K. (1956). *Z. Krist.* **107**, 451.
HOWELL, B., CHRISTENSEN, C. J. and MCLACHLAN, D. (1951). *Nature* **168**, 282.
HUGGINS, M. L. (1941). *J. Am. Chem. Soc.* **63**, 66.
HUGGINS, M. L. (1944). *J. Chem. Phys.* **12**, 520.
HUGHES, W. and TAYLOR, C. A. (1953). *J. Sci. Instr.* **30**, 105.
LIPSON, H. and BEEVERS, C. A. (1936). *Proc. Phys. Soc.* **48**, 772.
LIPSON, H. and TAYLOR, C. A. (1949). *Acta Cryst.* **2**, 130.
MCLACHLAN, D. and WOOLLEY, R. H. (1951). *Rev. Sci. Instr.* **22**, 423.
PATTERSON, A. L. and TUNELL, G. (1942). *Am. Mineralogist* **27**, 655.
PHILIPS, W. R. and MCLACHLAN, D. (1954). *Rev. Sci. Instr.* **25**, 123.
RADOSLOVICH, E. W. (1955). *Acta Cryst.* **8**, 456.
RADOSLOVICH, E. W. and MEGAW, H. D. (1955). *Acta Cryst.* **8**, 95.
ROBERTSON, J. M. (1936*a*). *Phil. Mag.* **21**, 176.
ROBERTSON, J. M. (1936*b*). *Nature* **138**, 683.
ROBERTSON, J. M. (1943). *Nature* **152**, 411.
ROBERTSON, J. M. (1948*a*). *J. Sci. Instr.* **25**, 28
ROBERTSON, J. M. (1948*b*). *J. Sci. Instr.* **25**, 216.
ROBERTSON, J. M. (1954). *Acta Cryst.* **7**, 817.
SHIMIZU, H. P., ELSEY, J. and MCLACHLAN, D. (1950). *Rev. Sci. Instr.* **21**, 779.
TAYLOR, C. A., HANSON, A. W. and LIPSON, H. (1953). *Proc. Roy. Soc. (London)* **218**, 371.
VAND, V. (1950). *J. Sci. Instr.* **27**, 257.
VAND, V. (1952*a*). *J. Sci. Instr.* **29**, 118.
VAND, V. (1952*b*). *Acta Cryst.* **5**, 390.
VAN DER WALT, N. T. (1956). *Rev. Sci. Instr.* **27**, 750.
WEBER, K. (1958). *Z. Krist.* **110**, 219.

Paper 4

A DIGITAL MECHANICAL COMPUTER
FOR FOURIER OPERATIONS

by J. Monteath Robertson

Chemistry Department, The University, Glasgow

The digital mechanical device mentioned by Dr. Niggli in the preceding paper, which generates accurate sine and cosine functions by means of special gear ratios, has now been in operation in the Chemistry Department at Glasgow University for several years under the code name of RUFUS. Demonstrations are being given during this conference.

The final version of this machine (see Figs. 1 and 2) differs in some respects from the preliminary description (Robertson, 1954). The simplifications outlined in the later paper (Robertson, 1955) have been incorporated. The completed machine has now only two banks of generators instead of two double banks. The ratios generated by the gears are the sines of the angles given in the body of Table 2 of the later paper (Robertson, 1955) and the arrangement is also given in that table.

In Fig. 1 the bank of sine generators is on the left, the cosine generators on the right, and the totalizer units with the output counters (visual instead of printing) in the centre. On the extreme left is the motor driving the sine generators, with the control switch in the foreground. Then follows seven rows of sine generators, each row corresponding to an even number (s) or an odd number (r) of the index h (see Table 2 of Robertson, 1955). In front of each of these rows can be seen the input counter and a vertical lever, which is used to push the row of generators into gear with the output shafts. The manner of engaging the successive rows of generators with the output shafts leading into the totalizers, and with the driving shafts from the motors at the extreme rear, has now been modified. Each row of generators is mounted on rails with guides for accurate positioning, and when pushed forward a set of specially cut sharp toothed bevel gears on the generators engage with a similar set of bevel gears on the output shafts. This simple mechanism works well. Engagement is usually immediate, and at most a slight turn of the hand control knob beside the input counter may be needed. Locking devices prevent disengagement and various electrical contacts ensure that the mechanism cannot be started until engagement of the gears is complete. Further details of the mechanism can be seen in Fig. 2, where the bank of cosine generators is exposed to view. The arrangement here is similar to that of the sine generators, except that there are now eight rows instead of seven, each corresponding to an even number (p) or an odd number (q) of the index h (see Table 2 of Robertson, 1955).

The purpose of the central bank of totalizer units is to produce the summation totals in four quadrants simultaneously, i.e. at θ, $180° - \theta$, $180° + \theta$, and $360° - \theta$, by forming the sums $p + q + r + s$, $p - q + r - s$, $p - q - r + s$, and $p + q - r - s$, where p, q, r and s represent the sums involving even cosines (i.e. with h even), odd cosines, odd sines and even sines respectively. This is achieved by employing two pairs of coupled differential gears as described and illustrated in a previous reference (Robertson, 1954). In the machine as now constructed, which has only two banks of generators instead of four, the totalizer units have been simplified by dispensing with the further coupled pairs of differentials at the ends of each unit and employing a reverse gear instead. (The central parts of the units, with their two coupled pairs of differentials, remain the same as already described.) The reverse gears are operated by pairs of solenoids situated at the ends of the bank of totalizer units (upper part of Fig. 2).

It is an important part of the mechanism that the shafts leading to the totalizer units should remain locked until one of the solenoids operates the gear shift mechanism. This prevents lost motion if, for example, the sine generators are being operated and the cosine generators are idle. Normally, both the sine and cosine generators may be operated simultaneously.

An essential feature of the mechanism as now constructed is that the same row of generators is employed for both odd and even values of the index h. For example, the eight rows of cosine generators are labelled 0, 2, 4, 6, 8, 10, 12, 14. By moving a slide, seen on the left of Fig. 2 just overlying the input counters, these numbers are concealed and the numbers 15, 13, 11, 9, 7, 5, 3, 1 appear in their stead. The movement of the slide at the same time switches the current from one solenoid to the other and reverse gears are thereby actuated on four of the shafts, in accordance with the scheme of sign changes shown in Table 2 of the earlier reference (Robertson, 1955). Similar arrangements are employed for the bank of sine generators, sign changes being made on three of the seven shafts in this case.

The present machine effects Fourier summations at the basic interval of 12° or 30ths of the cell side. However, summations at intermediate points, giving 6° intervals or 60ths, may be effected in accordance with the scheme previously outlined (Robertson, 1955) by running the machine through a second cycle of operations. To facilitate this work the indices of certain rows, where sign changes in the coefficients are required during the second cycle, are coloured red.

Another feature of the machine is that the range of indices of the terms employed is unlimited. Coefficients of all terms in the range $h = 16 - 30$ may be combined with the coefficients of the terms in the range $h = 0 - 15$ in accordance with the following scheme:

RUFUS

RULES FOR HANDLING TERMS WITH INDICES BETWEEN 16 AND 30

	EVEN intervals (i.e. 0°, 12°, 24°...)		ODD intervals (i.e. 6°, 18°, 30°...)	
	h EVEN	*h* ODD	*h* EVEN	*h* ODD
COSINES	ADD to (30 − *h*) i.e. 16 to 14 18 to 12	ADD to (30 − *h*) i.e. 17 to 13 19 to 11	SUBTRACT from (30 − *h*) i.e. 16 from 14 18 from 12	SUBTRACT from (30 − *h*) using sine bank i.e. 17 from 13 change signs if red
SINES	SUBTRACT from (30 − *h*) i.e. 16 from 14 18 from 12	SUBTRACT from (30 − *h*) i.e. 17 from 13 19 from 11	ADD to (30 − *h*) i.e. 16 to 14 18 to 12	ADD to (30 − *h*) using cosine bank i.e. 17 to 13 change signs if red

This machine has now been in fairly steady operation for a number of years and has given very satisfactory service in the course of a large number of two-dimensional crystal structure determinations. The driving motors, with variable speed controls, are capable of setting any two- or three-figure coefficient, positive or negative, in a few seconds. As soon as all the coefficients have been run in, the summation results are of course immediately available on the output counters. As only complete revolutions are counted, gear backlash can be neglected and numerically exact results are obtained.

At one time we had planned to build a larger machine designed for a basic interval of 7·2° or 50ths, with 13 rows of cosine generators and 12 rows of sine generators. Summation intervals would then have been 50ths of the cell edge direct and 100ths by means of a second summation cycle. Owing to the increased availability of fast electronic digital computers we have not proceeded with this development. However, the existing machine still plays a useful part in effecting small two-dimensional Fourier syntheses in this laboratory. It may be remarked that in contrast to electronic digital computers no programme writing or card punching is required, and as the operation is entirely mechanical there is very little time lost by faults. For larger syntheses, and especially in three-dimensional work, it does not, of course, compare in speed with modern electronic equipment.

I take this opportunity of expressing our indebtedness to Mr. J. Rae who has constructed most of the machine in its present form, and who maintains it in working order. Messrs. Barr & Stroud, Ltd., built the eight totalizer units with their differential gears, and I thank Mr. T. H. O'Beirne for many helpful discussions. The revolution counters were supplied by Messrs. English Numbering Machines Ltd. I also thank Miss S. Sutherland for preparing the illustrations.

REFERENCES

ROBERTSON, J. M. (1954). *Acta Cryst.* **7,** 817.
ROBERTSON, J. M. (1955). *Acta Cryst.* **8,** 286.

FIG. 1. General view of RUFUS.

FIG. 2. The bank of cosine generators with output shafts leading into the totalizer units with the output counters (top).

548   C76

c. 1   [5]

Paper 5

CRYSTALLOGRAPHIC COMPUTING
ON THE IBM 650

by G. A. JEFFREY and R. SHIONO

University of Pittsburgh, Pittsburgh 13, Pa., U.S.A.

and L. H. JENSEN

University of Washington, Seattle 5, Wash., U.S.A.

SUMMARY

Name and Maker of Machine: IBM 650 Electronic Data Processing Machine. International Business Machines Corporation.

Storage Capacity:
   Word: 10 digits and an algebraic sign.
   Magnetic Drum: 2000 words (20,000 digits)
                  4000 words (40,000 digits)

Optional Equipment:
   Magnetic Core: 60 words (600 digits)
   Magnetic Tape: Max. of 6 units
                  A tape reel contains the maximum of 25,043 of 80 digits records
   Disk Storage: Max. of 4 units
                  IBM 355 I   6,000,000 digits/unit
                  IBM 355 II 12,000,000 digits/unit

Input and Output:
   IBM 533   Card Read Punch Unit   (Input and Output)
   IBM 537   Card Read Punch Unit   (Input and Output)
   IBM 407   Accounting Machine   (Input and Output)
   IBM 543   Card Reader   (Input only)
   IBM 544   Card Punch   (Output only)
   IBM 46   Paper Tape to Card Punch   (Input only)
   IBM 47   Paper Tape to Card Printing Punch (Input only)
   Up to three input and output units of any combination may be used.

Calculating Time:
   Fixed Point Addition   0·672 msec
   Fixed Point Multiplication   2·496 ~ 19·584 msec
   Floating Point Addition   5·956 msec
   Floating Point Multiplication 4·800 msec

25

C

FOURIER SUMMATIONS

Written by	Application	Speed	Remarks	Machine requirement	Available
D. P. Booth (Bell Labs. Murray Hill, N.J.)	General projection and program for summing	$(H_1 \max + 1)(H_2 \max + 1) \leqslant 1581$ variable subdivision, with max. of 65 points in either x_1 or x_2.	100 terms in 15×15 grid ~ 10 min	Bell board	B	A
L. H. Jensen	General projection Fourier–Patterson difference	1/200th or multiple, centro-symmetric.	200 reflections, 1326 grids, 20 min	Special board $1 \sim 2$ passes	B	W
L. H. Jensen	Three-dimensional	1/1000th in one direction, 1/200th in other two	1st sum 20/sec + time for section	3 passes	B	W
A. Tulinsky (Yale Univ., New Haven, Conn.)	General projection	h_1 direction 1/1000th or multiple h_2 direction 1/100th or multiple		80-80	B	A
D. R. Fitzwater, D. E. Williams (Iowa State Univ., Ames, Iowa).	Three-dimensional	$h, k, l \leqslant 39$, 1/40th or 1/80th up to 1/4 of cell		Special board, expand on 402 or 407	B	A
E. E. Hellner, E. R. Wolfel, modified by R. Shiono	General projection and program for summing	$h_2 \max. \leqslant 99$ $(h_1 \max + 1)(h_2 \max + 1) \leqslant 976$, variable division of up to 1/250th	70 reflections, 30×30 grids ~ 13 min	80-80	B or I.C.T. with or without O	P

FOURIER SUMMATIONS—*continued*

Written by	Application		Speed	Remarks	Machine require-ment	Avail-able
R. Shiono	Three-dimensional, Fourier-Patterson difference	No limit on the first index to sum 1/60th or multiple in the first direction 2nd and 3rd summation uses the above program		80–80 The input is the output of SF program. Mono-clinic or higher	I.C.T. O (optional)	P
R. Shiono	Three-dimensional differential synthesis	Triclinic, monoclinic, orthorhombic (or higher)	$P2_1/c$ 1200 refl. $P2_12_12_1$ 600 refl. ca. 40 min/atom	80–80 9 derivatives	B also I.C.T.	P

LEAST SQUARES

Written by	Application		Speed	Remarks	Machine require-ment	Avail-able
M. E. Senko, D. H. Templeton	LS II. Orthorhombic or lower	Isotropic temp. factors 5 kinds. 20 atoms. Diagonal terms only. Standard deviations also calculated.	Approximately No. of atoms × No. of reflections in seconds	80–80	B	P

Structure Factor Calculations

Written by	Application		Speed	Remarks	Machine requirement	Available
D. Booth	$P1$	$f_i(hkl)$'s are needed for input, no temperature factor, 200 atoms		Bell board	B	A
R. Shiono	Triclinic, monoclinic, orthorhombic	Isotropic or anisotropic temp. factors 8 kinds, 50 independent atoms by one pass	$P2_1/c$, 9 atoms, 2 kinds, 3·5 sec/refl (2·1 sec/refl) $P2_12_12_1$, 7 atoms, 2 kinds, anisotropic temp. factor: 20 sec/refl, (10 sec/refl)	80-80	B also I.C. and I.C.T.O.	P
D. H. Templeton et al.	See Incor 1 and LS II	5 kinds of atoms, 20 atoms, isotropic		80-80	B	P
B. W. Brown, L. H. Jensen, E. C. Lingafelter, J. M. Stewart	$P1$ or $P\bar{1}$	Isotropic or anisotropic temp. factors. 8 kinds of atoms, 100 atoms, $P1$; 200 atoms $P\bar{1}$, by one pass	$P2_1/c$, 10 atoms, 3 kinds. Isotropic, 2 sec/refl., anisotropic 5 sec/refl.	80-80	B	W
A. Tulinsky	Two-dimensional, $\cos 2\pi(hx + ky)$ or $\sin$	49 atoms of 4 kinds, $\sin\theta$ required, isotropic temp. factors			B	A

MISCELLANEOUS PROGRAMS

Written by	Application	Speed	Remarks	Machine require-ment	Avail-able
A. Zalkin, R. E. Jones	Incor 1, data reduction of equi-inclination Weissenberg		80–80 preparation for LS II program	B	P
R. Shiono	Data reduction of equi-inclination Weissenberg		80–80 output is in-put for SF and Fourier	B	P
B. W. Brown, J. M. Stewart	Data reduction of Weissenberg and Precession	Weissenberg, 1·2 sec/refl. Precession, 1·4 sec/refl.	80–80 preparation for SF	B	W
A. Tulinsky	L.P. correction			B	A
A. Tulinsky	Conversion of trans-lational reciprocal lattice coordinates to spherical			B	A
B. W. Brown	Wilson Plot, scale and temperature factors		80–80	B	W
J. M. Stewart	Absorption correction		80–80	B	W

(Application notes: "Calculate $f(hkl)$ for 5 kinds"; "Principal or non-principal axis rotation"; "Monoclinic or higher"; "Orthorhombic or higher, requires 2θ value"; "Monoclinic or higher"; "Up to 8 different f's"; "Approximately rectangular parallele-piped-shaped crystal. Zero layer Weissenberg only.")

MISCELLANEOUS PROGRAMS—continued

Written by	Application	Speed	Remarks	Machine requirement	Available
D. E. Sands	Absorption correction	Crystal of constant convex-polygon cross section	80–80 zero layer only	B	W
D. H. Templeton	Interatomic distances	Any symmetry up to 20 atoms within 27 unit cells	$P2_12_12_1$, 8 atoms less than 4 Å 5 min 80–80	B	P
J. M. Stewart, E. C. Lingafelter	Bond lengths, angles, hydrogen coordinates	Generate hydrogen coordinates for tetrahedral chain, tetrahedral terminal, trigonal and linear bonds	80–80 Monoclinic or higher	B	W
R. Shiono	Distance and angle	Any symmetry, also for standard deviation of angle	80–80	B	P
J. M. Stewart	Least squares plane	Monoclinic or higher from up to 98 atoms. Also perpendicular distance to a plane	80–80	B	W
R. Shiono	Standard deviations of electron density, its first and second derivatives			B	P
R. Shiono	Anisotropic temp. factors from curvatures of differential synthesis	Based on Cruickshank's derivations, Acta Cryst. 9, 747 (1956)	80–80 2 parts	B	P

Programming Language:
  Basic machine code

Machine Features:
  Self checking automatic operations, ease of operation. Can be tailored to individual needs, because it can consist of varying numbers and types of units, up to a total of 31 units.

Normal Commercial Charge:
  $80/hour for basic 650

Abbreviations for machines used in following tabulation of programs:
  B   Basic 650 with 2000 drum locations
      One 533 Card Read Punch
  C   Magnetic cores
  D   Disk storages
  F   Automatic floating point arithmetic unit
  I   Indexing accumulators
  O   On-line 407 Accounting Machine
  T   Magnetic tape unit

Abbreviations for the source of Programs:
  A   from the author;
  P   from the University of Pittsburgh;
  W   from the University of Washington

Paper 6

CRYSTALLOGRAPHIC CALCULATIONS ON THE FERRANTI PEGASUS AND MARK I COMPUTERS

by D. W. J. CRUICKSHANK and DIANA E. PILLING
and in part A. BUJOSA, F. M. LOVELL and MARY R. TRUTER

School of Chemistry, The University,
Leeds 2, England

ABSTRACT

The Ferranti Pegasus I computers have 55 words of immediate-access storage, 4096 words on a magnetic drum and can have 10 magnetic tape units. Input and output is by punched paper tape. The time for fixed-point addition is 0·3 msec, for multiplication 2 msec. Nearly all crystallographic programs have been written in machine code, a few in Autocode. The commercial hire charge is up to £40 per hour.

The Pegasus SFLS program written at Leeds University handles all space groups. There are no program limitations on the maximum number of reflections. The possible variables are the $|F_o|$ scale, the average isotropic vibration, atomic coordinates, individual isotropic or six-component anisotropic vibrations. The matrices computed are a 2×2 for scale and average vibration, chains of 3×3, 1×1 and 6×6 for coordinates, isotropic and anisotropic vibrations. A standard allocation of storage space typically allows the refinement of up to 60 atoms isotropically or 25 atoms anisotropically. E.S.D.'s are computed. The approximate total times required per cycle of 1000 F's, 10 atoms, centrosymmetric monoclinic, are 100 and 130 minutes with isotropic and anisotropic vibrations respectively. An analysis of the appropriateness of the weighting scheme is given with each cycle.

The Fourier program written at Leeds University is for two- or three-dimensional syntheses and covers all plane and space groups. The maximum number of reflections allowed is approximately 10,000. The intervals of the coordinate mesh, which can be different in each direction, must be $\leqslant 1/120$ths. The machine time needed for 30 sections of 30×60 points for 1000 independent reflections in a centrosymmetric monoclinic space group is about 10 hours, including input and sorting of data and punching of results. The data can be input in a random order with any orientation of indices; they are then sorted into the order required for efficient computation. The method of calculation of the Fourier summations is very similar to that used with Beevers–Lipson strips.

Other programs written at Leeds include a contact-seeking dimensions program, one for the analysis of anisotropic vibrations in terms of rigid-body motions and one for the reduction of triclinic cells to standard forms.

Many programs for Pegasus have been written by other user groups (see §5).

The paper includes a discussion of the experience gained on the Ferranti Mark I computer.

32

1. BACKGROUND

1.1. Introduction

This paper chiefly describes the use of the Ferranti Pegasus series of computers for crystallographic calculations. Most of this description is devoted to the programs written at Leeds University by members of Professor E. G. Cox's crystallographic group, which have been used in numerous structure analyses. As these Pegasus programs were designed in the light of the rather considerable use which we made from 1952 to 1957 of the Ferranti Mark I computer installed at Manchester University, it is relevant first to describe some aspects of this work (§1.2) and the lessons learnt from it (§1.3). The Mark I programs are of some interest in themselves, first because they used the differential synthesis method for the refinement of structures, including anisotropic vibrations, and second because the uncommon method used for the structure factor calculations was particularly efficient for certain very large calculations.

A short description of the Pegasus computer is given in §1.4. Our comprehensive structure factor least-squares (SFLS) program for Pegasus is described in some detail in §2. §2.2.6, incidentally, contains some remarks on the correct formulae to be used in calculating E.S.D.'s in the LS method. Our comprehensive Fourier program, which uses the Pegasus magnetic tape system, is described in §3.

We have also developed a number of ancillary programs for crystallography, some of which are described in §4. An account of a dimensions program is given in §4.1; this finds and calculates all inter- and intramolecular distances and angles of interest, given the coordinates of the asymmetric unit. §4.2 describes a program for the analysis of the atomic vibration tensors U_{ij} in terms of the molecular rigid-body translation and rotation vibration tensors T_{ij} and ω_{ij}. §4.3 describes a program for the reduction of triclinic and monoclinic cell dimensions to unique standard forms.

A large range of crystallographic calculations has also been programmed for Pegasus by other user groups; some of these are summarized in §5.

1.2. Work on the Ferranti Mark I computer

1.2.1. *Introduction*

Our work on the Ferranti Mark I computer at Manchester University began in 1952 and continued to 1957. The one detailed description (Ahmed and Cruickshank, 1953) of this work which has been published covered only the early stages of the development of the program system, though brief reports of some of the later developments were given at the International Congresses in Paris and Montreal (Cruickshank, 1954 and 1957a) and at an

XRAG meeting in London in 1956 (summarized by Finch *et al.*, 1958). These programs also provided the basis for the generalized program system built up by Ahmed and Barnes (1958) on the other Ferranti Mark I computer, FERUT, at the University of Toronto.

The Ferranti Mark I computer (known at Manchester University as the Manchester University Mark II computer) was in operation from 1951 to 1958. It was probably the first serviceable computer to be built anywhere in the world which had both an adequate fast-access store and a large capacity magnetic drum. It was thus very well suited to crystallographic calculations. The fast-access electrostatic store consisted of 8 " pages " each of 32 " words ", while the magnetic drum had 512 tracks, each equivalent to one page, which gave a total capacity of 16,384 words or 655,360 bits. The single-address instructions were of half-word length and the whole instruction could be modified by the content of one of seven B-line registers. The actual computing was done with instructions or numbers taken from the fast-access store; addition or subtraction took 1·2 msec and multiplication 2·2 msec. The transfer of material to or from the magnetic drum took approximately 50 msec per track. Data were fed to the computer through a 200 character per sec photoelectric tape reader; output was much slower and was through a 15 character per sec punch or a 6 character per sec teleprinter.

Altogether we used the computer for work on about 40 crystal structures. This needed a total machine time of about 1750 hours, of which 1000 hours went on production runs, 500 hours on program development and some 250 hours were wasted due to machine faults. Most of the work involved the detailed refinement of relatively small structures by cycles of three-dimensional differential syntheses and structure factors, including, if required, anisotropic temperature factors. Considerable use was also made of two three-dimensional Fourier programs. One of these calculated the electron density directly in an arbitrary plane and adjacent parallel planes, and was used, for example, in the calculation of difference maps for the central molecular plane of anthracene (Cruickshank, 1956*a*, 1957*b*). The other was a relatively orthodox program for $P2_12_12_1$, which was written specially to achieve efficiency in the calculations on the wet vitamin B12 (Hodgkin *et al.*, 1957).

1.2.2. *Structure Factor Programs*

It would be of only antiquarian interest to describe the details of the programs developed by us for the Ferranti Mark I computer, but some aspects of the general tactics used are still valid. We will consider first the programs developed for structure factor calculations on wet vitamin B12, where the main problems arose from the size of the computations with over 100 atoms in the asymmetric unit and 2600 reflections and the consequent need for very efficient programming. $P2_12_12_1$ is a non-centrosymmetric space group so that both real and imaginary parts of the structure factors are required:

$$A(hkl) = \Sigma\, f_r\{ \underset{\substack{\text{indep.} \quad \text{equiv.} \\ \text{atoms} \quad \text{atoms}}}{\Sigma}\, \cos(hx_s + ky_s + lz_s)\},$$

(1.1)

$$B(hkl) = \Sigma f_r\,\{ \Sigma \sin(hx_s + ky_s + lz_s)\}.$$

As discussed by Ahmed and Cruickshank (1953), two computing schemes suggest themselves as possibilities, either to treat each plane separately by computing and adding the contributions of the different atoms to one plane and then repeating the process for the next plane, or to compute the contribution of the first atom to all the planes (or at least to a large set of them) and then to repeat for the other atoms, adding contributions to the running totals of each plane. The latter scheme is possible only on a machine with a large auxiliary store but then proves to be much faster if the data is in an ordered sequence.

In an orthorhombic space group for atoms with isotropic vibrations the method of computing the trigonometric contributions of the independent atoms is also very important. The choice lies between the addition formulae,

$$\underset{4}{\Sigma} \cos(hx_s + ky_s + lz_s) \text{ and } \underset{4}{\Sigma} \sin(hx_s + ky_s + lz_s),$$

(1.2)

where the summation is over the four symmetry related atoms, or the product formulae which, for $h + k$ and $k + l$ even, are of the type

$$(\cos hx_r \cos ky_r)\cos lz_r$$

(1.3)

and

$$(\sin hx_r \sin ky_r)\sin lz_r.$$

If the planes are arranged in batches with constant h, k and if tables of $\cos lz_r$ and $\sin lz_r$ (for all l) are prepared in advance, the basic inner loop in the computation of the trigonometric contribution of one atom to a sequence

TABLE 1

INNER LOOP IN $P2_12_12_1$ SF CALCULATIONS

(1) Pick up l.
(2) Place $\cos lz_n$ on multiplier.
(3) Multiply $(\cos hx_n \cos ky_n)\,(\cos lz_n)$.
(4) Add in $\underset{n-1}{\Sigma} \cos hx_r \cos ky_r \cos lz_r$.
(5) Store $\underset{n}{\Sigma} \cos hx_r \cos ky_r \cos lz_r = A$.
(6) Place $\sin lz_n$ on multiplier.
(7) Multiply $(\sin hx_n \sin ky_n)\,(\sin lz_n)$.
(8) Add in $\underset{n-1}{\Sigma} \sin hx_r \sin ky_r \sin lz_r$.
(9) Store $\underset{n}{\Sigma} \sin hx_r \sin ky_r \sin lz_r = B$.
(10) Test if next plane has same h, k.

of planes is simply the set of ten instructions shown in Table 1. On the other hand with the addition formulae (1.2), no specific tables of the trigonometric functions can be prepared and at least a linear interpolation is necessary in a general trigonometric table (a series expansion would be still slower). Some 18 instructions are needed for each atom and the process must be repeated three times to cover the symmetry related atoms. Consequently, the ratio of the times needed by (1.2) and by (1.3) is roughly 72:10. The product formulae (1.3) are thus much more efficient in an orthorhombic space group if the atoms are isotropic.

The conclusions led to a scheme for SF calculations for $P2_12_12_1$ very similar to that described by Ahmed and Cruickshank (1953) for $P2_1/a$. We have discussed the matter in a little detail here in order to show the efficiency of the method, which in fact enabled us to do SF calculations for wet B12 in times comparable with those required for other B12 crystals on very much faster machines. It was possible to improve the details of Ahmed and Cruickshank's scheme in a number of ways. For instance, in it the slowest operation was the interpolation in the tables of f against $\sin^2\theta$. Much of this operation was redundant, as a similar process had to be repeated for each kind of atom. The program was therefore revised so that the machine computed for each plane in advance the relative address (common to all atoms) of the appropriate entry in an f table and the fractional increment required in the linear interpolation formula. The actual evaluation of the f's during the main calculations was thus much simplified. As a result of this and similar improvements (especially the calculation of the A and B parts in the same process) the speed of the main computation was doubled.

1.2.3. *Control of Progress of Calculation*

On further experience the SF scheme developed by Ahmed and Cruickshank proved unsatisfactory in one respect. Their method was to compute a complete set of F_c and store these on the drum, and then to repeat the process, at the end checking the two sets for possible mistakes. If any were found a third and further complete sets were computed until two agreed. At first mistakes were few and this extravagant method produced results, but later much trouble was caused by computer errors. The method was clearly unsuitable for the lengthy calculations on B12. The SF scheme was therefore revised and brought under the control of a Master program, which was designed on the assumption that the computer would be unreliable. The program broke the whole calculation down into stages each lasting a few seconds, each of which was repeated until a complete check was obtained. The progress of the whole calculation was recorded by the Master program on a " score-board " stored on the drum, and the program was designed so that, in the event of the computer stopping or going out of control, a restart by the operator recommenced the calculation at the last stage which had been successfully completed. This method of controlling large calculations on a machine, which was very slightly unreliable and lacked any built-in automatic checks, proved entirely satisfactory.

In the cycle in which 105 atoms were placed in the asymmetric unit of wet B12, the SF calculations for 2600 planes required a total machine time of about $16\frac{1}{2}$ hours, of which 9 hours were for the calculations proper including their repeats and $7\frac{1}{2}$ hours were for the input and output of programs, data and results. The latter was inevitably tedious on a machine with a rather slow output punch.

1.2.4. *Fourier Syntheses*

The three-dimensional Fourier calculations for wet B12 with 16 sections each with 61×61 points also took about $16\frac{1}{2}$ hours. Some trouble was taken with the programming to ensure that the electron densities in the different quadrants were generated in an efficient manner. These methods have been more fully exploited in our Fourier program for the Ferranti Pegasus machine and are described in §3.

A Fourier program for the density in an arbitrary plane section, which was used for difference maps of benzene, naphthalene, anthracene and β-succinic acid, calculated the totals for the first two summations in the usual way with, say, x and y at successive increments of 1/60ths. In the third summation the trigonometric contributions were evaluated for the precise values of z which satisfied the equation of the plane for the appropriate incremental values of x and y.

1.2.5. *Refinement*

The refinement of atomic coordinate, scale and vibration parameters was achieved by differential syntheses. At each trial atomic position the program evaluated the density, its three first derivatives and six second derivatives. We speeded up the scheme described by Ahmed and Cruickshank by about 25% by evaluating at each position the totals from the F_o, F_c and ΔF series and checking that the differences of the first two agreed with the latter.

Differential syntheses were originally intended for the refinement of coordinates, with shifts computed from the differential totals by the equations given by Booth (1946). Experience with them on the computer soon showed, from the differences between observed and calculated peak heights, that the various atoms in a particular crystal often had appreciably different vibrational amplitudes. Further the values of the six second derivatives of the ΔF series showed that the vibrations were often appreciably anisotropic. A theory of the determination of anisotropic vibrations from differential syntheses was therefore devised (Cruickshank, 1956b). This required the setting up of sixth order linear equations, in which the right-hand side was the set of six derivatives just mentioned and the left-hand side was a matrix of quantities such as $\Sigma h^4 f$, $\Sigma h^2 k^2 f$, etc. Since great accuracy in these quantities was not required, it was sufficient to evaluate them once for each structure. Thus the differential synthesis method yielded a means of refining the anisotropic vibrations of atoms with only a small additional effort beyond that needed for coordinate refinement.

Some trouble was encountered with the oscillation of the shifts of vibration parameters in successive cycles and it was necessary to introduce " fudge factors " of 0·50 to 0·90 to obtain quicker convergence. It was suggested by Cruickshank (1956b) that this was probably due to certain effects of the accidentally absent reflections. This has been confirmed by Sparks (1958).

1.2.6. *Anisotropic SF*

The simple product formulae for structure factors are no longer applicable when the vibrations are anisotropic. Formulae of the product type may still be used however, but in an orthorhombic space group the usual single product has to be replaced by the sum of four products each multiplied by a different combination of exponentials (see, for example, Rollett and Davies, 1955). Because our isotropic SF programs were based on product formulae, we developed our anisotropic SF programs for the Ferranti Mark I computer in the same way, though our grouping of the exponential terms with the b_{ij} as parameters was rather different from that of Rollett and Davies.

1.3. Conclusions from experience on the Ferranti Mark I

The chief lesson we learnt from our experience with the Ferranti Mark I computer is easily stated. Since the volume of crystallographic computing is so great, it is much the most economical, in the long run, to design programs from the start to deal with every conceivable parameter in very large structures for all space groups. Inevitably our programs for the Pegasus Computer have fallen short of this ideal! In more detail the lessons we felt we had learnt were:

(a) Programs should handle all space groups and in an efficient manner. Our programs for the Mark I computer were written for particular space groups and though the originators of the programs could usually modify them quickly for similar space groups, it was decidedly troublesome for other people.

(b) By the end of our Manchester work, most structures were being refined with anisotropic vibrations, not only because the anisotropic vibrations were of interest in themselves and because the residuals were much reduced, but also because significant changes in the coordinate back-shift corrections often occurred. In the analyses of nitronium perchlorate (Truter, Cruickshank and

Jeffrey, 1960) and 1,2-diphenyl-tetrafluoroethane (Cruickshank, Jeffrey and Nyburg, 1959) reasonable molecular dimensions were not obtained until the anisotropic vibrations were considered. The refinement of anisotropic vibrations was therefore taken as essential in planning our Pegasus programs. On the programming side this meant that the arguments in favour of the product formulae for the trigonometric contributions to structure factors lost much of their force.

(c) Our experience with the differential synthesis method for refinement was very satisfactory. However, we decided to make a least-squares scheme our first program for Pegasus, partly to gain experience of the other method of refinement, but chiefly because the greater symmetry of the calculations makes an SFLS scheme a little faster than an SFDS scheme. Further the calculation of standard deviations is a trivial matter in SFLS, whereas it requires an additional type of calculation in SFDS. An SFLS scheme also allows new kinds of parameter to be introduced without seriously disrupting its general framework.

(d) In our Ferranti Mark I work coordinates were expressed as fractions of the cells and anisotropic vibration parameters as the dimensionless coefficients b_{ij} of the exponential

$$\exp\{-(b_{11}h^2 + b_{12}hk + \ldots)\}.$$

When following the progress of a refinement, we always found it essential to translate the fractional coordinate shifts into Å in order to judge the x, y and z shifts on an equivalent physical basis. Similarly no interpretation of the anisotropy of vibrations is possible immediately from the b_{ij}; the physically meaningful quantities are the components of the mean square vibration tensor in $Å^2$:

$$U_{11} = b_{11}/(2\pi^2 a^{*2}),$$
$$U_{12} = b_{12}/(4\pi^2 a^* b^*), \text{ etc.}$$

For our Pegasus programs the coordinates were therefore expressed in Å and the vibrations in $Å^2$, despite the slight disadvantages of the method for the coordinates of atoms in special positions. A further advantage is that overflow difficulties with the LS totals can be avoided, because these do not then vary much with the cell dimensions.

1.4. Description of the Ferranti Pegasus computer

About 30 Ferranti Pegasus computers have been built since 1956. They are medium-size computers of a well-balanced economical design. Essentially, a Pegasus has a magnetic drum store with just sufficient immediate-access store to allow rapid calculation and easy programming. The machine order-code has been particularly well thought out from the programmer's point of view.

Two models of Pegasus are available; of which Pegasus II is now the standard production model. All the crystallographic programs described in this paper were written for Pegasus I but they can be used on Pegasus II.

PEGASUS I

Pegasus operates in fixed point with a word length of $1 + 38$ bits for numbers; two instructions are packed into one word. The magnetic drum stores 4096 words together with 1024 words of " isolated " store containing input routines, engineers' test programs, etc. The immediate-access computing store consists of nickel delay lines, arranged in 6 blocks of 8 words each, together with 7 accumulators. Each accumulator can also be used to modify the address part of an order and, at the same time, to count the number of cycles of an operation. The time for addition or subtraction, etc. is 0·3 msec, multiplication is 2 msec and division 5·5 msec. Including access time, the average time for the transfer either of a single word or a block of eight words between the drum and the computing store is about 10 msec. All words in both the computing and drum stores carry a parity check digit and the computer stops if any word it uses is found to have incorrect parity. Input to the computer is by punched paper tape through two photoelectric tape readers working at up to 200 characters per sec, and the output is from one punch working at 33 characters per sec.

Magnetic tape equipment can be added to the standard Pegasus computer. The tape, which is available in reels of various lengths, is pre-addressed in sections containing either 16 or 32 words. The maximum capacity of a tape reel is about 250,000 words. A 32-word buffer store, composed of nickel delay lines, is built into the magnetic tape control unit. Computation can be continued in the central computer while information is transferred from buffer to magnetic tape or vice versa. Orders are also provided for searching for a given section on the tape and for rewinding at high speed. The standard control unit controls up to five mechanisms and two such units can be attached to one computer. Reading and writing operations are automatically checked, and if necessary, repeated up to five times. After five unsuccessful attempts, the computer stops.

Our Pegasus at Leeds, which is a Pegasus I, has at present (March, 1960) one control unit with three tape mechanisms. Later this year, we hope to add another tape mechanism and to have the larger drum and punched-card facilities of the Pegasus II model.

PEGASUS II

The currently available model, Pegasus II, is basically similar to Pegasus I, but has double the capacity of drum store and also has 16 long-delay lines of eight words each. These effectively replace track 0 of the drum and so give fast access to part of the main store. Extra logical equipment has been provided to allow on-line punched-card equipment for input and output to be added at any time. The paper tape input and output operate at higher speeds.

2. SFLS PROGRAM FOR PEGASUS

2.1. General description of the program

In this section we give a general description of the Pegasus SFLS program from the point of view of the user. In §2.2 we explain more fully some general aspects of the program and describe some results of our experience with it. In §2.3 we consider the details of the programming.

2.1.1. *General Specification*

The SFLS program calculates structure factors and accumulates least-squares totals, which are later solved for the parameter changes. The function minimized is

$$R' = \Sigma w(\,|\,F_o\,|\,-\,|\,F_c\,|\,)^2/\Sigma w\,|\,F_o\,|^2.$$

All space groups can be handled. The parameters which can be refined are:
  (i) the $|\,F_o\,|$ scale;
  (ii) the average vibration parameter of the whole structure, $\bar{U} = \overline{u^2}$ (the mean square amplitude of vibration in Å^2);
  (iii) atomic coordinates;
  (iv) individual atomic isotropic vibration parameters U;
  (v) the six components of the individual atomic anisotropic vibration tensors U_{ij}.

There is virtually no limit to the number of $|\,F_o\,|$ which may be included, as these are read off paper tape with their indices, one at a time as the calculation proceeds. The number of parameters which can be handled depends on the space group and decreases as the number of symmetry related positions rises. For convenience a standard allocation of the magnetic drum storage is ordinarily used which allows the refinement of up to 60 atoms isotropically or 25 atoms anisotropically in an orthorhombic space group. By preparing a " drum-list " specifically for a particular job, problems up to about twice these sizes can often be tackled.

2.1.2. *Data needed*

The crystallographer supplies the following data on standard question-naires:
  (a) *Basic data.* Cell dimensions, numbers of atoms, type of refinement, etc.
  (b) *Equivalent positions.* These are used to prepare symmetry code words (see §2.3.2).

D

(c) *Choice of weighting scheme.* The program found most useful is for $w = 1/(a + F + cF^2)$, where a and c are of the order of $2F_{min}$ and $2/F_{max}$ respectively. Programs for $w = $ constant, the Hughes' scheme, and "artificial" weights, such as $w = 1/(\sin \theta/\lambda)$, etc. are also available.

(d) *f tables.* Most standard f curves are available in tabular form. The values of f are given at $\sin \theta/\lambda = 0\cdot0$ $(0\cdot025)$ $0\cdot20$, $0\cdot20$ $(0\cdot05)$ $0\cdot60$, $0\cdot6$ $(0\cdot1)$ $1\cdot4$ Å^{-1}.

(e) *Initial parameters,* including the $|F_o|$ scale. Coordinates are given in Å and mean square vibration amplitudes in Å^2, as this eases the interpretation of parameter changes and the analysis of the vibrational motion. The chemical symbol and a number are given with each atom.

(f) *Planes data.* $hkl |F_o|$. Accidental absences may be included (either as 0 or $\frac{1}{2}F_{min}$, etc.) but as they require a separately adjusted weighting scheme (see §2.2.5), they are grouped together at the end of the data.

When punched appropriately, items (a) to (d) are joined to form one tape, known as the Basic Data tape. This changes little from cycle to cycle and is always fed first into the computer.

2.1.3. *Operation*

The Basic Data tape, (a) to (d), the main program, and the Parameters (e) are first fed into the computer. The SFLS calculations then proceed as the computer reads the Planes tape (f), one plane at a time. It then computes F_c and makes contributions to the LS totals. For each plane the printing is

$$h \ k \ l \quad s|F_o| \quad F_c \quad \sqrt{w}|\Delta|$$
$$\text{or} \quad h \ k \ l \quad s|F_o| \quad |F_c| \quad A_cB_c \quad \sqrt{w}|\Delta|$$

for centrosymmetric and non-centrosymmetric space groups respectively, where s is the $|F_o|$ scale factor. $\sqrt{w}\Delta$, which is proportional to $\Delta/\sigma(F)$, is printed so that "bad" planes can be easily spotted. The LS totals accumulated (together with r.h. sides) are for a

2×2 matrix for scale and $\bar{U}$;

3×3 matrices for atomic coordinates;

1×1 matrices for individual isotropic U;

6×6 matrices for individual anisotropic U_{ij}.

It is not necessary to do a complete cycle in one computer session, as the LS totals can be binary punched at any time and re-loaded later.

2.1.4. *LS Output*

The LS output at the end of each cycle provides:

(i) The residual $R = \Sigma |\Delta|/\Sigma |F_o|$ and $R' = \Sigma w\Delta^2/\Sigma w |F_o|^2$, etc.

(ii) An analysis of the appropriateness of the weighting scheme, by printing average values of $w\Delta^2$ in ranges of $|F_o|$ and of $\sin\theta/\lambda$.

(iii) Shifts of the $|F_o|$ scale and $\bar{U}$, and their E.S.D.'s and correlation coefficient.

(iv) Coordinate shifts (and the mean and maximum of both Δx and $\Delta x/\sigma$) and E.S.D.'s.

(v) Individual U_{ij} and/or U shifts (and means and maxima) and E.S.D.'s.

(vi) Contributions to the expected drop in R' from scale, coordinate and vibration shifts and the predicted R' for next cycle.

(vii) LS totals.

Reduced shifts may be applied by " fudge factors " if desired. Experience of this is discussed in §2.2.3.

2.1.5. *Computing Times*

The approximate total times required per SFLS cycle with $1000\,|F_o|$ for 10 atoms in a centrosymmetric monoclinic space group are about 100 and 130 minutes for isotropic and anisotropic refinements respectively. Ortho-rhombic and higher space groups are somewhat slower, triclinic rather faster. The absence of a centre of symmetry adds less than 5% to the time, as all the contributions to $B(hkl)$ are needed for the coordinate LS derivatives.

2.2. Methods and experience

2.2.1. *Method of Determining the $|F_o|$ Scale Shift*

When refined, the $|F_o|$ scale is always coupled with the average vibration $\bar{U}$ in a 2×2 matrix. If individual atomic vibrations are being refined, $\bar{U}$ although formally a redundant parameter is made use of in two ways. First, its introduction allows good estimates of the scale shift to be made. As the correlation coefficient between scale and $\bar{U}$ is typically 0·75–0·85, it would be quite impossible to obtain a satisfactory scale shift from LS equations which were diagonal in the scale. Second, to allow for the effect of the scale change, the individual ΔU or ΔU_{ij} are augmented appropriately by the difference between the $\Delta\bar{U}$ obtained (along with the scale shift) from the 2×2 equation and the $\Delta\bar{U}$ obtained from a 1×1 equation corresponding to a fixed scale. For the reasons indicated in International Tables, Vol. II (1959), §6.4.1.1, the 2×2 equation is actually set up to give the change of scale of $|F_c|$, and the new scale is later applied reciprocally to $|F_o|$. Since all derivatives with respect to scale of $|F_c|$, except the first, are exactly zero, the least-squares equations are valid even for *large* changes of scale if the other parameter shifts are small. We inadvertently confirmed this on one occasion, in the first cycle of a structure otherwise almost correct, when the LS process rightly doubled the $|F_o|$ scale.

This method of treating the scale and $\bar{U}$ in a 2×2 matrix has generally proved very satisfactory, and we can recommend it as a simple way of overcoming the important off-diagonal correlations between the scale and individual vibration parameters.

2.2.2. *Choice of LS Matrix Elements Computed*

The calculation of a full LS matrix with all off-diagonal elements is impractical on Pegasus for structures of even moderate size; for a structure with 15 atoms over 10,000 elements would be involved. On the other hand, the diagonal approximation is known to be bad for

(a) vibration and $| F_o |$ scale interactions;

(b) coordinates, if the axes are not orthogonal;

(c) anisotropic vibrations.

A simple method of treating (a) has already been described in §2.2.1. The straightforward method of overcoming (b) and (c) is to compute 3×3 and 6×6 matrices for the coordinates and vibrations. However, an attempt was made to have the best of both worlds by actually computing only the diagonal elements of these matrices and then, at the matrix inversion stage, estimating the off-diagonal elements in terms of the cell angles α, β, γ and the diagonal elements by the approximations given by Cruickshank (1956*b*). This technique was sufficiently satisfactory for the coordinate refinement, but for the anisotropic vibration refinement it was catastrophically bad. The predicted shifts were often wrong by a factor of 10 and were much worse than those given by the simple diagonal approximation, which would give eventual convergence with a fudge factor of 0·3, say. Trial calculations were therefore made with a *full* LS matrix (§2.2.8) on a small triclinic structure (oxamide, Ayerst and Duke, 1954). The approximate estimates of the off-diagonal terms were found to be about as good as had been expected, with errors of the order of 5% of the on-diagonal terms, but the 6×6 matrices proved very poorly conditioned and their solutions were very sensitive to approximations in the off-diagonal terms. These calculations with a full matrix also confirmed that for a structure with three-dimensional data and a fixed origin the inter-atom off-diagonal terms could be neglected without serious error. The SFLS program was therefore developed for 3×3 and 6×6 matrices.

2.2.3. *Fudge Factors*

It is well known that the parameter shifts in successive cycles of SFLS refinement are liable to oscillate, especially if the LS matrix is assumed to be diagonal. This can be ameliorated empirically by taking only a proportion of the indicated shifts, that is by introducing " fudge factors " less than 1·0. The experience with the present scheme, with its 2×2 matrix for scale and $\bar{U}$ and chains of 3×3 and 6×6 matrices, has been that fudge factors have not been needed for many structures with complete three-dimensional data.

However, as a compromise and to avoid keeping a close watch on the progress of the refinement of each structure, a fudge factor of 0·80 is ordinarily used. Some structures (particularly non-centrosymmetric ones without a fixed origin) had otherwise shown a tendency to oscillate. Oscillation also occurred in the refinement of the anisotropic vibrations of pyrimidine (Wheatley, 1960) and had to be checked by a fudge factor of 0·67. This was probably due to the same effects of accidental absences as caused trouble in the differential synthesis method, §1.2.5, which were analysed by Cruickshank (1956b). It would probably not have occurred if the average anisotropic vibrations of the structure (which is decidedly anisotropic) had been determined before the start of the refinement of the individual anisotropic vibrations.

For two-dimensional data the customary fudge factor is 0·50. The smaller value is necessary because of the overlapping of atoms in projection and the neglect in our program of the corresponding inter-atom off-diagonal terms in the LS matrix.

2.2.4. *Analysis of the Weighting Scheme*

Maximum accuracy can be obtained with the least-squares method only when the weights assigned to the observations are correct. Further, as explained below in §2.2.6, the usual LS formula for estimated standard deviations is *invalid* unless the weights are correct. The requirement is that the averages of $w\Delta^2$ must be constant when the set of $w\Delta^2$ values for a given structure is analysed in any significant systematic fashion. *A priori* w is likely to depend on $|F_o|$ and $\sin\theta/\lambda$. The SFLS program therefore provides an analysis of the average values of $w\Delta^2$ in groups of increasing $|F_o|$ and increasing $\sin\theta/\lambda$. For well-refined structures w usually proves to depend chiefly on $|F_o|$. For some structures the Hughes' (1941) weighting scheme has been satisfactory ($w = $ constant for small $|F_o|$, $w \propto 1/|F_o|^2$ for larger values), but for others the necessary weighting has been of the form

$$w = 1/(a + |F_o| + c|F_o|^2),$$

where a and c are of the order of $2F_{min}$ and $2/F_{max}$. This scheme is essentially $w = 1/|F_o|$, suggested to us by G. B. Carpenter, with some downweighting of the very large and very small $|F_o|$. Sometimes an $|F_o|^3$ term is needed as well. In no structure has $w = $ constant been satisfactory. We have not yet written any weighting routines with a dependence on $\sin\theta/\lambda$ as well as $|F_o|$, though there is evidence from some structures that the planes of medium $\sin\theta$ are the most accurate, as might be expected from the form of the polarization factor. The weighting analysis will, of course, be misleading on this point, unless both anisotropic vibrations and any hydrogen atoms have been allowed for in the F_c, as the former will reduce the Δ for high-order planes and the latter for low-order planes.

Some weighting routines exclude from the LS totals any planes of uncertain phase, say when $|F_c| < \frac{1}{3}|F_o|$. In the early stages of refinement of a structure we sometimes use artificial weighting schemes to speed convergence; one simple scheme is $w = 1/(\sin\theta/\lambda)$, which is coupled with the rejection of planes of uncertain phase.

2.2.5. Allowance for Accidentally Absent Reflections

The LS method of refinement allows the inclusion of the " accidentally absent " reflections which were too weak to be observed. For each of these reflections an estimate can usually be made of the minimum $|F_o|$ which could have been observed in that part of the spectrum, so that in a centrosymmetric space group the expected value of $|F_o|$ for the reflection can be estimated as $\frac{1}{2}F_{min}$ and its variance σ^2 as $(F_{min})^2/12$. Thus we have both $|F_o|$ values and absolute weights

$$w = 1/\sigma^2 = 12/(F_{min})^2 \qquad (2.1)$$

for these planes.

This procedure was used in the analysis of nitronium perchlorate (Truter, Cruickshank and Jeffrey, 1960) in which there were 364 $|F_o|$ and 102 accidental absences. The weighting for the observed planes, $w = 1/(F + 0.02\,F^2)$, was necessarily on a relative scale and was adjusted so that the average $w\Delta^2$ for the whole set was unity. Since (2.1) expresses the weights of the accidental absences on an absolute scale, their average $w\Delta^2$ should also have been unity. It was actually 2·4, which implied that (2.1) had seriously over-weighted the accidental absences. On closer examination it was seen that the $w\Delta^2$ values for some of the smaller $\frac{1}{2}F_{min}$ were unreasonably large (there was a ratio of 5 : 1 between the largest and smallest of the $\frac{1}{2}F_{min}$). The weighting scheme (2.1) was therefore abandoned and the accidental absences were all given the same constant weight, adjusted to give an average $w\Delta^2 = 1$. This worked satisfactorily. With the inclusion of the accidental absences, it would be roughly expected that the standard deviations would decrease by a factor of $[364/(364 + 102)]^{\frac{1}{2}} = 0.89$; the actual improvement in the coordinate E.S.D.'s was rather better than this, from an average of 0·010 Å to 0·008 Å.

The same procedure was also used in the analysis of thioacetamide (Truter, 1960), which had 922 $|F_o|$ and 485 accidental absences. In this problem the E.S.D.'s decreased by a factor of 0·84, close to the $(922/1407)^{\frac{1}{2}} = 0.81$ roughly expected.

Since the weighting schemes for the observed and unobserved reflections are on different relative scales, it is necessary to accumulate their LS totals separately, and then to add them together after the weighting ratio, which gives both the same average $w\Delta^2$, has been determined.

2.2.6. *Formulae for Standard Deviations*

The point that the usual LS formula (2.6) for standard deviations is invalid unless the weights are correct can be demonstrated briefly by deriving the formulae appropriate to the diagonal LS approximation (for a general derivation see e.g. Cruickshank and Robertson, 1953). The diagonal LS equations for coordinate refinement are

$$\Sigma wg^2 . \epsilon_x = \Sigma wg\Delta, \qquad (2.2)$$

where $g = \partial \mid F_c \mid /\partial x$. Hence

$$\sigma^2(x) = [\Sigma w^2 g^2 \sigma^2(hkl)]/[\Sigma wg^2]^2, \qquad (2.3)$$

which is similar to the formula in the Fourier method (Cruickshank, 1949). If the weights are correct, $w = 1/\sigma^2(hkl)$ and (2.3) simplifies to

$$\sigma^2(x) = 1/(\Sigma wg^2), \qquad (2.4)$$

which is the LS formula if the *absolute* weights are known. If the *relative* weights only are known, then on the second assumption that the Δ's are independent (apart from their coupling through the n parameters determined), we may estimate

$$\sigma^2(x) = [\Sigma w\Delta^2]/[(m - n)(\Sigma wg^2)], \qquad (2.5)$$

where m is the number of observations and n the number of unknowns. This is simply the version in the diagonal approximation of the usual LS formula

$$\sigma^2(x) = a^{jj}(\Sigma w\Delta^2)/(m - n), \qquad (2.6)$$

where a^{jj} is the appropriate element of the matrix inverse to the normal equation matrix. On the other hand, if the weights are incorrect, we cannot simplify (2.3) to give (2.4). The estimate for *arbitrary* weights, again assuming independent Δ's, which is derived directly from (2.3) is

$$\sigma^2(x) = (\Sigma w^2 g^2 \Delta^2)/(\Sigma wg^2)^2, \qquad (2.7)$$

apart from a factor of order $m/(m - n)$. This is the proper formula to use when the weights are incorrect.

To test the difference between (2.5) and (2.7) some calculations were done with the data for oxamide (Ayerst and Duke, 1954). With constant weights, known from the weighting analysis to be a poor scheme, both (2.5) and (2.7) give an average coordinate E.S.D. of 0·0037 Å. With $w = 1/\mid F_o \mid$, a better approximation to the true weights, (2.5) gave 0·0035 Å and (2.7) 0·0032 Å. However, for the E.S.D. of the isotropic mean square vibration amplitude, the analogue of (2.7) gave the larger value for both weighting schemes, 0·00064 Å² against 0·00060 Å² for the first and 0·00059 Å² against 0·0052 Å² for the second.

When there are multiple observations of each $\mid F_o \mid$, a set of absolute weights is sometimes derived from a study of the random errors in the experimental data. In such a case, it is perfectly proper to use (2.4), but the E.S.D.'s which result cover only these random experimental errors. When the weights are chosen to give constant average $w\Delta^2$, that is " correctly " in the above sense, the E.S.D. formula (2.5) covers a larger range of errors, not only the random experimental errors but also those features of the systematic experimental errors which cannot be mirrored in the electron density model used for the F_c, together with some of the errors of the model itself. A procedure which is *formally invalid* is to derive a set of absolute weights from the random experimental errors and then to calculate the E.S.D.'s due to the larger range of errors by (2.5) instead of (2.7), unless of course $(\Sigma w\Delta^2)/(m - n)$ is close to unity, which shows that only the random experimental errors are significant.

2.2.7. *Experience with SFLS Program*

The SFLS program has been used at Leeds, at Blackley by Dr. C. J. Brown and colleagues of I.C.I. Ltd., and at King's College, Newcastle, by Dr. H. P. Stadler and colleagues. Over 60 structures have now been refined, drawn from all crystal classes and ranging in size up to 70 atoms in the asymmetric unit. The total machine time used for production runs is approaching 1000 hours; the average number of cycles computed for each structure is about 10. This number is perhaps larger than might be expected from the fact the maximum parameter shifts in one cycle are generally about one-half to a third of those in the previous cycle. However, because of minor changes in the $|F_o|$ data, introduction of hydrogen atoms, revision of the weighting scheme, etc., a refinement is often not a completely smooth progression. Refinements are usually continued until the largest shift of any parameter is less than one-third the corresponding E.S.D.

The greatest coordinate change, which a series of cycles has successfully achieved, is one of 0·6 Å for an oxygen atom in $(NO_2)_2S_3O_{10}$; space group *Cc*, data given by Eriks and MacGillavry (1954). The success was partly due to the fact that the other atoms required only small shifts.

In a Fourier method peak heights give a good indication of whether an atom has been correctly placed. In the SFLS scheme a similar indication is given by the behaviour of the individual atomic vibration parameters U. If an atom is completely misplaced in a trial structure, the value of U steadily increases in successive cycles to an absurd value. If the atom is misplaced by, say, 0·3 Å the value of U is likely to increase at first, and then to decrease to a physically reasonable value as the position becomes correct.

2.2.8. *Treatment of Atoms in Special Positions*

An atom with one or more fixed coordinates causes no trouble, as the r.h.s. of LS normal equations is zero for the coordinate in question. It is necessary only to include an appropriately scaled-down f table for this atom. However, an atom at a position such as $(X,2X,z)$ in a hexagonal space group requires more care. Here X is the independent parameter and it is a function of the coordinates x and y; consequently

$$\frac{\partial \mid F_c \mid}{\partial X} = \frac{\partial \mid F_c \mid}{\partial x} + 2 \frac{\partial \mid F_c \mid}{\partial y}$$

and

$$\Sigma w \left(\frac{\partial \mid F_c \mid}{\partial X} \right)^2 = \Sigma w \left(\frac{\partial \mid F_c \mid}{\partial x} \right)^2$$

$$+ 4\Sigma w \left(\frac{\partial \mid F_c \mid}{\partial x} \right) \left(\frac{\partial \mid F_c \mid}{\partial y} \right) + 4\Sigma w \left(\frac{\partial \mid F_c \mid}{\partial y} \right)^2.$$

The method for such positions is therefore to accumulate the LS totals in the usual way during the main program, as though x, y, z were independent, and then, immediately before solving the normal equations, to combine together the elements in the 3×3 matrices to form the appropriate equations of reduced order. The anisotropic vibrations of atoms in this type of position are dealt with similarly. As this type of treatment is rather rarely needed, the short programs for regrouping the LS equations are prepared when the requirement arises.

2.2.9. *Full Matrix Refinement*

The layout of the SFLS program (see §2.3) is sufficiently general to allow it to be easily altered to compute the full LS matrix. This is only feasible for small structures, as the drum storage space is insufficient when there are more than about six independent atoms.

A full matrix program has been very profitably prepared by Mr. L. N. Becka for the anisotropic refinement of hexamethylenetetramine, for which a number of distinct sets of data had to be processed. The structure belongs to the cubic space group $I\bar{4}3m$ and has only three independent atoms, each at special positions, carbon at (x,o,o), nitrogen at (x,x,x) and hydrogen at (x,x,z). The ordinary program would have had to be modified in any case to deal with the special positions (§2.2.8), but since there are only a few independent parameters and the $\mid F_o \mid$ data are sparse, it was anticipated that the off-diagonal interaction terms in the LS matrix would be important (and, if neglected, would upset the proper estimation of standard deviations).

The program gives very rapid convergence. For instance, with the 38 independent $\mid F_o \mid$ obtained at liquid nitrogen temperature and with the full indicated shifts applied in each cycle, the successive values of R' were 0·01114, 0·00660, 0·00654 and 0·00654. In this instance where the trial structure was unusually good, the final parameters were effectively reached in the first cycle.

2.3. SFLS program details

2.3.1. *SFLS Equations*

If all parameters are regarded as functions of $|F_c|$ the aim of the LS method is to minimize

$$\Sigma w(|F_o| - |F_c|)^2 = \Sigma w \Delta^2. \tag{2.8}$$

The normal equations which give the small changes ϵ_i to any parameter p_i are

$$\sum_{i=1}^{n} \epsilon_i \left\{ \Sigma w \frac{\partial |F_c|}{\partial p_j} \frac{\partial |F_c|}{\partial p_i} \right\} = \Sigma w \Delta \frac{\partial |F_c|}{\partial p_j}, \quad (j = 1, \ldots, n) \tag{2.9}$$

where

$$|F_c| = A \cos \alpha + B \sin \alpha \tag{2.10}$$

Now

$$A = \sum_r \sum_s f_{rs} \exp\{ -2\pi^2[(ha^*)^2 U_{rs,11} + \ldots]\} \\ \times \cos 2\pi[(h/a)x_{rs} + \ldots], \tag{2.11}$$

where the summation over s is over the symmetry equivalent positions in the cell and that over r is over the atoms of the asymmetric unit, f_{rs} is a scattering factor, $U_{rs,11}$ is the 11 component of the vibration tensor of atom rs, and x_{rs} is a coordinate. For simplicity we write

$$A \equiv \sum_r \sum_s A_{rs} \\ \equiv \sum_r A_r, \tag{2.12}$$

where A_{rs} is the contribution to A of an atom at one equivalent position and A_r is the contribution from atom r and its symmetry equivalents. B_{rs} and B_r may be defined similarly for the sine parts.

Hence

$$\frac{\partial |F_c|}{\partial p_i} = \frac{\partial A_r}{\partial p_i} \cos \alpha + \frac{\partial B_r}{\partial p_i} \sin \alpha. \tag{2.14}$$

Since any symmetry operation is a combination of a rotation matrix $\mathbf{R}$ and a translation vector $\mathbf{t}$ the coordinate of an atom equivalent to r can be written

$$\mathbf{x}_{rs} = \mathbf{R}\mathbf{x}_r + \mathbf{t}. \tag{2.15}$$

Consequently, the argument of the cos in A_{rs} may be written

$$(h/a)x_{rs} + \ldots = (h_s/a)x_r + \ldots + ht_x + \ldots \\ = (h_s/a)x_r + \ldots + t_s, \text{ say,} \tag{2.16}$$

where (h_s, k_s, l_s) are a set of " equivalent " indices and $t_s = \mathbf{h} \cdot \mathbf{t}$ is a scalar quantity, independent of the particular atom r of the asymmetric unit. Further, the argument of the exponential in A_{rs} may be written

$$(ha^*)^2 U_{rs,11} + \ldots = (h_s a^*)^2 U_{r,11} + \ldots, \tag{2.17}$$

with the same (h_s, k_s, l_s). Hence

$$A_{rs} = f_{rs} \exp\{- 2\pi^2[(h_s a^*)^2 U_{r,11} + \ldots]\}$$
$$\times \cos 2\pi[(h_s/a)x_r + \ldots + t_s], \qquad (2.18)$$

and
$$\frac{\partial A_r}{\partial x_r} = \sum_s (- 2\pi h_s/a)B_{rs}, \qquad (2.19)$$

that is the derivative of A_r is expressed as a combination of the contributions to B_r.

If we define

$$\left.\begin{array}{l} G'_{rs} = A_{rs} \cos \alpha + B_{rs} \sin \alpha, \\ J'_{rs} = B_{rs} \cos \alpha - A_{rs} \sin \alpha, \end{array}\right\} \qquad (2.20)$$

and

we then find

$$\frac{\partial |F_c|}{\partial x_r} = \sum_s (- 2\pi h_s/a)J'_{rs}. \qquad (2.21)$$

For computational convenience we make a slight change of definition and put

$$\begin{array}{l} G_{rs} = vG'_{rs} = v(A_{rs} \cos \alpha + B_{rs} \sin \alpha), \\ J_{rs} = vJ'_{rs} = v(B_{rs} \cos \alpha - A_{rs} \sin \alpha), \end{array} \qquad (2.22)$$

where v is the sign of $\cos \alpha$. In centrosymmetric space groups $\sin \alpha = 0$, so that

$$G_{rs} = A_{rs} \text{ and } J_{rs} = B_{rs}, \qquad (2.23)$$

and calculations corresponding to equations (2.20) can be avoided. To take advantage of this the program computes for all space groups, not (2.21) but,

$$v\frac{\partial |F_c|}{\partial x_r} = \sum_s (- 2\pi h_s/a)J_{rs}. \qquad (2.24)$$

Similarly, we can show for an anisotropic parameter

$$v\frac{\partial |F_c|}{\partial U_{r,11}} = - \sum_s 2\pi^2(h_s a^*)^2 G_{rs}, \qquad (2.25)$$

and for an isotropic one

$$v\frac{\partial |F_c|}{\partial U_r} = \{ - 2\pi^2(2\sin \theta/\lambda)^2\}\sum_s G_{rs}. \qquad (2.26)$$

Since $v^2 = 1$ the l.h.s. of the normal equations is unaltered by these modifications. The r.h.s. is computed as

$$\sum w(v\Delta) \left(v\frac{\partial |F_c|}{\partial p_j} \right). \qquad (2.27)$$

The above formulation of the SFLS equations illustrates two important methods used in the program. First, symmetry has been dealt with in terms of equivalent indices (h_s, k_s, l_s) and translation scalars t_s, which are common to all atoms generated by a particular operation, rather than in terms of sets of equivalent coordinates and equivalent vibration tensors. Apart from reducing the number of equivalent quantities which have to be generated, the method makes the treatment of vibration tensors in space groups with 3-, 4- or 6-fold axes of symmetry as simple as with 2-fold axes.* Second the derivatives of $| F_c |$ with respect to any coordinate or vibration parameter are all linear combinations of the individual atomic contributions A_{rs} and B_{rs} to F_c. For a given structure factor, the program therefore lays out the complete set of A_{rs} and B_{rs} so that all derivatives can be calculated conveniently.

2.3.2. Symmetry

As has just been mentioned, symmetry has been dealt with in terms of equivalent indices rather than equivalent positions. This is chiefly because it allows a very simple treatment of the anisotropic vibrations of symmetry related atoms. To speed up the calculations still further the possible symmetry operations have been classified as

(a) a centre of symmetry at the origin;
(b) pure translation operations (in non-primitive cells);
(c) " alternations ";
(d) " permutations ";

and combinations of any of these.

Atoms generated by (a) and (b) are not individually included in the calculations since it is sufficient to multiply the f_{rs} of the other atoms by an appropriate integer M and, with a centre of symmetry, to omit the B contribution to F_c. (The B_{rs} are still calculated since they are needed for the LS derivatives.)

By (2.15) the equivalent point x_{rs} generated by the effect of a symmetry operation on a point x_r is

$$\mathbf{x}_{rs} = \mathbf{R}\mathbf{x}_r + \mathbf{t}, \qquad (2.15)$$

where $\mathbf{R}$ is a 3×3 rotation matrix, whose elements are all either 0, $+1$ or -1, and $\mathbf{t} = (t_x, t_y, t_z)$ is a translation vector. For instance the equivalent point generated by a 3_1 operation in the space group $P3_1$ is

$$x_{rs} = -y_r,$$
$$y_{rs} = x_r - y_r,$$
$$z_{rs} = z_r + \tfrac{1}{3},$$

* The advantages of this method were stressed to us by A. R. Curtis in 1956.

which can be written

$$\begin{pmatrix} x_{rs} \\ y_{rs} \\ z_{rs} \end{pmatrix} = \begin{pmatrix} 0 & -1 & 0 \\ 1 & -1 & 0 \\ 0 & 0 & 1 \end{pmatrix} \begin{pmatrix} x_r \\ y_r \\ z_r \end{pmatrix} + \begin{pmatrix} 0 \\ 0 \\ \frac{1}{3} \end{pmatrix}$$

Symmetry operations, which involve diagonal rotation matrices,

$$\mathbf{R} = \begin{pmatrix} \pm 1 & 0 & 0 \\ 0 & \pm 1 & 0 \\ 0 & 0 & \pm 1 \end{pmatrix} \tag{2.28}$$

are called " alternations " and those which involve non-diagonal matrices, as in the above example, are called " permutations." The alternations thus cover the 2-fold rotation and mirror plane symmetries, and the permutations the 3-, 4- and 6-fold rotations. The equivalent indices are given by

$$\mathbf{h}_s = \mathbf{hR}. \tag{2.29}$$

The reason for the division into alternations and permutations is to speed up the calculation of the arguments

$$(h_s/a)x_r + (k_s/b)y_r + (l_s/c)z_r + t_s$$

of the trigonometric functions. Since addition or subtraction on the Pegasus computer is seven times as fast as multiplication, it is much quicker in an orthorhombic space group to do just the three multiplications needed to get

$$(h/a)\,(x_r), \quad (k/b)\,(y_r), \quad (l/c)\,(z_r)$$

and then to get the four arguments desired by additions and subtractions (which is possible since all the $\mathbf{R}$ are diagonal), than to do the four arguments separately each with three multiplications.

Apart from the point group 1, four slightly different sets of program sub-routines are automatically selected for the point groups 2, m, $mm2$ and 222 ($2/m$ and mm are centrosymmetric and can be dealt with as either of appropriate pair). These sub-routines calculate the trigonometric arguments for the relevant set of alternations with the minimum number of multiplications. Similar savings are achieved with the exponential arguments and with the coordinate and anisotropic vibration derivatives. For alternation symmetry operations, only the translation vectors $\mathbf{t}$ have to be fed in with the Basic data (a), §2.1.2, as the effects of the rotation matrices $\mathbf{R}$ are built-in to the selected sub-routines.

No such saving in the number of multiplications is generally possible with non-diagonal rotation matrices, so that permutation operations are explicitly specified in the Basic data by their $\mathbf{R}$ (actually a single binary coded word) and $\mathbf{t}$. The SFLS program automatically combines all permutations with all alternations, so that only independent permutations unrelated by any alternations have to be specified. For instance, in the space group $P23$, of which the point group 222 is a subgroup, the symmetry is completely specified by the translation vectors for the alternations of 222 (actually all zero) and by the two rotation matrices for the left-handed and right-handed 3-fold operations and their translational vectors (the latter also zero).

2.3.3. *SFLS Program Design*

The first design decision which had to be made was as to whether the major outer loop of the program should deal with the contributions of one atom to many planes (as in our SF program for the Ferranti Mark I computer, §1.2), or whether the planes should be dealt with completely one by one. A choice of the latter was dictated by the smaller magnetic drum of the Pegasus and this was reinforced by the loss of advantage of the SF product formulae with anisotropic vibrations. The main program consequently deals with one plane at a time, computing its F_c and adding to the LS totals. The program deals with symmetry in the method already discussed and lays out the individual atomic contributions A_{rs} and B_{rs} in a manner suitable for calculating the LS deviations by equations (2.24), (2.25) and (2.26).

As the immediate-access computing store of Pegasus is small, it is not possible to do all the calculations which relate to one atom and its symmetry equivalents without many transfers of sub-routines from the drum to the computing store and a consequent loss of time. Hence the better policy, in the main program loop covering one plane, is for each sub-routine to complete its calculations for all the atoms before the program advances to the next sub-routine. For example, the exponential sub-routine, which assumes that the exponential arguments for all atoms have been stored on the drum by the earlier part of the program, has the object of replacing this set of arguments on the drum by the corresponding exponentials. Since there are 8 numbers in a block, 8 exponentials can be calculated between each set of drum transfers and the proportion of time spent in transfers is small.

The flow diagram for the main part of the SFLS program is shown in Table 2. Sub-routines (1)–(14) cover the SF part and (15)–(21) the LS part. The only points which require amplification concern sub-routines:

   (5)   The weighting routine can be chosen arbitrarily.
   (6) M is the multiplicity integer which allows for a centre of symmetry and non-primitive translations.
   (13)   The parts in curly brackets are not calculated for non-centro-symmetric space groups. s is the $|F_o|$ scale factor.

The program is actually set up in a manner precisely suited to the problem in hand during the input of the data and program tapes. This is achieved partly by the standard Pegasus Assembly routine which selects sub-routines from a crystallographic library tape and partly by a " Supermaster " program which makes appropriate alterations to the sub-routines and their controlling Master program.

TABLE 2

SFLS FLOW DIAGRAM

(1) Read one set $h, k, l, | F_o |$ from paper tape.
(2) Generate translation scalars t and permuted indices.
(3) Generate $h^2a^{*2}, hka^*b^*, \ldots, h/a, \ldots$ and permutations.
(4) $(\sin \theta/\lambda)^2$ and $(\sin \theta/\lambda)$.
(5) Weight w and $\sqrt{w}$.
(6) Mf_i $(\sin \theta/\lambda)$ for different atom kinds.
(7) $\theta_i = \mathbf{h}.\mathbf{x}_i + t$ for all atoms (including symmetry equivalents).
(8) All $\cos \theta_i$, $\sin \theta_i$.
(9) Any anisotropic quadratic forms $q = 2\pi^2(h^2a^{*2}U_{11} + \ldots)$.
(10) Any isotropic exponents q.
(11) All exponentials, $\exp(-q)$.
(12) All $A_{rs} = Mf \exp(-q) \cos \theta$, (2.18), and B_{rs}.
(13) $A = \Sigma A_{rs}$, $\{B\}$, $| F_c |$, $s | F_o |$, Δ, $\sqrt{w}\Delta$, $\{\cos \alpha, \sin \alpha\}$ and punch out.
(14) Contributions to residuals and weight analysis. (Jump back to (1) if no LS.)
(15) Accumulate 2×2 scale and $\bar{U}$ LS equations.
(16) For non-centrosymmetric s.g., all G_{rs} and J_{rs} by (2.22).
(17) Any anisotropic derivatives, $v\delta| F_c|\delta/U_{ij}$.
(18) Accumulate any 6×6 anisotropic U_{ij} equations.
(19) Accumulate any 1×1 isotropic U equations.
(20) Any coordinate derivatives, $v\delta| F_c |/\delta x$.
(21) Accumulate any 3×3 coordinate equations.
Return to (1) to read next plane.

The program for the output of LS results at the end of a refinement cycle (§2.1.4), though rather elaborate, calls for no special comment as the problems are all straightforward.

2.3.4. *Numerical Formulae*

The program finds $\cos \theta$ and $\sin \theta$ from an eight-entry table which has $\cos \phi$ for $\phi = 7\frac{1}{2}° (15°) 82\frac{1}{2}°$, with the aid of the formulae

$$\left.\begin{array}{l} \cos \theta = \cos(\phi + \delta) = (1 - \tfrac{1}{2}\delta^2) \cos \phi - \delta \sin \phi, \\ \sin \theta = \sin(\phi + \delta) = (1 - \tfrac{1}{2}\delta^2) \sin \phi + \delta\cos \phi, \end{array}\right\} \quad (2.30)$$

where ϕ is the nearest table entry to θ and $\delta = \theta - \phi$, and appropriate care is taken of the quadrant. The method gives 4 decimal-figure accuracy. The average time required to pick up a θ from the drum and plant back $\cos \theta$ and $\sin \theta$ is 25 msec, which is about twice as fast as can be achieved with the standard maximum accuracy series expansions.

Exponentials $\exp(-q)$ for the range $0 \leqslant q < 10$ are calculated by the formulae

$$\exp(-q) = \exp(-ma).\exp(-nb).(1 - c + \tfrac{1}{2}c^2), \quad (2.31)$$

where $\qquad q = ma + nb + c$

and $a = 10/8$, $b = 10/64$ and m and n are positive integers $0 \leqslant m, n < 8$ chosen to make $| c |$ as small as possible. $\text{Exp}(-ma)$ and $\exp(-nb)$ are selected with the aid of the Pegasus 3-bit modification instructions, from eight-entry tables of exponentials with arguments of 0 (10/8) 70/8 and 0 (10/64) 70/64. This method also gives 4 decimal-figure accuracy and works at an average rate of 17 msec per number, again about twice as fast as the standard expansions.

The scattering factor values f are found by second-order interpolation in the appropriate one of three tables for the ranges sin $\theta/\lambda = 0\cdot0$ (0·025) 0·200 0·20 (0·05) 0·60, and 0·6 (0·1) 1·4 Å^{-1}.

3. THREE-DIMENSIONAL FOURIER SUMMATION PROGRAM

3.1. Introduction

The electron density ρ at a point (XYZ) in a unit cell of volume V, is given by,

$$\rho(XYZ) = \frac{1}{V} \sum_{-\infty}^{\infty} \sum_{-\infty}^{\infty} \sum_{-\infty}^{\infty} [A(hkl) \cos 2\pi(hX + kY + lZ) \\ + B(hkl) \sin 2\pi(hX + kY + lZ)]. \tag{3.1}$$

By taking symmetry into account, this formula can be simplified for each space group (International Tables, Vol. I, 1952) and can be expressed as a combination of product functions of the type cos $2\pi hX$.sin $2\pi kY$.cos $2\pi lZ$, whose coefficients may be combinations of $A(hkl) \pm A(h\bar{k}l) \pm A(\bar{h}kl)$ $\pm A(hk\bar{l})$, etc. To compute $\rho(XYZ)$ efficiently for any given space group, the data $A(hkl)$ and $B(hkl)$ must be arranged in a predetermined order, and either a different program must be written for each space group or a general program must be written in such a way that the symmetry operations of any space group may be fully utilized. It has been our aim to produce a program of the latter type which is simple to use, flexible and efficient.

The program works on the " Beevers–Lipson strips " principle, carrying out three one-dimensional Fourier summations and in each summation handles the cosine and sine contributions for even and odd indices separately. By using this system, it is necessary to compute each summation only over the coordinate range 0 to 1/4 and then to combine the results in different ways by additions or subtractions for the complete coordinate ranges 0 to 1 (see, for example, §3.3.3). Since this replaces a large number of multiplications by a smaller number of faster addition or subtraction orders a considerable reduction in computing time is achieved. It will be seen (§3.3.2) that the trigonometric tables used are analogous to Beevers–Lipson strips with unit amplitudes. The general sequence of the main summation program (§3.3) is similar to that described (in detail for two-dimensional series and by an example for three-dimensional series) in the International Tables, Vol. II (1952), §2.5.4.7 and §6.5.1.

Since there are eight possible trigonometric product functions of the type $\cos 2\pi hX . \sin 2\pi kY . \cos 2\pi lZ$, the analytical expression for $\rho(XYZ)$ in a given space group can be regarded as a selection from these eight terms. The crystal symmetry may impose certain restrictions on the indices of the data contributing to each term (e.g. $h + k = 2n$, etc.). If the data are divided into different " parity groups " (of which there may be up to eight according as their three indices are even or odd), it is possible, for any space group, to define $\rho(XYZ)$ in terms of certain trigonometric functions whose coefficients are selected from one or more parity groups. The selection of the appropriate functions and the selection and combination of data (e.g. $A(hkl) - A(hk\bar{l})$, etc.) for the corresponding coefficients for a given space group can be completely defined by up to four " space group code words " (§3.2.4) together with a special 6-bit code word for non-centrosymmetric structures (§3.3.3).

The input data for the program are obtained by processing the paper tape output from the SFLS program by routines which produce paper tapes containing data for observed, calculated or difference Fourier syntheses or Patterson syntheses. To avoid any restriction on the ordering of the input data or on the orientation of the indices h, k, l, the Fourier summation program is in two distinct parts. In the first part, described in §3.2, the input data, corrected if necessary for multiplicity, when any of the indices are zero, are labelled according to the parities and signs of their indices, the indices being reorientated if necessary (Stage Oa), and are then sorted into batches according to their labels (Stage Ob). Stage Oc selects and combines the data under the control of the space group code words to form the different sets of coefficients required for each trigonometric product. It also forms a " control word " for each set, which defines the parities of the indices in the set and the trigonometric product to be associated with it. In the second part of the program, described in §3.3, $\rho(XYZ)$ is computed one section at a time by means of three one-dimensional Fourier summations (Stages I, II, III). Each stage is divided into two parts, of which the first, or a part is the Fourier summation proper and the second, or b part, is a combination of coefficients for the next stage or final output.

To compute a Fourier synthesis the following information must be provided:

   (i) $|h|_{max}$, $|k|_{max}$, $|l|_{max}$;
   (ii) The ranges of X, Y, Z over which ρ is to be computed and the intervals required in each direction;
   (iii) $F(000)$ and $1/V$;
   (iv) Three integers I_1, I_2, I_3 to define the orientation required (see §3.2.2);

E

(v) Up to four space group code words, whose construction is described in §3.2.4;

(vi) Whether the structure has a centre of symmetry; and, if not, the relation between the trigonometric products associated with any $A(hkl)$ and the corresponding $B(hkl)$. Note this *relation* is constant for all reflections of a given space group but may vary from one space group to another. It is stored in the computer as a 6-bit mask which is used in Stage I to change the appropriate bits of each control word.

3.2. Input routines (Stage 0)

3.2.1. *Introduction*

The input routines to the Fourier summation program have been designed to overcome the restrictions imposed by the paper tape input system used with Pegasus, and to be sufficiently general to deal with all space groups.

In the main summation program, the calculation is carried out by successive one-dimensional summations made over each of the reflection indices. There are, of course, six sequences in which the summations may be performed, each one requiring a properly ordered input tape. However, the introduction of suitable sorting routines (Stage Ob, §3.2.3), makes it possible to get any of the six possible orientations of the indices from one input tape.

The coefficients of the different trigonometric product functions in the electron density formula are combinations of the original reflection data. For example, in the space group $P2_1/c$, with the b-axis unique, the coefficients for the product function $\cos 2\pi hX . \cos 2\pi k Y . \cos 2\pi lZ$ are,

$$C(hkl) = F(hkl) + F(hk\bar{l}) \qquad (3.2)$$

with the restriction that $k + l = 2n$. The purpose of Stage Oc, §3.2.4, is to select the reflection data with the correct parities from the groups of data of types $F(hkl)$ and $F(hk\bar{l})$, and to add them together to form the correct coefficients. The program is controlled by space group code words which are easily constructed and are general enough to deal with any space group; their structure will be considered in greater detail below.

For the efficient working of Stages Ob and Oc, each reflection must be first classified according to the parities and signs of its indices. This is carried out in Stage Oa, §3.2.1.

It should be noted that the sorting routines to be described are necessary mainly because of the paper tape input system. For a machine equipped with punched card facilities these steps could be carried out more economically by using a sorting machine. The slowest part of the input routines is the group sorting operation, §3.2.3. The time taken depends very much on the order in which the data are punched; for a monoclinic space group with 1800 reflections in the worst order the time taken was forty minutes, of which ten minutes were spent in rewinding and searching the magnetic tape.

3.2.2. *Stage Oa: Labelling*

The input to this stage consists of a paper tape punched with the reflection data, together with the three integers I_1, I_2, and I_3 (§3.1), the function of which will appear below. In what follows it will be assumed that a three-dimensional electron density synthesis is to be computed for a non-centrosymmetric space group. Then, the data for any reflection will consist of the indices h, k, l, and the components A and B of the observed structure factors. No restriction is placed upon the order in which the indices are punched or upon the sequence of the reflections on the paper tape. It is assumed that data for not more than half the reciprocal lattice are presented and that only non-equivalent reflections are used. For space groups with 3-, 4-, or 6-fold symmetries the extra reflections, necessary in the electron density summation, are generated by the program.

It is convenient to denote the indices in the main summation program by the symbols h_1, h_2 and h_3. Then, the first summation is carried out over the index h_1, the second over h_2 and the third over h_3. The first function of Stage Oa is to distribute h, k, and l into h_1, h_2, and h_3; the correct permutation of the indices is determined by the values of I_1, I_2, and I_3 read in at the beginning of the program. After this, the sign of h_3 is examined. If this is negative it is set positive and the signs of h_2, h_1, and B are changed.

With this arrangement of the indices the reflection data may be divided into four main groups. These are:

Group 0: h_3, h_2, h_1 positive;
Group 1: h_3, h_2 positive; h_1 negative;
Group 2: h_3 positive; h_2 negative; h_1 positive;
Group 3: h_3 positive; h_2, h_1 negative.

Within each of these groups there are eight parity groups determined according to the even or odd nature of the indices. Any reflection may fall, therefore, into one of thirty-two different groups. The next step in this part of the input program is to determine to which group each reflection belongs and to form a 5-bit binary label to specify this. The group label together with the moduli of the indices are packed into one machine word; quantities A and B are also packed into one word and the two machine words representing the reflection data are stored until data for sixteen reflections have been processed. Then, the data in the machine are written on to one section of the output magnetic tape. When all the data on the input tape have been dealt with in this way, the magnetic tape is ready to serve as input to Stage Ob.

The only restrictions imposed in Stage Oa are that no index must be greater than 63, while $|A|$ and $|B|$ must be stored on such a scale as to be less than 2^{18}.

3.2.3. *Stage Ob: Sorting*

This section of the program consists of two sorting routines. The first sorts the data on the output tape produced in Stage Oa into the thirty-two possible reflection groups by making use of the group labels now attached to each reflection. A second magnetic tape, which is used for the sorted output, is divided into thirty-two equal parts, each large enough to hold the data for 512 reflections.

The second routine is a numerical sort carried out on each of the thirty-two groups of data formed by the group sorting operation. Numerical sorting is carried out by a radix sorting procedure making use of the values $|h|_{\max}$, $|k|_{\max}$, $|l|_{\max}$ of the indices h, k, and l. If the maximum values of the moduli of the reorientated indices are H_1, H_2, and H_3, then, since in each of the thirty-two groups all the data have the same parity, the radices needed are given by the equation,

$$R_i = [H_i/2] + 1, \ (i = 1, 2, 3), \tag{3.3}$$

where the square brackets denote the integral part of $H_i/2$. For any indices, h_1, h_2, h_3 the address, relative to zero, of the properly sorted location for the word containing the indices is given by

$$N = 2\{R_1 R_2[\,|h_3|/2] + R_1[\,|h_2|/2] + [\,|h_1|/2]\}. \tag{3.4}$$

The address of the word containing A and B is then $(N + 1)$.

The numerical sorting routine begins by transferring the first of the thirty-two groups of data from the input tape to the one part of the drum and clearing a second part. The data are then sorted on to the cleared part of the drum. When all the data of the group have been dealt with the sorted data are transferred from the drum to the output tape, and the drum is cleared in preparation for the sorting of the next group. If reflection data corresponding to any pair of locations on the sorted tape are missing, then these locations will contain zeros.

It is in this part of the program that the most stringent restriction is applied. In order that the numerically sorted data in any group shall not exceed the space allotted for them, the radices must obey the condition,

$$R_1 . R_2 . R_3 < 512. \tag{3.5}$$

By (3.3) this can be roughly expressed as,

$$|h|_{\max} . |k|_{\max} . |l|_{\max} < 4000. \tag{3.6}$$

This condition is, therefore, usually more restrictive than the one imposed at the end of §3.2.2. It will be relaxed when the programs are adapted for the Pegasus II machine with a larger drum.

3.2.4. *Stage Oc: Formation of Coefficients*

After the sorting procedures described in Stage Ob the data are ready to be combined, according to the space group requirements, to form the final coefficients for the main summation program. In the most general case (space group $P1$), the coefficients for each trigonometric function are formed by combining data, all belonging to the same parity group, from each of the four main data groups determined by the signs of the indices h_1, h_2, and h_3. There are eight different trigonometric product functions; the coefficients of four of these are formed by combining the A components of the structure factors, and of the remaining four, by combining the B components. Since the A and B components of each reflection are packed into one word (Stage Oa), it is convenient to process them in pairs and to pack the resulting coefficients in pairs so that one word contains an A part and a B part, which are coefficients for one pair of the eight trigonometric functions.

For each product function present in the series, selected groups of the sorted data have to be combined in some particular way to form the coefficients. The correct main groups and parity groups together with the operations to be used on the data are specified by one space group code word for each pair of trigonometric functions. (For centrosymmetric space groups one space group code word is required for each trigonometric function.) By using this system, a program has been developed which is sufficiently general to handle any space group. It should be noted that no attempt is made to use the full symmetry of space groups with 3-, 4-, or 6-fold axes. Thus, for example, the cubic space groups are treated as orthorhombic by generating the symmetry related reflection data from the non-equivalent data provided as input.

Each space group code word consists of twenty-three binary digits of one machine word. Three bits are used to define one of the trigonometric functions for which the code word is written, with the convention that a zero represents a cosine and a one represents a sine. The eight different parity groups are each represented by one bit whose value, one or zero, indicates whether data from the parity group should or should not be included. Similarly, four bits denote the presence or absence of the main groups. Finally, for each main group present two binary bits are necessary to specify the ways in which the A and B components of any reflection are to be treated. If a group operation bit is a zero the component is to be added when forming the coefficients, while if it is a one the component is to be subtracted.

As an example, consider the construction of a code word in the space group $P2_1/c$, b-axis unique, for the coefficients (3.2) of the function $\cos 2\pi hX . \cos 2\pi kY . \cos 2\pi lZ$. Let the indices be distributed so that,

$$h = h_3, \quad k = h_2, \quad \bar{l} = h_1. \qquad (3.7)$$

In this case since all three functions are cosines, the bits representing the product function must each be zero. The parity condition, $k + l = 2n$, implies that only four of the eight parity groups are used in forming the coefficients. Since the space group is monoclinic, only two of the main groups of data are required, namely those with all indices positive and those with one index negative. For both the Group 0 and Group 1 data the A parts are to be added, while, because the space group is centrosymmetric, all the B parts are zero and the group operation bits for these components are irrelevant. The code word for this trigonometric function is, therefore,

TF		Parity Groups								Main Groups				Group Operations			
										0	1	2	3	0	1	2	3
		eee	eeo	eoe	eoo	oee	oeo	ooe	ooo								
000		1	0	0	1	1	0	0	1	1	1	0	0	00	00	00	00

in which zeros are written for any of the group operation bits not used.

The program first decodes the code word into the four different parts. Then, the data belonging to the first main group and parity group specified by the code word are selected from the magnetic tape and distributed on the drum according to the operation bits for these data. For the same parity group, the next main group data are selected from the input tape and are added or subtracted from the partial coefficients already on the drum, according to the new group operation bits. This procedure continues until all the main group bits have been dealt with. The complete set of coefficients on the drum are then written on the output magnetic tape. Before repeating the process for the next parity group bit a control word is formed for use in the main summation program. This contains six bits, specifying the trigonometric function and parity group for the coefficients just formed. It also indicates how many coefficients have been transferred to tape, and the address of the section containing the first coefficient of the set. Finally, after all the space group code words have been processed, the sign of the first control word is made negative if the space group is non-centrosymmetric, and then, all the control words are transferred to the output tape.

In a non-centrosymmetric space group a given code word contains sufficient information for selecting the appropriate data and forming the coefficients for two trigonometric functions. The TF bits in the word refer to the trigonometric function for which the A parts of the input data are used to form coefficients. To obtain the trigonometric function for the coefficients formed from the B parts, the trigonometric bits of the control words formed at the end of Stage Oc are transformed in Stage I of the main summation program (§3.3.3), by a suitable mask fed in with the structure data. For a given non-centrosymmetric space group this mask is common to all the control words used in Stage I. For example, in the space group $P1$, one code word is used to specify the data to be used for both

$$\cos 2\pi hX . \cos 2\pi k Y . \cos 2\pi lZ \text{ and}$$
$$\sin 2\pi hX . \sin 2\pi k Y . \sin 2\pi lZ$$

functions. Similarly the functions

$$\sin 2\pi hX . \cos 2\pi k Y . \sin 2\pi lZ \text{ and}$$
$$\cos 2\pi hX . \sin 2\pi k Y . \cos 2\pi lZ$$

are represented by one code word, so that the mask used to find the second function needs only to complement the bits representing the first function. This, however, is not always true, and in the space group $Pna2_1$ one of the related pairs of functions is

$$\cos 2\pi hX . \cos 2\pi k Y . \cos 2\pi lZ \text{ and}$$
$$\cos 2\pi hX . \cos 2\pi k Y . \sin 2\pi lZ.$$

Here, only the last of the three terms is changed and this is true for all the code words in this space group. So, even in the general case of $P1$, not more than four space group code words are required.

To complete this section, all the space group code words will be derived for the space group $Pna2_1$ (No. 33, International Tables, Vol. I, 1952). The electron density formula is,

$$V\rho(XYZ)/8 = \overset{h+k=2n,\ l=2n}{\Sigma\ \Sigma\ \Sigma} | F(hkl) | \cos 2\pi hX . \cos 2\pi k Y . \cos[2\pi lZ - \alpha(hkl)]$$
$$- \overset{h+k=2n,\ l=2n+1}{\Sigma\ \Sigma\ \Sigma} | F(hkl) | \sin 2\pi hX . \cos 2\pi k Y . \sin[2\pi lZ - \alpha(hkl)] \quad (3.8)$$
$$- \overset{h+k=2n+1,\ l=2n}{\Sigma\ \Sigma\ \Sigma} | F(hkl) | \sin 2\pi hX . \sin 2\pi k Y . \cos[2\pi lZ - \alpha(hkl)]$$
$$- \overset{h+k=2n+1,\ l=2n+1}{\Sigma\ \Sigma\ \Sigma} | F(hkl) | \cos 2\pi hX . \sin 2\pi k Y . \sin[2\pi lZ - \alpha(hkl)].$$

This space group is orthorhombic so that only Group O data, with positive indices, are present. Suppose that the indices are orientated so that $k = h_1$, $h = h_2$, and $l = h_3$. Then expanding and rearranging the terms, the expression for the electron density becomes,

$$V\rho(XYZ)/8 = \overset{h_1+h_2=2n,\ h_3=2n}{\Sigma\ \Sigma\ \Sigma}[A \cos 2\pi h_3Z . \cos 2\pi h_2X . \cos 2\pi h_1 Y$$
$$+ B \sin 2\pi h_3Z . \cos 2\pi h_2X . \cos 2\pi h_1 Y]$$
$$- \overset{h_1+h_2=2n,\ h_3=2n+1}{\Sigma\ \Sigma\ \Sigma}[A \sin 2\pi h_3Z . \sin 2\pi h_2X . \cos 2\pi h_1 Y$$
$$- B \cos 2\pi h_3Z . \sin 2\pi h_2X . \cos 2\pi h_1 Y] \quad (3.9)$$
$$- \overset{h_1+h_2=2n+1,\ h_3=2n}{\Sigma\ \Sigma\ \Sigma}[A \cos 2\pi h_3Z . \sin 2\pi h_2X . \sin 2\pi h_1 Y$$
$$+ B \sin 2\pi h_3Z . \sin 2\pi h_2X . \sin 2\pi h_1 Y]$$
$$- \overset{h_1+h_2=2n+1,\ h_3=2n+1}{\Sigma\ \Sigma\ \Sigma}[A \sin 2\pi h_3Z . \cos 2\pi h_2X . \sin 2\pi h_1 Y$$
$$- B \cos 2\pi h_3Z . \cos 2\pi h_2X . \sin 2\pi h_1 Y].$$

64 D. W. J. CRUICKSHANK *et al.* [6]

The coefficients for the function $\cos 2\pi h_3 Z . \cos 2\pi h_2 X . \cos 2\pi h_1 Y$ are formed from the A components of structure factors having the parity restriction $h_1 + h_2 = 2n, h_3 = 2n$. This restriction implies that the parity groups for which h_1, h_2, and h_3 are even and for which h_1, h_2 are odd and h_3 is even, are required. The coefficients for the function $\sin 2\pi h_3 Z . \cos 2\pi h_2 X . \cos 2\pi h_1 Y$ are formed from the B components of the same data. One code word is necessary, therefore, for these two functions, and one for each of the remaining three pairs of functions. The complete set of space group code words, needed to control the program in forming the coefficients for this space group are, therefore,

TF	Parity Groups	Main Groups	Group Operations			
000	10010000	1000	00	00	00	00
110	00001001	1000	10	00	00	00
011	01100000	1000	11	00	00	00
101	00000110	1000	10	00	00	00.

In constructing the code words care must be taken to ensure that they are written in terms of the orientated indices, since they are decoded after the data have been reorientated.

3.3. Fourier summation program

3.3.1. *Introductory Remarks*

As already indicated (§3.1), this part of the program computes $\rho(X_3 X_2 X_1)$ by three one-dimensional Fourier summations, with coefficients prepared by the input routines (§3.2). Let these be denoted by $C(h_3 h_2 h_1)$. Although the same program can be used for Fourier or Patterson syntheses and for any part or " patch " of the unit cell, the description given here is for a Fourier synthesis at sections along the X_1 axis, for $X_2 = 0 \to 1$, $X_3 = 0 \to 1$, as this enables the fullest advantage to be taken of the Beevers–Lipson technique. The intervals at which ρ is to be computed may be different along each axis, with the restriction that no intervals may be smaller than 1/120th. (The limit will be lowered when the larger drum has been installed.)

Output is by paper tape punch, at present operating at 33 characters per sec, with ρ expressed in electrons/Å^3, and is described in §3.3.5c. Modifications, due to be made to our Pegasus in the summer of 1960, will include faster output equipment.

§3.3.2 describes the preparation of the trigonometric table required for the summations and Stages I, II and III are described in §§3.3.3 to 3.3.5. Each a or b part of these stages is self-contained in the sense that one can restart at the beginning of any of them, in the event, for example, of a computer fault occurring or of there being insufficient time available to complete a given section.

3.3.2. *Trigonometric Tables*

The layout of the cosine and sine tables greatly affects the speed of a Fourier summation program, but is governed to some extent by the capacity of the immediate-access store of the computer. When this is large—as on the Ferranti Mark I machine—it is convenient to keep a complete cosine table of $\cos 2\pi X$, for $X = 0 \rightarrow 1$, in the computing store. No interpolation is needed and $\sin 2\pi X$ can be read directly from the same table. With Pegasus, however, the problem is complicated by the small capacity of the computing store. To keep such a table on the drum would be very inefficient.

In this program a different scheme is used. Since the main Fourier summation is done by the Beevers–Lipson method, it is convenient to store cos and sin " strips " of unit amplitude. Twelve tables are computed, corresponding to cos or sin, even or odd indices and the required intervals of X_1, X_2 or X_3. In each table for each even (or odd) value of h_i there are entries for all values of X_i from 0 to 1/4. By storing twelve tables instead of four, the intervals chosen along the three axes may be independent of one another.

The cos and sin tables are computed in pairs. A standard sub-routine is used to calculate the first two entries in each table and the recurrence relations,

$$\left.\begin{array}{l} u_{n+2} = 2u_{n+1} \cos \delta\theta - u_n \\ v_{n+2} = 2v_{n+1} \cos \delta\theta - v_n \end{array}\right\}, \qquad (3.10)$$

where u_n, v_n denote $\cos(\theta + n\delta\theta)$, $\sin(\theta + n\delta\theta)$ respectively, are then used to build up the cos and sin tables simultaneously.

3.3.3. *First Summation*

(a) *Stage Ia*. For one value of X_1, the one-dimensional Fourier summation,

$$\sum_{h_1} C(h_3 h_2 h_1) . T(h_1 X_1),$$

is carried out, where $T(h_1 X_1)$ is $\cos 2\pi(h_1 X_1)$ or $\sin 2\pi(h_1 X_1)$ as appropriate for each set of coefficients $C(h_3 h_2 h_1)$, (a " set " being defined as all the data of a given parity in h_1, h_2, h_3 which contribute to a given trigonometric product). The summation is carried out for one set of data at a time, the control word for that set having first been decoded into its components. Two binary digits of the control word cause the correct trigonometric table to be selected. All the data of the set are transferred from magnetic tape to the drum and are then processed, two words at a time, the first word of each pair containing h_3, h_2, h_1 and the second the A and B parts of the coefficient $C(h_3 h_2 h_1)$. The A part is handled first and the results are stored on magnetic tape in pairs of words, the first containing the values of h_2 and h_3 and the second, the corresponding summation over h_1 for the one value of X_1.

As each set is completed a new control word is constructed, containing the tape address of the results, the number of totals stored, and the same 6-bit code, defining the trigonometric function and parities associated with h_3, h_2, h_1, as was contained in the corresponding data control word, formed in Stage Oc (§3.2.4). The sign of the first data control word is then tested to see if the structure is centrosymmetric. If it is, the next set of data is processed immediately. If not, those bits of the data control word which defined the trigonometric function for the A part are transformed to the values appropriate for the B part, by means of the 6-bit mask already referred to (§3.1 and §3.2.4), and the summation process is repeated using the B part of the $C(h_3h_2h_1)$ words. When all sets have been processed, the list of new control words is copied on to magnetic tape at the head of the results, and the next part of the program, Stage Ib, is entered.

(b) *Stage Ib*. The results of Stage Ia are combined so as to form coefficients $C(h_3h_2X_1)$ for the second summation. Each control word, formed in Stage Ia, is decoded and all sets of totals for which the h_3h_2 code bits are 00 00 (i.e. cos.cos. coefficients for h_3, h_2 even) are added together for corresponding values of h_3, h_2. The results are then written on to magnetic tape and the process is repeated for the h_3h_2 code bits, 00 01, and so through all sixteen possible sets. Note that this may result in the addition of A totals to B totals. For example, suppose that, for a given parity group in a non-centrosymmetric orthorhombic space group, the A's contribute to

$$\cos 2\pi h_3 X_3 . \cos 2\pi h_2 X_2 . \cos 2\pi h_1 X_1,$$

and the B's to

$$\cos 2\pi h_3 X_3 . \cos 2\pi h_2 X_2 . \sin 2\pi h_1 X_1.$$

Then, the corresponding Stage Ia totals will be

$$\sum_{h_1} A(h_3 h_2 X_1) \cos 2\pi h_1 X_1$$

and $$\sum_{h_1} B(h_3 h_2 X_1) \sin 2\pi h_1 X_1,$$

and these will be added together in Stage Ib. As before, a list of control words is prepared to control the sequence of operations in Stage IIa, but now only the four code bits referring to h_3 and h_2 are included.

3.3.4. *Second Summation*

(a) *Stage IIa*. In Stage IIa the totals

$$\sum_{h_2} C(h_3 h_2 X_1) . T(h_2 X_2),$$

are computed for every value of h_3 and all $X_2 = 0\rightarrow1/4$, where T has the same significance as in Stage Ia. For one set of coefficients $C(h_3h_2X_1)$, the corresponding control word is decoded into its various parts. The four code bits are separated into two pairs and the appropriate trigonometric tables for $T(h_2X_2)$ selected. One tape section, containing sixteen coefficients, is read from magnetic tape to the drum via the buffer store and while these coefficients are being processed, the next tape section is read into the buffer and is held there until needed. The access time to the magnetic tape is thus minimized.

To process each coefficient, the values of h_2 and h_3 are obtained from the first word of the pair, and the modifier which selects $T(h_2X_2)$ from the table is adjusted to the first entry of the " strip " for h_2. The coefficient $C(h_3h_2X_1)$, contained in the second word, is multiplied by consecutive terms in the table corresponding to $X_2 = 0\rightarrow1/4$. The products, for each X_2, are accumulated for constant h_3, and the value of h_3 is stored at the head of the corresponding totals. The process is repeated for all coefficients of the set. The totals are then transferred to tape and a record kept of the number of different values of h_3 which occur. A new control word is formed containing this counter, the tape address of the first results and the 4-bit code defining the set. When all sets have been completed, the list of control words is copied on to the magnetic tape.

(b) *Stage IIb*. This stage is similar to Stage Ib, in that sets of Stage IIa results with the same h_3 code bits are combined to form coefficients $C(h_3X_2X_1)$ for the third Fourier summation. They are here combined in one of four different ways according to the following rules:

$$C(h_3X_2X_1) = \begin{cases} Ce + Co + Se + So, \text{ for } X_2 = 0\rightarrow1/4; \\ Ce - Co - Se + Se, \text{ for } X_2 = 1/4\rightarrow1/2; \\ Ce - Co + Se - Se, \text{ for } X_2 = 1/2\rightarrow3/4; \\ Ce + Co - Se - Se, \text{ for } X_2 = 3/4\rightarrow1; \end{cases} \quad (3.12)$$

where Ce, Co denote $\sum\limits_{h_2} C(h_3h_2X_1) \cos 2\pi(h_2X_2)$
and Se, So denote $\sum\limits_{h_2} C(h_3h_2X_1) \sin 2\pi(h_2X_2)$

for $X_2 = 0\rightarrow1/4$ and $h_2 = 2n$ or $2n + 1$ respectively. The first time that Stage IIb is entered for a given section X_1, the coefficients $C(h_3X_2X_1)$ are formed according to the first of the above rules. These coefficients are used immediately for the third summation and the results for the whole quadrant, $X_2 = 0\rightarrow1/4$, are computed and punched out (§3.3.5) before returning control to Stage IIb to apply the second rule for the quadrant $X_2 = 1/4\rightarrow1/2$. A list of control words for use in Stage III is formed each time Stage IIb is obeyed; in each of these, only two code bits are needed to select the appropriate trigonometric terms $T(h_3X_3)$ in Stage IIIa.

3.3.5. *Third Summation and Output Routine*

(a) *Stage IIIa*. Each set of coefficients prepared by Stage IIb is processed according to the required trigonometric expression to form

$$\sum_{h_3} C(h_3 X_2 X_1) . T(h_3 X_3), \text{ for } X_2 = 0 \rightarrow 1/4 \text{ and } X_3 = 0 \rightarrow 1/4.$$

For a given value of h_3, one coefficient $C(h_3 X_2 X_1)$ is multiplied by each term in the appropriate $\cos 2\pi h_3 X_3$ or $\sin 2\pi h_3 X_3$ table, for $X_3 = 0 \rightarrow 1/4$. This is repeated for all $X_2 = 0 \rightarrow 1/4$ for the same value of h_3. The coefficients for succeeding values of h_3 are treated similarly and results for each point $(X_3 X_2)$ are accumulated. When one set has been processed the results are written on to magnetic tape and the remaining sets of coefficients are dealt with in the same manner. As before, a table is built up of control words describing the sets of totals.

The actual computing is done in blocks of eight values of X_3 at a time (the number of words involved in a drum transfer), and it is possible to keep the whole loop of instructions for processing one set of coefficients within the computing store, thus making this part of the program very fast.

(b) *Stage IIIb*. Finally, the sets of Stage IIIa results (of which there may be up to four) are combined, according to rules analogous to those given for Stage IIb, for $X_3 = 0 \rightarrow 1/4$ and these results are punched out (see output routine). The second rule is then applied for $X_3 = 1/4 \rightarrow 1/2$ and so on, until the whole quadrant $(X_2 = 0 \rightarrow 1/4, X_3 = 0 \rightarrow 1)$ has been output.

(c) *Output Routine*. The output routine is entered after each sixteenth of a section has been computed (e.g. $X_2 = 0 \rightarrow 1/4$, $X_3 = 0 \rightarrow 1/4$). $\rho(X_3 X_2 X_1)$ is obtained by reading the Stage IIIb totals sequentially from the drum, adding $F(000)$ and multiplying by S/V, where a scale factor, S, may be applied (if, for example, it was necessary to scale $A(hkl)$ and $B(hkl)$ on input). Each value of ρ is punched as a signed integer in electrons/Å^3. The punched paper tape is printed off-line.

At the end of the output routine, control is returned to either:

(i) Stage IIIb to recombine the Stage IIIa totals for the same range of X_2 and next range of X_3;

(ii) Stage IIb to recombine the Stage IIa totals for the next range of X_2;

or (iii) Stage Ia to begin the next section for the next value of X_1.

Note that the sequence of printing such areas as $X_2 = 1/4 \rightarrow 1/2$, $X_3 = 1/4 \rightarrow 1/2$ is in the correct order—although these terms are in fact computed and stored in the computer in the order $X_2 = 1/2 \rightarrow 1/4$, $X_3 = 1/2 \rightarrow 1/4$.

3.4. Operating speed

The program has been used for observed and difference Fourier syntheses and for Patterson syntheses. For an observed Fourier synthesis in the space group $P2_1/n$, the time of input of 1800 independent reflections from paper to magnetic tape (Stage Oa) was 20 minutes. The time taken for the group sorting depends very much on the order in which the data are supplied. In this case, the data were badly ordered on the paper tape and the group sorting took 40 minutes, while the numerical sorting took 10 minutes. The formation of the coefficients (Stage Oc) took 30 minutes, giving a total time of 1 hour 40 minutes for input and sorting. Sorting the data with only two mechanisms is unavoidably slow, and it is hoped to improve these times in the near future when more magnetic tape mechanisms will be available. We now (March, 1960) have a third mechanism installed and undergoing tests and hope to have a fourth one this summer. Further time can be saved by combining Stage Oa with the group sorting; as each reflection is read from paper tape it can be placed immediately in the correct group according to the signs and parities of its indices.

The total time required for computing each section of 60×30 points in this example is approximately 28 minutes. Due to the slow output equipment, almost half this time was spent in punching results (12 minutes per section); this situation will be improved when faster punches become available. Of the remaining 16 minutes, Stage Ia and Stage Ib together took about 4 minutes and Stage IIa, 3 minutes. Stage IIb took $1\frac{1}{2}$ minutes each time it was obeyed, i.e. 6 minutes in all, and Stage IIIa 3 minutes in all. The computing time for Stage IIIb was a matter of seconds and was included in the output time. The time for computing the trigonometric tables (which, for $\delta X_1 = 1/15$, $\delta X_2 = 1/60$ and $\delta X_3 = 1/30$, and for $|h_1|_{max} = 7$, $|h_2|_{max} = 25$, $|h_3|_{max} = 15$, required 1200 entries) was 30 seconds.

4. ANCILLARY PROGRAMS

4.1. Dimensions

4.1.1. *Introduction*

The program is designed to determine the distances between an atom and its nearest neighbours, and the angles between the directions of contact. Production of next-but-one-neighbour distances and angles within molecules is excluded as far as possible.

Two separate sets of distances are of interest to the crystallographer. The first set are those between bonded atoms. These will be distances less than some maximum l_1, dependent on the compound being studied. The second set are the van der Waals distances, which will be less than a value l_2 (usually larger than l_1). The latter are generated by symmetry and/or translational operations on the asymmetric unit. For maximum efficiency in the program the atoms chosen for the asymmetric unit should form a molecule or part of a molecule. If this is not done, some genuine bond lengths will be listed among the van der Waals contacts. If the asymmetric unit contains more than one molecule, it is necessary to make $l_1 = l_2$ to obtain intermolecular contacts.

It is neither necessary nor possible to specify which bonds or which contacts are to be produced; all those less than l_1 or l_2 are produced automatically.

4.1.2. *Operation of the Program*

The crystallographer must supply the unit cell dimensions, space group, a list of atomic coordinates (with a chemical symbol and a number for each atom as in §2) and the maximum lengths l_1 and l_2.

The program operates in five stages:

stage A   The coordinates supplied, which refer to the crystal axes, are transformed to standard orthogonal axes and these new coordinates are printed. This stage is omitted for orthogonal space groups.

stage B   Distances less than l_1 within the asymmetric unit are calculated and printed; the direction cosines are calculated and stored.

stage C   The angles subtended at each atom by those vectors in B, which include this atom, are calculated and printed.

stage D   Interatomic distances, less than l_2, between each atom in the asymmetric unit and all surrounding atoms (other than those in the asymmetric unit) are calculated and printed; as in stage C, the direction cosines are stored.

stage E   For each atom in the asymmetric unit all possible angles between the vectors found in B and those found in D and also all the angles between the vectors found in D (which include this atom) are calculated and printed.

The direction cosines can be printed if required. Any of stages C, D or E can be omitted if desired.

The results are printed unambiguously; every atom involved in a quoted distance or angle appears with its chemical symbol and number. Enough information is also printed in stages D and E to show how each atom is related by symmetry and translation to the corresponding one in the symmetric unit. Each distance appears twice in stage D (e.g. as O $2' -$ C 3 and C $3' -$ O 2); this acts as a check that vectors have not been missed and is necessary for the operation of stage E.

4.1.3. *Programming Methods*

In stage A the coordinates are transformed to refer to a standard set of orthogonal axes, in which $\mathbf{b_0}$ coincides with $\mathbf{b}$, $\mathbf{a_0}$ is the projection of $\mathbf{a}$ on the plane perpendicular to $\mathbf{b_0}$, and $\mathbf{c_0}$ is perpendicular to $\mathbf{a_0}$ and $\mathbf{b_0}$. The orthogonal coordinates X, Y and Z in Å are related to the original x, y and z, also in Å, by

$$X = x \sin \gamma + z(\cos \beta - \cos \alpha \cos \gamma)/\sin \gamma,$$
$$Y = y + x \cos \gamma + z \cos \alpha, \qquad\qquad (4.1)$$
$$Z = z[\sin^2\alpha - \{(\cos \beta - \cos \alpha \cos \gamma)/\sin \gamma\}^2]^{\frac{1}{2}}.$$

Both the original and the orthogonal coordinates are stored.

If only bond lengths and angles are required, these orthogonal coordinates are used in stages B and C. If the van der Waals distances be required, the original coordinates are adjusted so that all the fractional coordinates x/a, y/b and z/c lie between $-\frac{1}{2}$ and $\frac{1}{2}$; these and the corresponding orthogonal coordinates (which are also printed) are stored and used for further calculation.

In stage B, since the square root routine is comparatively slow, the exact interatomic distance r is only calculated when the sum of squares is less than l_1^2. For each relevant distance, the atom designations and r are printed and also stored together with the direction cosines.

In stage C the atom designations for all the vectors obtained in B are compared in pairs and for vectors with a common atom the angles are calculated from the direction cosines. The angles are punched out and printed but not stored.

For stage D two processes are required in addition to those in stage B; these are the generation of all the atoms related to those of the asymmetric unit by the space group symmetry and the generation of atoms in unit cells bounding the one containing a given atom.

Consider first, contacts between the asymmetric unit and atoms obtained purely by translation. Suppose there is a single molecule in the cell of a structure with space group $P1$. This molecule may be in contact with molecules in any one of the surrounding 26 cells (the full set forming a block of $3 \times 3 \times 3 = 27$ cells). If the coordinates of the original molecule are chosen (as is done in stage A) to lie within the ranges $-\frac{1}{2} < x/a$, y/b, $z/c \leqslant \frac{1}{2}$ it is not necessary to explore the full volume of this block of 27 cells for contacts between the molecule and its neighbours, but only the volume of a block of $2 \times 2 \times 2 = 8$ cells whose centre is the origin. Consequently the adjacent parts of the 26 possible molecules can be generated by only $8 - 1 = 7$ operations, corresponding to unit translation along each of the three axes, along any two or along all three at once. For a given coordinate the unit translation is negative if the coordinate is positive and vice versa. The new coordinates generated in this fashion are transformed to orthogonal axes and distances less than l_2 are calculated between these atoms and those of the asymmetric unit.

Coordinates for symmetry-related atoms are generated from the asymmetric unit in the form given in the International Tables, Vol. I (1952), for the equivalent positions, and then converted to the orthogonal system. Again the distances less than l_2 between these atoms and those of the asymmetric unit are printed. The symmetry-related atoms are generated again and the first translational operation applied, and this is continued until all the possible translations have been made to atoms generated by one symmetry element. The process is repeated until all the equivalent positions in the space group have been covered.

To carry out this part of the program it is necessary to have a number of sub-routines, one for each set of symmetry-related positions. These sub-routines are called for by a master program which is specific to the space group. At present, master programs and the necessary sub-routines are available for 12 of the most common space groups. Instruction sheets for writing other routines have been prepared for readers with no knowledge of programming. A new sub-routine or the master program for a new space group takes about an hour to prepare.

Stage E proceeds as stage C but only the designations of the atoms in the asymmetric unit are scanned.

4.1.4. *Experience*

We have used the program on some 40 structures in triclinic, monoclinic, orthorhombic and tetragonal space groups. It has frequently produced contacts that even model-conscious crystallographers had not expected. The calculations in parts D and E are often considerable. For instance in a $P2_12_12_1$ example with 12 atoms in the asymmetric unit and $l_2 = 4.3$ Å, about 100 inter-molecular contacts and 400 angles were found in a calculation lasting about 35 minutes. Stages A and B alone are often used to provide a quick check that a newly prepared coordinate list is reasonable before it is used in a lengthy refinement cycle. Except in stage D the rate of output is limited by the rate of punching.

4.1.5. *Molecular Plane*

Dr. A. M. B. Douglas has written a program in Autocode (a simple symbolic code) for determining the best plane through a set of atoms, whose coordinates are referred to orthogonal axes. The program uses the method described on p. 93 of the International Tables, Vol. II (1959), and finds the minimum characteristic value of the weighted second moment distribution. The printed results give the equation of the plane, the deviation of each atom from this plane and the centre of gravity of the molecule for the weights chosen.

4.2. Determination of the molecular vibration tensors T_{ij} and ω_{ij}

For molecules whose internal vibrations are much smaller than their rigid body vibrations in the crystal, the rigid-body translation and rotation vibration tensors T_{ij} and ω_{ij} can be determined from the individual atomic tensors U_{ij} by the least-squares method described by Cruickshank (1956c). Although not of the same magnitude as those in a SFLS refinement cycle, the necessary calculations are rather intricate, especially when the crystal axes are not orthogonal, and a program has therefore been written for this analysis. It also calculates the corrections to the atomic coordinates caused by rotational oscillations of the molecule (Cruickshank, 1956d).

It is not usually certain, however, that the internal vibrations can be neglected and it is necessary to check carefully that the rigid-body assumption is satisfactory. The program helps this to be done by providing rather full information about each observed and calculated U_{ij} tensor in several forms, including the values of the tensors (and coordinates) with respect to the principal axes of inertia of the molecule. A complete determination of the internal normal modes of a molecule, as well as T_{ij} and ω_{ij}, from the atomic U_{ij} is, of course, impossible as there are more unknowns than observations. The present least-squares method could, however, be extended to find the absolute magnitude of a limited number of internal normal vibrations in which the relative magnitudes of the vibrations of the different atoms were assumed.

The operation of the program requires the following data:

(i) The cell angles α, β, γ;

(ii) The coordinates of the molecular centre of symmetry, if any (this is the only molecular symmetry element automatically covered by the program);

(iii) The atomic coordinates x_i in Å and vibration tensors U_{ij} in Å² with respect to the crystal axes (coordinates should be given for any atoms, say hydrogens, whose U_{ij} are not known);

(iv) The atomic masses;

(v) The weights assigned to each U_{ij} for the LS equations;

(vi) The breadth parameters q^2 of the atomic peak shapes (required for the coordinate corrections, Cruickshank, 1956d).

The calculation proceeds in the following stages:

(1)   Transform the x_i and U_{ij} to the standard orthogonal axes defined by equation (4.1).

(2)   Find the principal vibration magnitudes and directions of each atomic U_{ij} tensor w.r.t. the standard axes.

(3)   Find the mass centre and principal moments of inertia of the molecule

F

and their directions. For a flat molecule, the best molecular plane is thus a by-product of the calculations.

(4)   Transform the x_i and U_{ij} to the inertial axes.

(5)   Set up the 12 × 12 least-squares equations for T_{ij} and ω_{ij}.

(6)   Solve for T_{ij} and ω_{ij} w.r.t. the inertial axes. This set of axes is chosen because the T_{ij} and ω_{ij} tensors are often then nearly diagonal.

(7)   Find the principal magnitudes and directions of T_{ij} and ω_{ij} w.r.t. the inertial and the standard axes.

(8)   Compute U_{ij}^{calc} from T_{ij} and ω_{ij} w.r.t. the inertial, standard and crystal axes. This is done for all atoms for which coordinates have been supplied.

(9)   Compute $\Delta U_{ij} = U_{ij}^{\text{obs}} - U_{ij}^{\text{calc}}$ w.r.t. the inertial axes.

(10)   Compute the r.m.s. ΔU_{ij}.

(11)   Find the E.S.D.'s of the elements of T_{ij} and ω_{ij}.

(12)   In the direction of the radius to the mass centre, find for each atom the observed and calculated values of U, also ΔU. Find the r.m.s. radial ΔU. If the rigid body approximation is justified, all the vibration in this direction arises from T_{ij}.

(13)   Find the principal magnitudes and directions of $(U_{ij}^{\text{obs}} - T_{ij})$ for each atom w.r.t. the inertial axes. The purpose of this is to assist the detection of any internal twisting vibrations.

(14)   Calculate the radial corrections to the coordinates caused by the angular oscillations.

(15)   Print revi sedcoordinates for all atoms w.r.t. the inertial, standard and crystal axes.

Apart from the elements of the 12 × 12 LS equations, the full results from each stage of the calculation are printed.

The program takes about 30 minutes to run for a molecule with 10 atoms; about half the time is absorbed in the punching of results.

The transformations of the coordinates in Å and the vibration tensors in Å² from the orthogonal standard axes, suffix S, to the orthogonal inertial axes, suffix I, is straightforward. If the coordinate transformation is

$$\mathbf{x}_I = \mathbf{A}\mathbf{x}_S, \qquad (4.2)$$

the tensor transformation is

$$\mathbf{U}_I = \mathbf{A}\mathbf{U}_S\mathbf{A}', \qquad (4.3)$$

where $\mathbf{A}'$ is the transposed matrix. Rather more care has to be taken with the transformation from the triclinic crystal axes, suffix C, to the standard orthogonal axes. If the coordinate transformation is

$$\mathbf{x}_S = \mathbf{B}\mathbf{x}_C, \qquad (4.4)$$

(equivalent to writing (4.1) as $\mathbf{X} = \mathbf{B}\mathbf{x}$) the tensor transformation is

$$\mathbf{U}_S = (\mathbf{D}\mathbf{B})\mathbf{U}_C(\mathbf{D}\mathbf{B})',$$

where **D** is a diagonal matrix whose elements are equal to the lengths of the axes reciprocal to the unit axes parallel to the crystal axes, e.g.

$$d_{11} = \sin \alpha / N, \tag{4.6}$$

where $N^2 = 1 + 2 \cos \alpha \cos \beta \cos \gamma - \cos^2 \alpha - \cos^2 \beta - \cos^2 \gamma$.

4.3. Reduction of triclinic and monoclinic cells

Of the many possible primitive cells which can be selected from a triclinic lattice, two are unique. One of these contains a pair of triobtuse-angled corners and the other contains a pair of triacute-angled corners. The triobtuse cell is known as the Delaunay reduced cell (Delaunay, 1933) and any primitive cell can be reduced to this form by a simple algorithm (Patterson and Love, 1957). The triacute cell is easily obtained from the Delaunay cell. One of these two primitive cells contains the three shortest non-coplanar translations of the lattice and is known as the Dirichlet cell. Thus the Dirichlet cell either coincides with the Delaunay cell or is the triacute form readily obtainable from it. Either of these forms provides a convenient method of classification of crystals (in terms of the ratio c/b, for example), particularly in the triclinic system.

A program has been written for use on the Pegasus computer, for reducing triclinic cells to both the Delaunay and Dirichlet forms. The axial lengths and interaxial angles of both reduced cells are printed with the convention $c \leqslant a \leqslant b$ (Donnay and Nowacki, 1952), together with the volume of the cell and the axial ratios a/b and c/b of the Dirichlet cell. The output also includes two transformation matrices showing the relation between the axes of each reduced cell and the experimental data provided.

A similar but simpler program is available for the reduction of monoclinic cells in the *ac* plane, to give the shortest *a* and *c*.

5. PEGASUS PROGRAMS BY OTHER GROUPS

In addition to the Leeds group, a number of other groups of users have prepared extensive series of programs for crystallographic calculations on Pegasus. Some of these programs which are available for general use are briefly described below.

5.1. Structure factor diagonal least squares program

This program written by Dr. H. Judith Milledge (University College, London) and Mr. D. Milledge (Ferranti, Ltd.) is a comprehensive least squares system on a scale similar to that of the SFLS program described in §2. It covers all space groups and refines, with the diagonal LS approximation, the $|F_o|$ scale, atomic coordinates, isotropic vibrations and the three magnitudes of the individual anisotropic vibrations for ellipsoids of specified orientations. Unit LS weights are ordinarily applied. E.S.D.'s are computed. Both the real and imaginary parts of the dispersion correction can be applied if desired.

The program has facilities for adding or subtracting one or more reflections at any stage of a cycle, which is very useful for testing whether, say, implausible bond lengths are due to the effects of some extinguished reflections. For the trial structure stage, the program has facilities for calculating successive cycles with expanding ranges of $\sin \theta / \lambda$ as the refinement proceeds; coupled to this is a facility for shifting a molecule as a whole.

5.2. Intensity data processing

This program by H. J. and D. Milledge produces $|F_o|^2$ or $|F_o|$ tapes for the SFLS program, §5.1, from an intensity tape. *Inter alia*, it applies the conventional Lorentz-polarization corrections, extinction corrections, the Phillips upper-layer Weissenberg correction and spherical or cylindrical absorption corrections.

5.3. HKL sequence

This program by H. J. and D. Milledge generates all possible (hkl) triplets for a given space group in a given $\sin \theta / \lambda$ range.

5.4. Molecular geometry

This program by H. J. and D. Milledge calculates, for desired atoms, bond lengths and cosines, bond angles, and the molecular plane and the deviations from it.

5.5. Contour output Fourier synthesis program

This program by Dr. P. A. Samet (University of Durham, King's College, Newcastle-upon-Tyne) has the special features of a single character output and a continuously variable coordinate mesh, which allows orthogonal sections to be printed out to scale ready for contouring.

The program is for two-dimensional Fourier synthesis, but has additional facilities to sum $F_l \genfrac{}{}{0pt}{}{\sin}{\cos} 2\pi l z$ for the preparation of sections.

The main program calculates

$$\frac{1}{C} \sum_{-H}^{H} \sum_{0}^{K} F \genfrac{}{}{0pt}{}{\sin}{\cos} 2\pi(hx + ky),$$

or one of the sums of the cos.cos, sin.sin, cos.sin or sin.cos terms. If required by the space group two or more such outputs can be added. The maximum indices are $H \leqslant 40$, $K \leqslant 45$, L unlimited, all K positive.

There is no limitation as to the interval of coordinate mesh or on the starting points of patch syntheses, but the number of points in any one synthesis must not exceed a maximum of 66 × 130. The output is in a single character code for direct contour plotting. The F's are input serially by a special input routine.

The times including print-out for a projection or section of 30 × 60 points with 500 coefficients are 15 min in $P2/m$, 35 min in $P2_1/c$.

Acknowledgments

Our thanks are due first to Professor E. G. Cox for his continuous encouragement of these projects and to Dr. F. R. Ahmed for his help and skill in launching our work at Manchester; to Dr. R. K. Bullough, Mr. J. F. P. Donovan and Mr. R. Shiono for help with programs for the Ferranti Mark I computer; to Mr. R. A. Brooker and members of the Manchester University Computing Machine Laboratory for their unfailing co-operation and the use of their facilities for six years; to Drs. A. M. B. Douglas, R. Hine, Messrs. L. N. Becka and G. Walker for help with programs for the Pegasus computer; to Dr. A. S. Douglas, Director of the Leeds University Electronic Computing Laboratory; to Miss Mary Jowett and Mrs. Barbara Hawkshaw who have done many production runs for us; and to the Department of Scientific and Industrial Research for financial support.

REFERENCES

AHMED, F. R. and BARNES, W. H. (1958). *Acta Cryst.* **11**, 669.
AHMED, F. R. and CRUICKSHANK, D. W. J. (1953). *Acta Cryst.* **6**, 765.
AYERST, E. M. and DUKE, J. R. C. (1954). *Acta Cryst.* **7**, 588.
BOOTH, A. D. (1946). *Trans. Faraday Soc.* **42**, 444.
CRUICKSHANK, D. W. J. (1949). *Acta Cryst.* **2**, 65.
CRUICKSHANK, D. W. J. (1954). *Acta Cryst.* **7**, 624.
CRUICKSHANK, D. W. J. (1956a). *Acta Cryst.* **9**, 915.
CRUICKSHANK, D. W. J. (1956b). *Acta Cryst.* **9**, 747.
CRUICKSHANK, D. W. J. (1956c). *Acta Cryst.* **9**, 754.
CRUICKSHANK, D. W. J. (1956d). *Acta Cryst.* **9**, 757.
CRUICKSHANK, D. W. J. (1957a). *Acta Cryst.* **10**, 747.
CRUICKSHANK, D. W. J. (1957b). *Acta Cryst.* **10**, 470.
CRUICKSHANK, D. W. J., JEFFREY, G. A. and NYBURG, S. C. (1959). *Z. Kristallogr.* **112**, 385.
CRUICKSHANK, D. W. J. and ROBERTSON, A. P. (1953). *Acta Cryst.* **6**, 698.
DELAUNAY, B. (1933). *Z. Kristallogr.* **84**, 109.
DONNAY, J. H. D. and NOWACKI, W. (1954). *Crystal Data.* Geological Society of America. Memoir No. 60.
ERIKS, K. and MACGILLAVRY, C. H. (1954). *Acta Cryst.* **7**, 430.
FINCH, J., GREEN, D. W., HOLMES, K. C. and NORTH, A. C. T. (1958). *Brit. J. App. Phys.* **9**, 1.
HODGKIN, D. C., KAMPER, J., LINDSEY, J., MACKAY, M., PICKWORTH, J., ROBERTSON, J. H., SHOEMAKER, C. B., WHITE, J. C., PROSEN, R. J. and TRUEBLOOD, K. N. (1957). *Proc. Roy. Soc.* A **242**, 228.
HUGHES, E. W. (1941). *J. Amer. Chem. Soc.* **63**, 1737.

International Tables for X-ray Crystallography, Vol. I. (1952). The Kynoch Press, Birmingham, England.
International Tables for X-ray Crystallography, Vol. II. (1959). The Kynoch Press, Birmingham, England.
PATTERSON, A. L. and LOVE, W. E. (1957). *Acta Cryst.* **10,** 11.
ROLLETT, J. S. and DAVIES, D. R. (1955). *Acta Cryst.* **8,** 125.
SPARKS, R. A. (1958). *Thesis,* University of California, Los Angeles, U.S.A.
TRUTER, M. R. (1960). *J. Chem. Soc.* (in press).
TRUTER, M. R., CRUICKSHANK, D. W. J. and JEFFREY, G. A. (1960). *Acta Cryst.* **13.** 855.
WHEATLEY, P. J. (1960). *Acta Cryst.* **13,** 80.

Paper 6a

CRYSTALLOGRAPHIC CALCULATIONS ON
THE FERRANTI PEGASUS COMPUTER

by H. J. MILLEDGE

Department of Chemical Crystallography, University College,
Gower Street, London, W.C.1, England

and D. MILLEDGE

Ferranti Ltd., 68 Newman Street, London, W.1, England

ABSTRACT

The main programmes written at University College, London, are:

1. Intensity Processing, for applying absorption, Lorentz-polarization, spot-shape and extinction corrections to X-ray intensities, obtaining the average scale and temperature factors from a Wilson plot, and printing $\sin \theta$ (or related functions) for any reflection (hkl). Reflections can then be sorted in ascending order of $\sin \theta$ and/or unitary structure factors obtained.

2. A comprehensive structure factor and diagonal least squares programme for refining the scale factor, co-ordinates x, y, z, individual isotropic temperature factors, anisotropic temperature factors along the axes of ellipsoids in specified orientations, and the percentage of an atom occupying a site x, y, z; preset fractions of the various shifts obtained can be applied to the next cycle of refinement. Weights may be specified, and e.s.d. obtained. Individual reflections may be subtracted from a completed refinement.

Special facilities intended for use at the trial structure stage can (a) generate fractional co-ordinates x, y, z for a molecule whose origin, orientation and co-ordinates in Å are specified; (b) shift the molecule as a whole along one or more axes; (c) calculate Pattersons or Fouriers serially or at specified points for up to 40 reflections at a time selected from the SFLS output tape; (d) exclude reflections from the refinement unless F(calc) exceeds a specified fraction of F(obs).

3. A molecular geometry programme which calculates, for specified atoms, bond lengths and cosines, bond angles, and the molecular plane and deviations from it in Å. It can also print orthogonal Å co-ordinates for drawing or model-building.

Three years' experience with these programmes suggests that certain other facilities would be desirable, and some are briefly discussed.

1. Introduction

A group of programmes designed to carry out almost all the operations involved in the solution and refinement of crystal structures has been based on the following assumptions:

1. There should be as few actual programme tapes and as little repunching of data between the various stages of calculation as possible.

2. All programmes should be self-resetting, so that any job can be broken in the middle (e.g. if a data-tape error is noticed) and another job of a completely different kind commenced at once.

3. Almost all parameters should be capable of being readily altered *independently* between cycles of calculation.

4. Adequate printing should appear at the beginning of the calculation to enable the operator to detect unacceptable data (e.g. negative temperature factors) and to indicate at a later date exactly what calculation was performed.

5. Crystallographic criteria should appear at the end of a calculation in a form which permits snap decisions to be taken before continuing.

6. Adequate facilities should be provided for salvaging refinements containing errors not detected on input (e.g. F(obs) punched as -104 instead of $-10{\cdot}4$), and for breaking and restarting the job at any point.

7. Versatility is much more important than speed.

2. The Intensity Processing Programme

At present this programme reads I(obs) and applies any or all of:

(*a*) Lorentz-polarization corrections for oscillation, rotation, powder or Weissenberg data (but not precession pictures).

(*b*) Spot-shape corrections for upper-layer equi-inclination Weissenbergs.

(*c*) Spherical or cylindrical absorption corrections, and approximate ellipsoidal absorption corrections derived therefrom by appropriate distortions of the reciprocal lattice (details to be published).

(*d*) Some empirical forms of extinction correction now under study.

(*e*) The programme prints (hkl) and $\sin \theta$ or related functions, and F(obs) or I(obs) on any desired scale. (hkl) can either be specified, or obtained from a routine for generating all possible (hkl) triplets for a given spacegroup in a given $\sin \theta/\lambda$ range.

(*f*) The sum of (F(obs))^2 is accumulated for 8 subdivisions of a specified $\sin^2\theta/\lambda^2$ range, and results are printed so that the average scale and temperature factor can be obtained from a Wilson plot.

(*g*) This information can be accepted and a set of unitary structure factors produced.

(*h*) Tabulated sharpening functions can be applied as though they were absorption corrections.

(*i*) An associated programme accepts the tape containing hkl $\sin \theta$ F(obs) and produces a tape with these values sorted in ascending order of $\sin \theta$. This is useful either for indexing powder photographs, or for dividing the data into successive ranges for least squares refinements.

A facility is also being added to index oscillation photographs for crystals of any symmetry in any orientation (or to provide the settings for crystal and counter for the measurement of individual reflections, which is almost the same problem mathematically).

Output tapes from this programme are the input data tapes for the Structure Analysis programme.

3. The Structure Analysis Programme

This is primarily a diagonal least squares programme by means of which positional co-ordinates x, y, z, the scale factor, individual isotropic temperature factors, and the anisotropic temperature factors along the *axes* of an ellipsoid in a specified orientation (or in any other chosen direction in the ellipsoid) can be refined. For the calculation of anisotropic temperature factors it generates the conventional six $(b(ij)$ components for the ellipsoids specified, but can accept such $b(ij)$ values directly if desired. A diagonal $b(ij)$ refinement is to be added.

The minimum time per structure factor is about 2 seconds, and increases with the complexity of the job. The whole programme is written in fixed point, and several scaling parameters are available to keep the calculations in the optimum range for which the programme is designed. It is at present restricted to positive fractional co-ordinates x, y, z and positive values of l (h and k may be negative), but these restrictions will shortly be removed.

The necessary equivalent points for the required spacegroup are specified according to a simple code, and for cubic (or rhombohedral) crystals the cyclic permutation $xyz \rightarrow zxy \rightarrow yzx$ can be accomplished by the programme. If all possible (hkl) values are to be generated for any spacegroup, the reflection conditions (as found in Vol. I of *The International Tables for X-ray Crystallography*) are also coded as a pseudo-machine order, so that absent reflections are eliminated.

If separate estimates of related intensities (e.g. $F(hkl)$, $F(\bar{h}kl)$, etc. for a crystal having spacegroup *Pbca*) are available, then instead of averaging these and using only the $F(hkl)$ quadrant of the reciprocal lattice, separate x, y, z co-ordinates can be supplied for each of the symmetry-related molecules, and these molecules can all be refined as though they were independent, providing a correspondingly increased volume of the reciprocal lattice is used to provide *independent observations*. The spread of the results for the symmetry-related molecules may be compared with errors derived from the usual type of calculation involving only one asymmetric unit. (Ideas similar to this were discussed by Prof. D. Harker at the Leningrad Conference in May, 1959).

Atomic scattering factors for up to eight different types of atom are tabulated at not more than 36 equal intervals for the $\sin \theta/\lambda$ range required, and each $f(hkl)$ value obtained from these tables by linear interpolation.

Tables stored at different intervals may be used in the same structure-factor calculation. Tabulated scattering factors have been punched as Pegasus Library subroutines, and the atoms required for any job may therefore be selected by the data tape from existing Library tapes (on which they may occur in any order), or special curves may be tabulated as better calculations become available. Some preliminary trials have been made with anisotropic scattering factors, but these routines have not yet been incorporated in the main programme. Anomalous dispersion corrections Df' and Df'' may be specified for each type of atom.

A different isotropic temperature factor may be applied to each scattering factor on input, and the whole curve may be multiplied by any fraction to allow for atoms in special positions or non-stoichometric structures. The whole scattering-factor calculation may be dispensed with if point-atoms are used (for example in neutron diffraction calculations, or for unitary structure factors).

The programme has various options for dealing with unobserved reflections, and can be used with arbitrary weights or unit weights (either by not specifying any weights, or by ignoring those specified); it provides standard deviations for the parameters refined, and all necessary totals for combining the results of jobs run at different times. Thus a three-dimensional refinement can produce a single answer, or cumulative refinements layer by layer.

First, second, third and fourth moments of dF are obtained, and a routine is being added to analyse these moments of dF to indicate whether the differences between $F(\text{obs})$ and $F(\text{calc})$ are random, and if not, how the distribution differs from a normal one. It is hoped that experience with such an analysis will help in:

(*a*) the detection of systematic errors in the data,

(*b*) estimating the usefulness of various weighting systems,

(*c*) estimating the nature and effect of the remaining errors in the calculated structure factors, and hence

(*d*) deciding when reasonable convergence has been achieved.

The programme also has a facility for subtracting unwanted values after the job has been completed, so that a wrongly punched reflection can be subtracted and the correct value added. This facility is also useful for observing the effect of a few reflections suffering from extinction on the various parameters.

The programme can be used to refine very large jobs 40 atoms at a time by adding a set of partial structure factors into its present calculations. This saves time, for example, in a structure containing a lot of hydrogen, which ought to be included in the calculation, but is not worth altering every cycle. It could also be used to find the water molecules in Vitamin B_{12}, say, if the rest of the structure were considered known. It is worth noting that any refinement of an unlimited number of variables can be split up in this way; the same answers are obtained as would result from handling all the variables simultaneously, providing that cross-terms between parameters refined in different sections of the job are not required.

All the parameters can be readily varied independently, and the programme can easily be used by non-programmers, though obviously non-crystallographers cannot really be taught to react to the output as efficiently as an experienced crystallographer.

The programme has proved highly efficient on a wide variety of two- and three-dimensional refinements, both centrosymmetric and non-centrosymmetric, when used with properly chosen shifts. It is possible to apply a different fraction $1/n$ of the shift (where n is an integer) to atoms of different atomic number, and the fractions can be varied independently for co-ordinates and temperature factors. The most commonly successful fractions, or " damping factors " are half-shifts for the co-ordinates and quarter-shifts for the temperature factors of the heaviest atom present, and even greater damping factors for the lighter atoms present; rough approximations being an additional factor of $(Z_{heavy}/2 Z_{light})$. An inspection of the behaviour of the shifts in successive cycles and the corresponding changes in F(calc) relative to the changes still necessary to obtain good agreement with F(obs) usually provides a good enough guide to ensure rapid convergence, and some other rules of an empirical nature can also be employed.

4. Facilities for use at the trial structure stage

The most interesting features of the programme are its special facilities for use at the trial structure stage. These reflect a geometrical rather than a statistical approach to the problem, since one can be certain that the crystal will contain atoms in a sensible chemical arrangement. Frequently the configuration of the molecule itself is known, or at least some possible alternatives are known (e.g. that it is either a *cis-* or *trans-*isomer), whereas its position and orientation in the unit cell are unknown.

Accordingly, the programme has a range of facilities for reading the co-ordinates of a molecule in Å, rotating and/or shifting it in the unit cell, generating the corresponding fractional co-ordinates, and calculating structure factors for comparison with F(obs). This technique is especially useful if some preliminary information is available about the structure (such as diamagnetic anisotropy data), and the remaining degrees of freedom can be systematically explored in a single run on the computer, using an appropriate loop tape carrying the F(obs) list for the low-order reflections in one tape reader, and the variation instructions in the other.

In testing the convergence of SFLS refinements from rather poor trial co-ordinates for known structures, it has been found that while most of the parameters converge reasonably well towards the correct structure, a few tend to run amok. The only way in which this can be rapidly spotted is by calculating bond-lengths and angles after each cycle. At present this cannot be done within the main SFLS programme, and is certainly the most desirable facility which is to be added. The molecule can then be roughly " squared up " (or accurately repositioned using the co-ordinate generator routine) before continuing the refinement.

This combination of a co-ordinate generator programme and a bond-seeking programme will also permit experiments on the selection or rejection of trial structures on the *purely geometric criteria* of reasonable inter-molecular contacts (sensible intra-molecular distances having been incorporated already in the chemical model being tested), instead of by comparing F(obs) and F(calc). The systematic investigation of possible spatial arrangements may perhaps produce acceptable trial structures faster than other methods, and seems well worth investigating.

5. Point-Fourier calculations

In the early stages of a structure it is very useful to be able to compute Patterson or Fourier sections or projections, often only with a few large terms whose signs are known or are to be permuted. The SFLS programme can be made to print any (or none) of F(obs) [scaled], F(calc), dF, $w.dF$, or the corresponding A and B terms for non-centrosymmetric structures, for each reflection. It also has an input routine for extracting any one of these quantities for up to 40 reflections at a time in a specified intensity range from the F(calc) output tape. With these it can compute Fouriers (or Pattersons with their squares) at a few selected points (e.g. atom centres) at any desired subdivisions of the cell edges, or systematically over the whole cell. This is not intended to be a complete Fourier programme, since it is slow and of limited capacity, but it is exceptionally versatile, and does have provision for adding or subtracting a previous Fourier output tape placed in the second tape-reader, so that it can be a very efficient way of changing a few signs, or gradually building up the F(obs) Fourier as signs are progressively determined.

6. Elimination of terms with doubtful signs from the refinement

The other really valuable facility which has been provided sounds quite trivial. It is possible to exclude a term from the refinement process unless F(calc) exceeds a specified fraction of F(obs)—i.e. unless its sign is determined with a fair degree of certainty. This idea seems to have been first used by Gillis (unpublished), and provides an extremely powerful method of speeding up the convergence of a least squares refinement. Empirical rules governing the choice of this " acceptable fraction " in different structures at different stages of refinement are still being worked out.

7. Method of operation of the Structure Analysis Programme

The programme could, for example, combine its various facilities by starting with the F(obs) tape for the pgg projection of a heavy-atom structure. The Patterson–Harker lines could be computed using the 40 strongest terms (thereby fixing the origin of a molecule whose orientation had previously been determined from diamagnetic anisotropy measurements). The programme could then generate the necessary fractional co-ordinates and enter a least squares refinement for the low-angle reflections only, with suitable fractional shifts and an " acceptable percentage " of F(obs) chosen in relation to the importance of the heavy atom relative to the rest of the structure. Such a SFLS refinement may be expected to converge from quite a poor trial structure.

(An alternative solution in such a case could be obtained by using the co-ordinates of the heavy atom to calculate structure factors for this atom only, and thereby fix signs so that an F(obs) or difference Fourier could be prepared from the output tape, but this must be taken away from the computer to be interpreted, and does not permit the rapid iteration process possible with least squares.)

In such favourable cases the solution of a structure could be literally automatic and accomplished in a single run on the computer, the operator having only to select the co-ordinates of the peaks of the Patterson–Harker sections by inspection, and punch them as the origin for the co-ordinate generator routine, but in most crystals a more sophisticated use of all the available facilities is necessary.

In the final stages of refinement, difference Fouriers can be calculated for important regions of the molecule to give information about the electron distribution, without having to calculate the electron density over the whole cell.

8. Molecular geometry

This programme provides bond lengths and angles, the direction cosines of the bonds, the mean molecular plane and the deviations of atoms from it, and orthogonal Ångstrom co-ordinates for making drawings or models of the structure. At present the atoms to be involved in these calculations have to be specified. It is proposed to convert this into a bond-seeking programme which will also produce standard deviations for bond-lengths and angles.

Acknowledgments

Our thanks are due to Dr. M. Ehrenberg for assistance in production runs and programme testing, and to several members of the staff of Messrs. Ferranti, Ltd. Most of the computations involved in this work have been carried out with the help of a grant for computing made from the Wellcome

Trust, and with the use of tape-editing equipment purchased by means of a grant from the University of London Central Research Fund. Messrs. Babcock and Wilcox have also kindly enabled us to use their Pegasus computer. The absence of references does not mean that we are unaware of the many standard works on the mathematical processes involved in such programmes, and we have drawn upon them freely.

Paper 7

GENERAL PROGRAMS FOR CRYSTAL STRUCTURE ANALYSIS ON THE ENGLISH ELECTRIC DEUCE COMPUTER

by J. S. ROLLETT

Oxford University Computing Laboratory,
9 South Parks Road, Oxford

MACHINE

The DEUCE is built by the English Electric Co. Ltd., and is the commercially available computer based on the Pilot ACE, which was designed at the National Physical Laboratory (Wilkinson, 1954). DEUCE has a working store of 21 mercury delay lines, 4 of which hold one word of 32 binary digits, 3 hold two words each, 2 hold four words each and the remaining 12 hold thirty-two words each. Eight of the twelve long lines can be used to hold instructions, one per word. There is a backing store of 8192 words, thirty-two on each of 256 tracks of a magnetic drum. Input and output is by means of Hollerith cards, which are read at 200 cards/minute and punched at 100 cards/minute. The machine available to the author (at the National Physical Laboratory) used 32 columns of the card, but later models of DEUCE are able to read and punch either 64 or 80 columns. All arithmetic facilities are of fixed point form and floating arithmetic is obtained by programming.

The instructions take the form of transfers from a specified source to a specified destination, the next instruction is also specified so there is a 2 + 1 address system. Either one, two or more than two words may be transferred by one instruction. Certain source numbers are used for special purposes, such as to obtain half or twice the contents of certain stores, to take the 32-bit number provided by the card reader or the handswitches and to provide either constants or logical operations on two of the one word delay lines. Similarly, some destinations are reserved for additions and subtractions in the 32 and 64 digit accumulators, to choose a different next instruction if the source is negative or non-zero, and to trigger off the automatic multiplier, the divider, the Hollerith equipment, and transfers to and from the drum.

A simple addition or subtraction takes 64 μsec (2 word times) or more if the next instruction and the data are not in the optimum positions in the delay lines. The multiplier and the divider each take just over 2 msec to operate, and a transfer of 32 words to or from the drum requires 13 msec (plus 40 msec if it is necessary to move the reading or writing heads to the correct position). It is not necessary to wait for the completion of a multiplication, division, drum transfer or Hollerith operation before going on to the next instruction and this makes it possible to practise " time-sharing " to the point of doing four different things at once. Certain interlocks are provided to prevent disastrous attempts to use the same equipment for two things at once.

Clearly the speed of a program on DEUCE depends not only on the numerical methods chosen, but also on the care with which the instructions are planted in suitable stores, the efforts made to ensure that information is collected from the drum in advance, and use of the available time during multiplications. The author's experience is that in some routines involving little multiplication DEUCE can be made to carry out about ten instructions per millisecond but that more usually the rate is near five per millisecond. With care, the multiplier can often be kept busy for about three-quarters of the time.

CHOICE OF PROGRAMS

At the time that the programming of DEUCE was undertaken (Jan. 1956) there were no generally available crystallographic refinement programs for any machine in this country which would carry out the heavier refinement calculations for structures of any desired symmetry. It was not uncommon to hear of large three-dimensional calculations which had been waiting for periods of up to two years for lack of suitable computing equipment. Among the outstanding problems were structures of triclinic, monoclinic, orthorhombic and hexagonal symmetry. Clearly any attempt to provide facilities for structure factor, Fourier series and least squares calculation based on special programs for particular spacegroups would have involved a great deal of programming labour, and would have meant undue delay for some problems. It was also clear that the only DEUCE computers which were likely to be available for a considerable time would be in government establishments and industrial laboratories, so that most of the machine operation and data punching would have to be done by skilled computers with no special knowledge of crystallography. For this reason it was desirable to keep the number of different programs small so that little confusion should arise in discussion between operators and authors. The availability of the machine also led to the decision to program only those operations which involved considerable arithmetic on each item of data. It was doubtful whether many crystallographers would be able to justify the expense of using DEUCE to transform intensities to structure factors or to work out distances and angles between atomic positions. Recently, DEUCE has been installed in some Universities (notably Glasgow) and these programs have been made available. Clearly, the situation which limited the scope of the original set of programs has changed and there is now justification for programs which carry out operations which would previously have been uneconomic. The priorities which were decided were:

1. A three-dimensional structure factor program for all spacegroups, designed primarily for large structures and therefore restricted to isotropic vibration.
2. A three-dimensional Fourier series program, to use the output of the structure factor program.
3. A three-dimensional least squares program for all spacegroups, primarily for smaller structures, to provide for refinement through successive cycles without hand calculation and punching of data, and to deal with the effects of anisotropic vibration.

This sequence was based firstly on the urgency of certain problems in Oxford and elsewhere and secondly on the greater difficulty of carrying out structure factor calculations rather than Fourier calculations on conventional punch card equipment. It turned out that the structure factor program was produced by April 1956 and the Fourier program by August, but that the least squares routine was not available until July 1957, by which time the other two programs had brought a number of problems to the point at which least squares refinement was required. The main decisions affecting the design of these three programs are discussed below. The facilities provided are summarized in the appendix.

THE STRUCTURE FACTOR PROGRAM

The most important decision which had to be faced in designing this program was that between the evaluation of $\binom{\cos}{\sin} 2\pi(hx + ky + lz)$ for all atoms in the (non-centrosymmetric, primitive lattice) unit cell and the use of the appropriate products $\binom{\cos}{\sin} 2\pi hx \binom{\cos}{\sin} 2\pi ky \binom{\cos}{\sin} 2\pi lz$ drawn from tables worked out in advance, summing only over the atoms in the asymmetric unit. It is evident that the first method involves more arithmetic, not only because more atoms are required in the summation but also because the angles whose functions are required are more various and hence less easy to tabulate. In either case the work involved or the length of the tables needed can be reduced by evaluation of the functions for $(h, k, l + 1)$ from those for (h, k, l) by the addition formulae. Apart from the disadvantage of requiring operations on reflections not appearing in the data, this would have led to difficulties with unusual orientations for crystals of certain symmetries. After some consideration the product form was discarded in

G

favour of $2\pi(hx + ky + lz)$ on account of the size of the tables of sines and cosines which would be needed. It would have been necessary to read parts of these from the magnetic drum, if they were to be large enough to allow for a sufficient range of index values. The resulting transfers would have been so numerous that the program would have been slower than the one which was in fact written. Further, the drum storage needed would have reduced the space available for other quantities and would have limited the scope of the program so that the largest calculations impending would have been impossible (some 82 quantities for each of 100 atoms would have filled the whole of the drum). It is worth noticing that these difficulties do not arise for a machine with a very large high speed store (some machines have working stores for 32,000 words) until much larger calculations are required. They are nevertheless, well worth consideration in view of the increasing availability of " desk size " electronic computers with relatively small stores.

The use of tables of sines and cosines at a small interval with linear inter-polation was discarded in favour of the direct evaluation of the series:

$$\cos \pi x/2 = 0{\cdot}9999930 - 1{\cdot}2334812x^2 + 0{\cdot}2525728x^4 - 0{\cdot}0190846x^6.$$

This is a Chebyshev " economized " series, slightly modified so that the answer shall not be negative in any part of the range $0 \leqslant x \leqslant 1$. The error of the approximation is about 10^{-5}. The time-sharing power of the machine was used to obtain the sign of the functions (and to decide which should be which) from the digits indicating the quadrant, while the position in the quadrant was being used in the series. Both cos and sin were found in $17\frac{1}{2}$ msec and the multiplier was in use for 14 msec of this time. A similar technique was applied to the individual isotropic temperature factors. The series used was:

$$2^{-x} = 0{\cdot}999944 - 0{\cdot}691327x + 0{\cdot}230832x^2 - 0{\cdot}039488x^3$$

with an error of about 10^{-4} for $0 \leqslant x \leqslant 1$.

The integral part of the argument was treated separately and used to shift the result the required number of binary places.

The innermost loop of the program generated the positions of all atoms related to the given atom by symmetry (except those produced by a centre at the origin, or a lattice translation) and added together the resulting sines and cosines. The next loop picked up the parameters $(x, y, z,$ temperature factor and chemical type) for each atom, determined the temperature factor and compiled a list of sums of contributions for atoms of each chemical type. By careful coding it was possible to hold all the instructions required for these two loops in the high speed store, so that the only drum transfers required during most of the running time were those fetching the atomic parameters, eight atoms per track. These could be arranged to take place while the machine was doing arithmetic and this shortened the calculation time by about 10% in a typical case. In the outer loop of the program, which was too large to go into the store in one piece, each track was fetched as the last was being obeyed, to minimize the time spent waiting for the drum.

The outer loop multiplied the contributions of chemical types by interpolated formfactors, added to find A_c and B_c, formed F_c and $\Delta = | F_o | - - | F_c |$, punched the answers and then picked up the indices and found $\sin^2\theta$ for the next reflection. It will be seen that it was decided to operate reflection by reflection rather than to calculate the contributions of one atom to all reflections before doing the next atom. This decision was based partly on storage space, partly on the possible need to guard against sporadic failures of the machine (which had only been working about six months when the program was designed) and partly on operational simplicity. Although some other arrangement might lead to a program formally faster than this the reflection by reflection scheme, combined with the fast and reliable input of DEUCE, gave a program which could use any period of several minutes which might become available, and which was therefore convenient for the machine operators. It was also possible to check the first few answer cards within a minute of the start of a run, so that an inexperienced user was unlikely to waste hours of machine time in calculations based on a gross error.

The methods of specifying and storing atomic formfactors raise points of general interest. Once again the relative merits of tables and of series approximations were in question. On this occasion it was decided to use tables, since a relatively small amount of information concerning relatively complicated functions was required and since it was felt that it should be possible for any crystallographer to produce a form factor based on a new wave function calculation or one corrected for special effects such as anomalous dispersion and ionic charge. He should also be able to determine the accuracy of his table, without recourse to the machine and without heavy hand calculation. The program carried out simple linear interpolation in a table of 32 values for each chemical type. The arguments were not equally spaced, because form factors, as functions of $\sin^2\theta$, fall off steeply at first and more slowly later. Consequently the values of the form factor for $64 \sin^2\theta$ (for the radiation in use) equal to 0 by 1 to 16, by 2 to 32, by 4 to 60 were punched. This complicates the interpolation routine somewhat but yields good accuracy. The practice of plotting against $\sin^2\theta$ rather than $\sin^2\theta/\lambda^2$ has been criticized as lacking generality, but it gives better accuracy, particularly since it would be necessary to carry tables for use with any radiation twice as far out as those for Cu $K\alpha$ radiation alone. In three years of heavy use of this and other programs the author has not been asked for tables for any other radiation than Cu $K\alpha$. It is, after all, usually only necessary to tabulate about four or five form factors for a crystal structure analysis, and often the one required will be on file already.

All thirty-two values for one type of atom were read into the machine before those for the next type, but inside the machine form factors for all types of atom for one particular value of $\sin^2\theta$ were stored on a single track of the drum. The first differences needed for interpolation were packed with the values so that it was only necessary to read one track into the store for each reflection. This system slowed down form factor input but saved about 0·1 sec per reflection on a typical calculation.

One other aspect of this program which affected its efficiency crucially was the arrangement of information on the data and answer cards. It was decided that the $h, k, l, |F_o|$ (or F^2) data should be in the same form, as nearly as possible, as the reflection answers, so that data for Patterson and Fourier series should be handled in the same way by the Fourier program to be written subsequently. (In this part of the work the author was fortunate in designing both programs at about the same time, so that little risk existed of allowing them to become incompatible). It was also decided that the advantage of being able to sort cards (so as to investigate functions of particular index values), and of being able to correct and select data by changing or extracting individual cards, outweighed the possible speed advantage of making one card carry more than one reflection. The remaining problem was the allocation of the thirty-two card columns. After some thought and experiment to establish the feasibility of the necessary reading and punching routines (not then in the subroutine library) the space was divided into 4 three column fields (for hkl and i where necessary, or $\sin^2\theta$ to 3 decimals) and 4 five column fields (for $\Delta, |F_c|, A_o, B_o$ or $\Delta, |F_c|, \cos\alpha$, $\sin\alpha$). It was unfortunate that insufficient space was available for F_o as well but it was held that small Δ values were the simplest sign of correct computation for the guidance of the operators. It certainly proved valuable to be able to check that no large Δ had been punched, by sighting through the appropriate zero holes, but for purposes of final inspection of the printed results F_o might have been more useful. This dilemma could, of course, be overcome easily on a DEUCE punching 64 card columns, but the author has not had access to such a machine. On the data cards the F_o were punched in the A_o, or $\cos\alpha$ position. As a standard practice all F were punched to 2 decimal places, which should be adequate precision and which allows values up to 999·99 electrons per unit cell. This limit is unlikely to be exceeded even by a structure of the size of vitamin B12 selenocyanide (the largest on which the program is known to have been used). The form factors were also punched to 2 decimals and since atomic numbers are not normally higher than 100, 4 card columns were sufficient and the 32 form factor values for an atomic type were put on 4 cards in 8 four column fields on each.

Partly to avoid the need for handling a large bulk of data cards for long periods on the machine, partly to save time on repeated input of the same F_o data in successive cycles and partly to simplify the main program and increase its capacity, a separate routine was used to convert the F_o data to binary beforehand. On the binary cards each term occupied one row only, F_o taking twenty bits and the l index ten. The h and k indices were not punched except at the start of each set of three cards and at any other point at which either of them changed. Rows holding h and k were distinguished by a hole in one of the two columns not used by l and F_o. The end of the data was marked by a hole in the other one of these two.

A similar program, written by D. A. Bekoe, converted the decimal parameters, type number, x, y, z, and temperature factor, to binary cards, on which each atom required four rows.

As a result of these precautions the input deck even for calculations with 100 atoms and 2000 hkl data was compact and easy to handle. The data were read in three cards at a time, and each set of structure factors was computed and punched before the next set of three cards was read. Should any machine failure occur it was only necessary to take out of the deck those sets of three data cards for which all the answers had been punched and put the remainder back in the machine in the same way as at the start. Exactly similar remarks applied to voluntary interruptions.

All other items of data such as scaling factors, counts of atoms and chemical types, codes for symmetry relations, and unit cell dimensions were converted to a suitable binary form by hand, and punched in binary on certain of the program cards. This simplified the program somewhat and kept down its bulk. It did not prove to be an important source of delays and errors, at least as far as the NPL operators were concerned.

It should perhaps be observed that no checking was built into the program. There is no good overall check on a structure factor calculation except repetition (and even this will not deal with consistent failure of the machine or errors in programming). Rather than tolerate a hundred per cent increase in the running time of every calculation, it was decided to ask the machine operators to repeat short sections at intervals and check that the two sets of answers agreed. (There were good facilities for doing this checking off the machine). Results were then sent to the users " on approval " on the understanding that any contaminated by error would be repeated without charge. Few errors slipped through.

THE FOURIER PROGRAM

There is a much greater advantage in a Fourier calculation in using the product form $\binom{\cos}{\sin} 2\pi hx \binom{\cos}{\sin} 2\pi ky \binom{\cos}{\sin} 2\pi lz$ than there is in structure factor work. Having decided to use the product form and so limited the problem to calculation at the points of a regular three dimensional net, one is faced with the decision of the choice of interval which shall be made available. At the time that the DEUCE program was written, earlier programmers (e.g. Sparks, Prosen, Kruse and Trueblood, 1956, on SWAC) had designed general programs to calculate at intervals of 1/60 of a unit cell edge, with the option of working at 1/120 of a cell edge in at least one direction. This scheme has the advantages of simplifying the program and of allowing a direct check against hand calculations with Beevers–Lipson strips and results from conventional punch-card machines (e.g. using the system of Schaffer, Schomaker and Pauling, 1946). It was clear that the system would soon be defeated by the problems awaiting the DEUCE, since the structure of cystine (Oughton and Harrison, 1959) had such a long c axis that the l indices ranged up to 72 and an interval of about 1/240 would be necessary. In view of the experimental difficulty of indexing the reflections correctly for this structure it seemed unlikely that there would be any need to provide a finer interval than this. On the other hand there did appear to be a real need for various intervals coarser than 1/60 so that time should not be wasted for a large number of smaller structures in calculating and punching unnecessary answers. A completely general choice of interval was not thought to be either feasible or necessary and the system used was that of allowing any interval which was an integral number of 240ths, so that 1/240, 1/120, 1/80, 1/60, 1/48, 1/40, 7/240, 1/30...1/16, 1/15,... were all available. This makes possible a table of sines and cosines in 1/240ths of a cycle (i.e. at 1·5° intervals) from 0° to 45°. It was found that the sine and cosine of an angle could be kept to 15-bit accuracy in the halves of a 32-bit word and that they could be " unpacked " in 5 msec, which is less than the time needed for advancing from one angle to another by the addition formulae. This would not, of course, have been true for a machine in which multiplication was quicker in relation to the time for addition. For this machine, however, the result of this discovery was a program in which every trigonometric function required was drawn straight from the table.

Although it may be possible to store the whole of the data and answers for a small Fourier series calculation inside the machine, the decision to do this in a general program for DEUCE would limit its usefulness intolerably. In order to allow the calculation of as large a map as might be required (up to 241 × 241 × 241 points in the worst case) it was decided to calculate one section, consisting of points with the same z coordinate, at a time and to punch it before doing the next section. The data would be scanned once per section and the parts of the first and second summations needed for that section only would be computed. Each summation would be accumulated as far as possible as soon as the relevant information was available, so that the totals for the previous summation could be cleared immediately. In this way the storage space for intermediate answers was minimized and restrictions (due to limits on storage space) on the ranges of the indices were avoided.

The program was designed to calculate the electron density expressions given in International Tables for X-ray Crystallography, Vol. I, so that on some occasions (e.g. with hexagonal symmetry) more than the independent *hkl* data would be required but, on the other hand, the types of function needed were very few. A survey showed that of the 32 possible types

$$\pm \frac{(A)}{(B)} \left(\begin{smallmatrix}\cos\\\sin\end{smallmatrix}\right) 2\pi hx \left(\begin{smallmatrix}\cos\\\sin\end{smallmatrix}\right) 2\pi ky \left(\begin{smallmatrix}\cos\\\sin\end{smallmatrix}\right) 2\pi lz \text{ only eight would be required:}$$

$$+ A \cos 2\pi hx \cos 2\pi ky \cos 2\pi lz$$
$$- A \cos 2\pi hx \sin 2\pi ky \sin 2\pi lz$$
$$- A \sin 2\pi hx \cos 2\pi ky \sin 2\pi lz$$
$$- A \sin 2\pi hx \sin 2\pi ky \cos 2\pi lz$$
$$+ B \sin 2\pi hx \cos 2\pi ky \cos 2\pi lz$$
$$+ B \cos 2\pi hx \sin 2\pi ky \cos 2\pi lz$$
$$+ B \cos 2\pi hx \cos 2\pi ky \sin 2\pi lz$$
$$- B \sin 2\pi hx \sin 2\pi ky \sin 2\pi lz$$

Space groups *Fdd2* and *Fddd* are awkward to handle in this way, but in all common cases there is no difficulty.

Full advantage was taken of this simplification to shorten the program and increase its speed. Since it was evident that problems with about 5000 *hkl* terms, each having an A and a B coefficient, would appear within the expected lifetime of the program, it was clear that there would have to be a version which did not store the terms, but read them from cards as they were required. If this had to be done from decimal cards once per section the process would be slow, so ways of gaining speed were sought. The solution adopted was to convert the data to binary, each term occupying two card-rows. The first of these held A and the l index and the second held B and an 8-bit signal in which each one digit indicated that one of the eight expressions above was to be calculated. The h and k indices were only punched once (on a separate pair of card-rows with a special sign) for each batch of data with constant h, k and varying l. With this arrangement, it was possible to carry out the first summation at the full speed of the card reader. After reading A and l, the machine found $A \cos 2\pi lz$ and $A \sin 2\pi lz$. After reading B and the signal, the machine found $B \cos 2\pi lz$ and $B \sin 2\pi lz$ and then obeyed the signal, accumulating the correct totals $C_1 \ldots C_4$ for the functions:

$$C_1 \cos 2\pi hx \cos 2\pi ky \qquad C_3 \sin 2\pi hx \cos 2\pi ky$$
$$C_2 \cos 2\pi hx \sin 2\pi ky \qquad C_4 \sin 2\pi hx \sin 2\pi ky$$

The time available between card-rows for calculations is given by the programming manual as $15\frac{3}{4}$ msec and the most demanded of the machine by this program was 15 msec. Little was wasted, therefore, and trouble has only been experienced on rare occasions when the reader speed has been allowed to rise above the maximum permissible at certain parts of the read cycle.

When a pair of rows carrying h and k was read, the rest of the card was stored and $C_1 \ldots C_4$ were used to calculate additions to the two second summations D_1 and D_2 for the previous k and all y in the section. $C_1 \ldots C_4$ were then cleared in readiness for the next set of terms. If the new h was the same as the previous h, the program returned to the first summation, dealing with the stored card-rows before restarting the reader. If the new h was different, then another pair of terms ($D_1 \cos 2\pi hx$ and $D_2 \sin 2\pi hx$) was added to the third summation for the previous h and all values of x and y in the section. The second summations were then cleared for the next h and k. It was only necessary at any time to store two values (new and previous) for hk, four totals (in the working store) for the first summations $C_1 \ldots C_4$, and a maximum of 482 totals (512 words on the drum were in fact allowed for convenience) for the second summations, apart from the third summation answers themselves. These last were kept on the drum, each line of constant y, z and varying x taking as many 32 word tracks as it required, having regard to the fact that every answer track on the drum held 31 function values and a check sum which was verified each time the track was read into the working store. A section of 61×81 points could be done in one pass, but a section of 61×121 points would have had to be split into two for lack of storage. This would probably be advisable, in any case, to cut down the fault-free time required for a successful run.

The program so obtained had no inconvenient limitations in the sense of being unable to do any particular piece of work because there were just too many terms or just too many answer points. In consequence, it proved a satisfactory standard routine, but it was recognized that the technique of taking the terms from cards for each section was somewhat slower than that of reading them from the drum, because the machine had to wait for the reader at h, k changes and between the end of one card and the beginning of the next. A " terms-on-drum " version of the program was eventually written for which about 14 terms were held per track of drum, and most of the third summation space was re-allocated in this way. This version of the program could handle up to about 2000 terms (strictly up to 400 binary cards of hkl data) and compute sections up to 31×48 points (or similar sizes of other shapes). By changing one instruction of the program the limit on the number of terms could be varied.

It will be noticed that the whole of the information about the crystal symmetry was added to h, k, l, A and B, by the subsidiary program which produced the binary cards with 8-bit codes defining the trigonometric functions needed. This subsidiary program was designed to read hkl, Δ, $|F_c|$, $\cos \alpha$ and $\sin \alpha$ or hkl, Δ, $|F_c|$, A_o and B_o (for F_o maps only) from decimal cards output by the structure factor program and to punch out binary cards for F_o, F_c or $(F_o - F_c)$ maps. The remainder of the information needed by the main program was punched in decimal on a set of " section cards " which carried xyz for the first point of this section, the intervals for x and y and the number of points to be calculated in each direction. In most cases the section cards were easy to make since all cards of the set were the same except for the z value. The advantage of this system was that sections were readily computed in any desired sequence, so that particularly interesting ones could be done first and repeats could be organized at any time as a check on the machine.

While all that has been said refers to sections at constant z, any given set of decimal data can be reproduced (off-line) so as to interchange index fields, and sorted so as to allow efficient calculation of sections at constant x or y. The reproducer works at 100 cards (i.e. 100 terms) per minute and the sorter is faster (though several passes are needed) so that the whole process is quick and requires no DEUCE time at all.

The program punched out the answers to four decimal accuracy (four decimal digits and a sign punched over the first) and could therefore put eight on a card. This was seldom as many as the number of points required in the corresponding (x) direction so that the results were produced in a series of " strips " of eight x values and as many y values as were required. In front of each strip a " lead card " was punched defining the position of the first point in the strip and the x, y intervals. The output punch also numbered the cards as a safeguard against any unwanted change of sequence. There was a very straightforward relation between the arrangement of the printed answers and the plotted sections for contouring and in favourable cases it was even possible to contour the tabulator results directly.

THE STRUCTURE FACTOR — LEAST SQUARES PROGRAM

There were a large number of superficial respects in which the least squares program and the isotropic structure factor program were closely similar. This had obvious advantages in that the bulk of the data (structure factors and form factors) for the one were interchangeable with those for the other and the answers from either program could be used for Fourier series calculations in the same way. The methods used to obtain the trigonometric and exponential functions were also numerically similar. The main difference between the structure factor parts of the two programs was that the least squares program handled the expression

$$2^{-(B_{11}h^2 + B_{22}k^2 + B_{33}l^2 + B_{23}kl + B_{31}lh + B_{12}hk)},$$

instead of $2^{-B\sin^2\theta}$ for each atom, so that more parameters were needed and a more detailed system of symmetry codes was interpreted. The ten parameters (x, y, z, B_{11}, B_{22}, B_{33}, B_{23}, B_{31}, B_{12} and chemical type) were punched in decimal on three cards for each atom and converted to one binary card per atom by a subsidiary program. The symmetry codes were punched in binary, as before.

The main program had three inner loops. In the first the structure factor was computed and the quantities

$$\frac{\partial A}{\partial x_i}, \frac{\partial B}{\partial x_i}, \ldots, \frac{\partial A}{\partial B_{12i}}, \frac{\partial B}{\partial B_{12i}}$$

were stored on the drum tracks for intermediate answers for every atomic position i in the calculation (i.e. the surroundings of one lattice point if there was no centre of symmetry, half one lattice point otherwise). The second loop replaced these quantities by

$$\frac{\partial |F_c|}{\partial x_j}, \ldots, \frac{\partial |F_c|}{\partial B_{12j}}$$

for the parameters of the independent atoms j in the refinement. The third loop read down the intermediate answers and added their squares and products to the accumulated totals on the drum tracks for normal equations. This three-stage process was required because of the limited size of the working store for instructions and at first sight appears inefficient because of unnecessary drum transfers. In fact, however, these were time-shared with the arithmetic so that they did not account for any appreciable extra running time.

The most difficult loop in which to arrange the drum transfers efficiently was the third, in which access was required to the intermediate answers and the normal equations alternately. Since the drum tracks were arranged in groups of sixteen and switching from one group to another required 40 msec for the reading heads to be shifted, such operations had to be avoided by interleaving the intermediate answer tracks with the normal equation tracks on the drum. As a result of this precaution, of calling for all data as far as possible ahead of the time at which it would be used, and of careful coding of the arithmetic, it was possible to keep the speed of the program close to that at which the multiplier could form the necessary products.

Another difficulty which had to be faced in this program, and which would have been trivial if the author had limited its application to his own problems, was that of scaling the normal equations. The diagonal term for B_{11j} has dimensions $f_j^2 h^4$ and since the atomic number and axial length can vary widely the normal equation term is not easy to predict. The DEUCE has no built in floating point facilities and any attempt to handle this problem by floating point subroutines would have led to serious difficulties of program space and speed. Other programmers have evaded a part of the difficulty by using a vibration term $e^{-(B_{11}(h^2/a^2) + \cdots)}$ but this still leaves the variation of f_j and, in DEUCE, destroys the advantage of handling the indices as integers. It was found that it was possible to retain sufficient accuracy in structures with carbon atoms and axes shorter than 10 A while avoiding overflow in all cases which were encountered, at least while the program was in use at NPL under the author's general supervision. This kept the program relatively simple and fast at the expense of a limitation which was hard to define and which may yet catch some user unawares.

As before, the data were read in and computed from three binary cards at a time. It was possible to put a " safety card " between any set of three data cards and the next three, in which case the machine would punch out the current normal equation totals immediately after reading the safety card. In this way it was possible to safeguard the main run against machine failures just as strongly as the condition of DEUCE appeared to demand (except in extreme cases!). The price paid in machine time for such a "dump" was about that for the calculations on four reflections. There remained the possibility of an arithmetic failure producing wrong normal equations but not disturbing the normal appearance of the actions of the machine. This was unlikely since most of the arithmetic facilities of the machine were used to construct instructions, but it did occur now and then. As a safeguard against this situation any run lasting more than two hours was divided into sections by clearing the drum and repeating program input (a quick process) about once per hour. This produced a set of independent partial totals to be added together subsequently. Should an error be discovered in any of these totals it was never necessary to repeat more than one hour of work.

A separate program was used to add together the partial totals and solve the resulting equations. Gauss–Seidel iteration with special discrimination against zero diagonal terms was used, so that projections, and atoms in most types of special position, would not give difficulty. Since the iteration does not in general converge unless the matrix concerned is positive definite, this method is a powerful check against machine errors which lead to ridiculous normal equations. The solving program punched the new parameters in binary, ready for the next cycle of the refinement, and could then be made to punch in decimal the totals $\Sigma \mid F_o \mid$, $\Sigma \mid F_c \mid$, $\Sigma \mid\mid F_o \mid - \mid F_c \mid\mid$, $\Sigma w \Delta^2$, and the elements of the normal equations solved.

The main program was provided with three alternative weighting schemes. Two of these were simple functions of $\mid F_o \mid$ with no special provision for terms with $\mid F_o \mid = 0$. These were:

Scheme 1. $\sqrt{w} = 1$ if $\mid F_o \mid < F_*$, $\sqrt{w} = F_*/\mid F_o\mid$ otherwise.

Scheme 2. $\sqrt{w} = \mid F_o \mid/F_*$ if $\mid F_o \mid < F_*$, $\sqrt{w} = F_*/\mid F_o \mid$ otherwise.
Where F_* is a constant.

It was possible to change from one scheme to the other by replacing three cards of the program and it was stated in the description of the program that other schemes could be produced if necessary. No user of the program suggested any variation or alternative. This may have been because of the flexibility of the third scheme provided but it reinforces the impression that dangerously little attention is paid to the appropriateness of the weighting scheme.

The third scheme allowed the square root of the weight for each $|F_o|$ to be punched on the decimal data card alongside the value as an integer in the range 0 to 31. (This had the unfortunate result that the binary data for the SFLS program differed from that for the SF program so that a separate converter program had to be written.) This meant that any scheme within reason could be adopted at the price of a small amount of extra work on the data and without any further programming at all. Few users chose this alternative.

A straightforward means (the substitution of two cards) was provided for eliminating the least squares part of the program entirely when it was to be used to calculate structure factors only. It was also possible to calculate normal equations for some but not others of the atoms in the structure factor. The parts of the normal matrix which were computed were:

(i) A three-by-three matrix for each atomic position.

(ii) A six-by-six matrix for each atomic vibration.

(iii) A two-by-two matrix which was solved for the overall scale factor. The other parameter (which was not adjusted by the program) was an overall vibration parameter Q, such that $\partial |F_o|/\partial Q = -F_c \sin^2\theta$.

This scheme normally produced satisfactory convergence when full hkl data were employed. On some occasions, particularly when the program was applied to projections with poor resolution, it was necessary to reduce the shifts calculated. Simple facilities for punching out parameters based on half or quarter shifts were provided with the program which solved the normal equations.

Acknowledgments

The author wishes to express his thanks to the staff of the Mathematics Division of the National Physical Laboratory both for providing facilities for the initial testing of these programs and also for operating a computing service based on them.

REFERENCES

OUGHTON, B. M. and HARRISON, P. M. (1959). *Acta Cryst.* **12**, 396.

SCHAFFER, P. A. Jr., SCHOMAKER, V. and PAULING, L. (1946). *J. Chem. Phys.* **14**, 648.

SPARKS, R. A., PROSEN, R. J., KRUSE, F. H. and TRUEBLOOD, K. N. (1956). *Acta Cryst.* **9**, 350.

WILKINSON, J. H. (1954). *Proc. Symp. Autom. Dig. Comput.* NPL 5–14.

APPENDIX

(a) Machine

English Electric DEUCE. 402 words (of 32 bits) in working store of mercury delay lines of various lengths, plus 8192 words on magnetic drum. Input and output on 32 columns of Hollerith cards (200 cards/minute input, 100 cards/minute output). Addition of 32-bit numbers 64 μsec (optimum coding, fixed point). Multiplication 2 msec (fixed point). Coding in machine language for all programs described here. No built-in floating point arithmetic. Standard commercial charge for crystallographic work £33 per hour.

(b) Programs

(i) *Structure Factors* (*SF*)

All space groups. No limit on number of reflections. Parameters are F_o scale, atomic positional coordinates, individual isotropic atomic vibrations and chemical types. Up to 1664 independent atoms of up to 16 chemical types allowed. Output is h, k, l, $\sin^2\theta$, ΔF, $|F_c|$, $\cos \alpha$, $\sin \alpha$ or h, k, l, $\sin^2\theta$, ΔF, $|F_c|$, A_o, B_o. Time for 1000 reflections, 10 independent atoms, centrosymmetric monoclinic space group 41 mins (35 mins if binary F_o data already exist).

(ii) *Fourier Series*

All space groups, but summation over at least all reflections with $h, k, l \geqslant 0$. Special precautions required for *Fdd2*, *Fddd* and some higher symmetries but otherwise multi-plicities applied automatically. No limit on number of reflections in standard version, limit of about 2000 reflections in faster version. Intervals are $n/240$ths where n is integral and may be different for each direction. Approximate time for 1000 reflections, 30 sections each 30 × 60 points: $4\frac{1}{2}$ hours (standard version).

(iii) *Structure Factors and Least Squares* (*SFLS*)

All space groups. No limit on number of reflections. Variables are F_o scale, atomic coordinates, six anisotropic vibrational parameters per atom (isotropic vibration para-meters not refined). Chains of 3 × 3 and 6 × 6 matrices calculated, also 2 × 2 matrix for F_o scale. Up to 64 independent atoms for anisotropic refinement. Estimates of standard deviations not provided. Cycle time for 1000 reflections, 10 independent atoms, centro-symmetric monoclinic space group, with anisotropic vibrations: 2 hours. Up to 16 chemical types of atom allowed.

(iv) *Ancillary Programs*

Programs exist to convert binary F^2 to binary $|F|$, to apply tabular modification functions to binary F^2 and to calculate interatomic distances and vectors between specified fractional coordinates.

Some additional crystallographic programs developed at Glasgow University are noted in the Discussion (p. 301).

Paper 8

PROGRAMMING AND CRYSTALLOGRAPHIC APPLICATION OF EDSAC II

by M. WELLS

Crystallographic Laboratory, Cavendish Laboratory, Cambridge

A DESCRIPTION OF EDSAC II

EDSAC II was designed and built entirely by the members and staff of the Cambridge University Mathematical Laboratory as an experiment in computer design rather than as the central unit in a data processing service, although it in fact provides many of the University departments with such a service.

EDSAC is a parallel binary machine, with a single address order code, operating in either fixed or floating point modes on a 40-bit word. The most significant bit is a sign digit and the binary point is immediately after this, so that in the fixed point mode the range of operands is $-1 \leqslant x < +1$, with an accuracy of about 1 in 10^{12}. In the floating point mode the 8 least significant bits are used to define a binary exponent, in the range $-128 \leqslant p < +128$, so the range of operands is now extended to about $\pm 10^{\pm 40}$ with an accuracy of about nine decimal digits. An overflow indication is provided, which shows whenever the correct result of an operation would exceed capacity; orders are provided which can discriminate on the state of this indicator.

There are two modifier registers, or B-lines, with a comprehensive range of arithmetic and logical orders; the current content of the sequence control unit, which contains the address of the order being obeyed can also be used as a modifier register. In addition there are orders which allow the address part of any order in the store to be used to modify the obeyed address of an order, although such " modifiers " cannot be used in making decisions.

The immediate access store consists of 1024 words, each of 41 bits, on ferrite cores and has an access time of 2 μsec and a cycle time of 7 μsec. Each word accommodates either a 40-bit number, or two 20-bit instructions and a parity bit, used only in error detection, so that in all the store has 2048 separately addressable locations.

Each 20-bit order has an 11-digit address (i.e. an integer in the range 0 to 2047) and 9 function digits; seven of these are used to specify the function number (i.e. an integer in the range 0 to 127) and two are used to indicate which modifier register or registers are to be used in constructing the final obeyed address. There are over 90 meaningful functions and one of these gives access to the subroutines in the " wired " store. As well as the computing store, freely available to the programmer, there is a second store identical in size and speed which contains a number of permanently wired in subroutines for evaluating simple functions such as square roots, logarithms, etc., and which also holds various input and output subroutines, the magnetic tape control and the " report stop." During the operation of the machine, any attempt to store a result which has exceeded capacity, or any improper entry condition to a wired store subroutine, or any undefined function number will cause the machine to report, i.e. print out the contents of the arithmetic unit, the control and modifier registers and the last order the machine attempted to obey, and then stop.

The wired store also holds the program input routine, which reads program in basic machine code, but includes facilities such as floating address working and input of numerical data that one normally associates with more elaborate interpretive schemes; an auto-code will shortly be available, but so far all the programs written for the machine have been in basic machine code.

Input and output are both via standard 5-hole punched paper tape and are not buffered in any way. There are two input channels, of which only one at a time may be active; input speed on either is 1000 rows of tape per second, at which speed the tape can stop between rows. There are two output channels, one driving a perforator at 300 rows per second the other a perforator at 33 rows per second. Also available are an oscilloscope graph plotter and an on-line line printer, which has only numeric characters and will print two lines of 80 characters each per second.

There are four magnetic tape units attached to the machine; again these are not buffered in any way. The unique control system on EDSAC allows for the provision of very complicated orders and advantage is taken of this to use the arithmetic unit for splitting up and assembling data for the magnetic tape. This reduces the total hardware, but means that magnetic tape operations cannot be carried out in parallel with computing; an automatic search is provided which enables any specified block to be positioned under the read/write heads. The information on the tapes is stored in pre-addressed blocks, each of which carries a label giving the number of the tape unit, the number of the block, the maximum permissible content of the block and a " key." If the key does not fit then the machine will not transfer information to or from that block, so that on one reel of tape the data for several programs may be stored with much reduced possibility of accidental use of wrong data or destruction of another users file by over-writing. As a further precaution against writing in to a file it is possible to suppress all writing operations on any tape-deck.

CRYSTALLOGRAPHIC APPLICATIONS OF EDSAC II

Structure refinement in two dimensions

A program has been produced for doing all the intermediate steps between a set of postulated atomic coordinates and the corresponding F(obs) or F(obs) — F(calc) synthesis; the data for a set of structure-factors are read in, the program allowing the option of a centrosymmetric or non-centro-symmetric structure and the choice of overall isotropic temperature factors on groups of atoms or individual anisotropic temperature factors. Then a table of the F(obs) is read and the corresponding F(calc) are stored, along with the F(obs) and various miscellaneous data. These two sets of F-values are then processed to give the differences and the reliability index; at the same time simple tests are carried out on the F-values which eliminate any large discrepancies. Finally, the machine will print out either the F(obs) synthesis or the F(obs) — F(calc) synthesis, or both, over any area of the unit cell and at intervals along each axis that the user has specified.

Structure refinement in three dimensions

A logical development of the previous program has been the refinement program, based on the differential synthesis. The F(obs) and F(calc) are stored and processed as in the previous program, except that it now becomes necessary to use the magnetic tape backing store to accommodate the file. Then the peak height, the three first derivatives and the six second derivatives of the F(obs) — F(calc) synthesis are computed for each atom in turn and used to refine the atomic coordinates, the scale factor and the temperature factors (isotropic or anisotropic, as the case may be). The program is very fully optioned and includes facilities for space group symmetry up to orthorhombic on both coordinates and thermal parameters and the sup-pression of refinement of thermal motion or any particular atomic coordinate. Available as auxiliaries to this program are a three-dimensional Fourier synthesis program and a program for estimating errors.

Computation of absorption corrections

A set of programs for the computation of absorption corrections in three dimensions, with Weissenberg (normal-beam or equi-inclination) and pre-cession cameras have been prepared and are in use. Also in preparation, though in one case not yet fully tested, are programs for evaluating the correction when the crystal is mounted in an absorbing container and has liquid adhering to it. It is possible to use any of these programs in such a way that the specimen is twinned.

Future applications

Two important developments are in the course of being programmed. The first, which is nearly completed, is the production of a data processing program for the interpretation of the output from an automatic X-ray diffractometer and the allied problems of producing control tapes for this instrument and developing automatic error detection and correction programs. The second is the direct display of a Fourier synthesis in contoured form on the oscilloscope graph plotter. At present the plotter suffers from rather poor resolution and long term instability, but it is hoped that when the new unit which is being built becomes available there will also be available a program for producing the direct display.

Acknowledgments

I am grateful to Dr. M. V. Wilkes for permission to use EDSAC and to the Commissioners for the Exhibition of 1851 for financial support.

APPENDIX

MACHINE

Cambridge University Mathematical Laboratory, EDSAC II.

Storage: 1024 words of 41 bits (40 data + 1 parity) on ferrite cores. Access time 2 μsec, cycle time 7 μsec.
Four magnetic tape units each holding approx. 8×10^5 words. Transfer rate approx. 1250 words per sec. No buffers.

Input: Standard 5-hole punched tape, at 1000 rows per sec on each of two channels, stopping between rows. No buffers.

Output: Standard 5-hole punched tape, at 30 or 300 rows per sec, depending on which channel is called. No buffers.
Oscilloscope graph plotter, with film transport etc. controlled by the machine.
On-line printer, 120 lines of 80 numeric characters per minute.

Add-time: Floating point; 120–200 μsec. Fixed point; 30 μsec.

Multiply: Floating point; 270–520 μsec. Fixed point; 290–540 μsec.

Programming: All programs are in basic machine code.

Advantages: Very flexible order code, with over 90 functions, and very comprehensive library of programs, some permanently available in the machine.

Disadvantages: Small high speed store and no fast backing store. Output devices inadequate for some crystallographic work, e.g. Fourier synthesis.

Charges: Commercial work is not normally undertaken, but if accepted the minimum rate is £75 per hour, increasing if high speed punch or magnetic tape are required. Normal charge for crystallographic work is £5 to £10 per hour.

H

PROGRAMS

SF: One program, fully optioned as regards thermal motion, and scattering factor representation. No symmetry other than $P1$ or $P\bar{1}$.

SFDS: All space groups up to orthorhombic. No limit to number of reflections. Variable include any or all of F(obs) scale, atomic coordinates, isotropic vibrations for groups of atoms and 6 individual anisotropic vibrations, all from differential synthesis. Max. numbers of atoms are approx. 150 for isotropic and 30 for anisotropic options. E.S.D.'s are evaluated by a separate auxiliary program. Computing times for typical structure problem
(a) approx. 3·5 minutes per cycle after the first.
(b) approx. 6 minutes per cycle after the first.

Fourier: Two-dimensional for plane groups $P1$ or $P\bar{1}$. About 1700 reflections. Input as table of F-values on punched tape; if $P1$ a table of phase angles will be supplied by the machine during the computation of F(calc).
Output as table of electron densities, in column format.
Intervals in each direction and area evaluated specified by each user.
Three-dimensional (Due to M. G. Rossman). Monoclinic space groups. Maximum no of reflections $\sim 5 \times 10^3$. Input as table of real and imaginary parts of each coupled F. Intervals of mesh selected by user. Output is in a table ready for contouring.
Time for suggested problem approx. one hour.
Three-dimensional (Due to M. Wells). This program is designed to follow the SFDS program, so that no input format is needed. Intervals selected by user. Output is in a table ready for contouring. Time for suggested problem approx. 40 minutes.

Absorption   Available for equi-inclination Weissenberg, Normal Beam Weissenberg
corrections: and Precession cameras, all with three dimensional specimens and non-zero layers. Also available for twinned specimens and/or specimens mounted in absorbing holders.

Paper 9

PROGRAMMING AND CRYSTALLOGRAPHIC APPLICATIONS OF THE FERRANTI MERCURY COMPUTER

by O. S. MILLS

Department of Chemistry, University of Manchester,
Manchester 13

and J. S. ROLLETT

Computing Laboratory, University of Oxford,
9 South Parks Road

INTRODUCTION AND DESCRIPTION

The MERCURY computer is a high-speed digital machine which has been developed by Ferranti Ltd., from the MEG prototype machine originally designed in the Department of Electrical Engineering of the University of Manchester. The computer design has been influenced by the requirements of flexibility in a wide variety of scientific calculations and for this reason ordinary arithmetic is performed with engineered floating point operation.

In common with most large digital machines, MERCURY employs a two-level system of storage. The fast store normally consists of 1024 words, each of 40 binary digits, held on ferrite cores, although it is possible for smaller-sized stores to be provided. The slower, auxiliary store consists of a number of drum units so that its total capacity can be varied considerably. The " standard " machine is fitted with two drum units which have a total capacity of 16,384 words. Up to two additional drums can be fitted, but to our knowledge, at the present time, the largest installation which is currently used for crystallographic work employs a store of 24,576 words. Information is transferred between these stores in blocks of 32 words. Each block comprises a *page* when in the high-speed store (maximum 32 pages) or a *sector* when on the drum (512 sectors on the standard machine). The transfer time in either direction is $7\frac{3}{4}$ msec, assuming that no time is wasted in allowing the drum to rotate to the appropriate position for transfer. The drum rotation time is slightly longer than that corresponding to two sectors and

107

the average waiting time prior to a single transfer is about $8\frac{3}{4}$ msec. When transfers involve alternately odd and even numbered sectors, little waiting time is involved between sectors and a few organization instructions can be obeyed.

Each 40-bit word can be used to hold any of (a) a floating point number of 30-bit argument and 10-bit exponent, which leads to an accuracy of better than 1 in 10^8 over a range of $10^{\pm 77}$, (b) two 20-bit instructions, (c) four 10-bit numbers which lie in the range $0 \leqslant x \leqslant 1023$ or $-512 \leqslant x \leqslant 511$ (fixed point), or (d) one instruction and two 10-bit integers.

Floating point numbers can be located anywhere in the core store but instructions and short integers are restricted to the first half of the store. The maximum number of instructions which can thus be held in the core store without recourse to supplementation from the drum is 1024. Instructions are obeyed sequentially and are of the single-address type.

The following table gives the times of the arithmetic and some other operations:

transfers between the core store and accumulator	120 μsec
floating point addition and subtraction	180 μsec
floating point multiplication	300 μsec
10-bit fixed point addition or subtraction	60 μsec
control instructions (jumps, tests etc.)	60 μsec
division (by sub-routine, not engineered)	4 msec

All the arithmetic instructions are capable of being address modified by any of eight B-lines. With the exception of B0, which always contains zero, a B-line can contain a 10-bit number in the range $-512 \leqslant x \leqslant 511$. The B-lines are used for counting operations as well as modification.

Usually, input of numbers and instructions is by way of 5-hole paper tape, with parity check on decimal and other key characters. The Ferranti TR2 tape reader operates at 200 characters/sec. Output is likewise normally on paper tape either by a Creed 25 punch (33 characters/sec) or by a Teletype punch (60 characters/sec). Recent modifications will permit, however, the use of a number of additional input/output mechanisms of increased speed, e.g. paper tape readers up to 1000 characters/sec and punches up to 300 characters/sec, as well as magnetic tape decks (1000 characters/sec). In addition, numbers and letters can be displayed on MUGO (Manchester University Graphical Output), and fast printers can be fitted, although we are unaware of any crystallographic use of them on this machine.

The machine operates on fields of 10-bit numbers associated with each of which is a parity digit. The parity of a number is checked when the number is withdrawn from the core store and generated when written into the store. Floating point numbers are always standardized to retain maximum accuracy and should the magnitude of any number exceed the machine capacity, the machine halts. The machine also halts if a parity check fails. We find that various machines differ markedly in their " mean free path " between parity failures, and thus for any calculation which requires more than 15 minutes, efficient RESCUE operations should be incorporated.

PROGRAMMING TECHNIQUES

Problems can be coded for the machine by means of:
 (i) An automatic coding method devised by R. A. Brooker (University of Manchester) called AUTOCODE,
 (ii) A paginated input which can be written in either fixed or symbolic address form, known as PIG, written initially by R. B. Payne (University of Manchester) and subsequently supplemented by the staff of Ferranti Ltd.,
 (iii) An octal input, IMP, which utilizes the form of instructions that occur within the machine, written by J. S. Rollett (University of Oxford), and
 (iv) Binary coding.

In most installations, method (i) is the most common form of programming as it permits the scientist, as distinct from the specialized programmer, to present problems to the machine in a language which can often be very similar to that of the problem. To illustrate the similarity which can often be achieved between the written form of the instruction and the language of the problem, consider the calculation of the geometric structure factor of a group of m atoms whose positional parameters are stored in symbolic locations, $x_1 \ldots x_m$, $y_1 \ldots y_m$, and $z_1 \ldots z_m$. In the following example, which is for space group $P\bar{1}$, the location " w " is used for working space, holding in turn the individual contributions to the G.S.F., whilst " g " finally contains the accumulated answer.

$g = 0$	clear accumulation site
$i = 1(1)m$	prepare to cycle m times
$w = \phi \cos(2\pi xih + 2\pi yik + 2\pi zil)$	form individual G.S.F.
$g = w + g$	add to current total
repeat	repeat cycle if necessary

Whilst automatic coding procedures inevitably result in some loss of programming efficiency, with MERCURY this loss is kept very low, in some programs, for example, the increase of time may only be of the order of 20%, which time can often be recovered because of the simplicity in developing the program. Certain aspects of a program (particularly magnetic transfers) can sometimes be speeded up by a knowledge of the exact locations of results, and this can be achieved by the incorporation into an otherwise AUTOCODE program, of machine instructions of the type normally written in PIG language. Work with matrices is made particularly simple and provision is made for the output of " check " values during the development or testing runs. When the program has been checked satisfactorily, these additional number prints can be suppressed without alteration of the tape itself, so that production runs can be started immediately. It is also possible to incorporate complete sub-programs from the AUTOCODE Library into users' programs.

With the use of conventional programming methods, e.g. (ii) or (iii), the full flexibility of the machine may be utilized. A comprehensive checking scheme is incorporated into the coding program PIG so that many errors in the program logic, or tape punching errors, can be detected automatically. The usual library of sub-routines is available to programmers. Some sub-routines, known as Quickies, are contained in the input scheme.

Binary coding is restricted almost completely to input and output procedures.

It is our view that AUTOCODE is the most powerful method available to a crystallographer who wishes to program a particular problem for MERCURY, and who has not a machine " on the doorstep " with unlimited amounts of free time, or who has not himself time to devote in large quantities to the intricacies of conventional coding. It may be desirable to speed up parts of the program by the judicious use of machine instructions. The reasons for using other programming systems have varied, but are usually concerned with the need to abandon the conventions of AUTOCODE in order to obtain more storage space, particularly on the drum. The octal input (which is very short) has been found particularly useful for programs which do not occupy any drum space, and for making corrections to large programs after they have been converted to binary form for routine use. The comprehensive post-mortem routines in PIG are an advantage not present in other systems.

Complete descriptions of the facilities available with AUTOCODE are contained in " The Manchester Mercury Autocode System " (Brooker, Richards, Berg and Kerr, 1959) and with PIG in the " Programmer's Handbook " (Ferranti List CS 225 and Addendum No. 1). Information concerning octal programming can be obtained from the author. A complete description of the machine has been given in a series of papers by Kilburn and co-workers.

SCOPE OF THE MACHINE FOR CRYSTALLOGRAPHIC CALCULATIONS

It is clear that the accuracy associated with the normal floating point working (1 in 10^8) is sufficient for all crystallographic calculations save perhaps cases where very ill-conditioned matrices may require the use of double-length arithmetic. Indeed, it is often convenient to throw away part of this possible accuracy. As far as storage is concerned, the standard machine cannot be regarded as luxuriously spacious. We will give two illustrations:

(1) The maximum number of atoms which could be refined anisotropically, if *all* cross-products of the least-squares matrix were calculated and if only the minimum number of terms were stored, i.e. the triangular matrix and the right-hand sides, is 19 (i.e. 172 parameters) on the standard machine or 28 on the full four-drum machine. Such allocation allows no space for program on the drum! Sparks (see Appendix) gives details of such a program, specific for $P2_1/a$;

(2) In Fourier work we require to store all the reflection data if recycling (to calculate a series of sections of the map) is to be made automatic, and hence for a problem of 5000 terms in a non-centrosymmetric space group we require a minimum of 10,000 locations for the Fourier coefficients with additional locations for the associated indices. If the latter are stored as 40-bit numbers the total storage requirements are 25,000 words. Indices can clearly be stored as signed 10-bit integers, with no practical restriction on their magnitude, and three such indices " packed " into a word. Such a system reduces the total storage requirements to 15,000 words. It is also possible to pack a single index, or indeed two indices if they are arbitrarily restricted to the range $-16 \leqslant h \leqslant 15$, into the least-significant 10 bits of a floating point number, an operation which reduces the accuracy of that number to about 1 in 10^6, but with still the same overall range of magnitude. By means of such a system of packing, it has been possible to hold the 5000 terms for a non-centrosymmetric space group, or double this number for a centrosymmetric one, together with the indices in about 10,500 locations. These values are rough limits to the size of problems which can be tackled by present programs with automatic recycling. Larger problems, with limitless terms, can be dealt with, of course, if the reflections are not stored in the machine, but here the data must be input once per section. If more obscure methods of packing are used some 7000–8000 terms may be incorporated.

The provision of floating point working means that there are virtually no problems of scaling to be overcome, as working rarely approaches numbers in the region of 10^{77} except in error.*

The times of operation of various programs are given in the Appendix. Here we merely note that the overall speed of calculation makes it possible for Fourier and least-square calculations to be carried out with the larger problems within a few hours, whilst smaller problems may be cycled within

---

*We warn users and potential users that machine overflow can sometimes be encountered with the $\phi 28$ (matrix division) instruction in AUTOCODE. This is due to the fact that the routine evaluates the determinant simultaneously, although this value is not used during the actual division process. If this happens, suitable scaling must be used, or AUTOCODE itself must be altered " behind the scenes." The same trouble may be experienced with sub-program–518, unless the user modifies it to omit the determinant calculation.

a few minutes. Input, and especially output, are disproportionately slow and such problems of data processing which occur, e.g. sorting, etc., could perhaps be done more cheaply on a slower machine which uses the same type of output punch, e.g. PEGASUS. However, this would need careful consideration, as MERCURY fitted with a Teletype punch would be about as cheap (or dear !) as PEGASUS fitted with a Creed 25 punch, assuming charges of £75 and £40 per hour respectively.

One of the difficulties which is met by anyone who wishes to use any program is that of convention. Restrictions of this type are by definition arbitrary and arise usually from two sources. In the first place a programmer uses sub-routines in which punching conventions for the particular machine are implied, e.g. number termination by a single space or by a double space, the latter as in the MERCURY AUTOCODE. The second source is that imposed by the programmer himself, usually for his own convenience. Such an example could be that quoted earlier, namely the restriction of indices to the range $-16 \leqslant h \leqslant 15$. Another similar convention, which has little to recommend it, is the insistence that coefficients, e.g. F values, or A and B terms for Fourier series be restricted to integers. There is good reason for outputs to be restricted to whole numbers (with some suitable scale factor), but as input tapes are often hand-punched, they should be allowed considerable flexibility so that users are free to punch numbers in the way most familiar to themselves.

With the rapid development of machines in the last ten years, we would like to see a parallel development in the attitude of programmers to data assimilation. The standard which we should strive to attain, we suggest, is that all the information which is required for a given calculation should be presented in a form which involves the least number of artificial conventions and is consistent with accepted crystallographic nomenclature. The print-out of such input should be intelligible to a trained crystallographer, not a programmer. This will mean that the programs must be more complicated more logical in their data-reading parts. The requirement is one of *interpretation* as well as search. Examples of such interpretive programs, where some progress has been made in this direction, include some listed below, and also the least squares program written for PEGASUS by Cruickshank.

One of the most useful features of an interpretive program should be cross-checks for incompatible items. If some incompatibility is detected, or if required information is missing at any stage, then the program should print out a statement of this condition. Such " error prints " are invaluable for fault detection at some distance from a machine; it is frustrating to be told " machine went into loop-stop consistently " when more fruitful information could be supplied, quite apart from the question of wasted machine time.

We should perhaps emphasize that we do not regard attention to convenience of presentation of data and results as being in any way more important than care in ensuring programs correct for all cases and appropriate methods. These things are fundamental, but they can usually be secured in a short time, whereas inconvenient forms of data may go on wasting effort for years.

SOME PROGRAMS WHICH HAVE BEEN WRITTEN
FOR "MERCURY"

In the Appendix we list some programs which have been written by members of various organizations and whose specifications have been received. In the present section we discuss some of these programs in the order in which they might be utilized during a structure analysis.

(a) *Data Reduction*

These programs permit the usual transformations of observed intensities obtained from equi-inclination and normal-beam Weissenberg photographs to F^2, $|F|$ or some function of F^2. Requests can be made for the determination of scale and temperature factors by Wilson's method as an optional extra. Corrections for spot-shape, spot-extension and absorption are also available. The scaling of data from different levels has been discussed recently (Rollett and Sparks, 1960) and the recommended procedure has been programmed. Facilities for scaling individual levels, averaging and sorting are available.

(b) *Solution and Refinement*

A general Fourier program for symmetries up to and including orthorhombic has been written. This covers three- and two-dimensional cases and the output can be contoured directly. The program comprehensively checks for data inconsistencies, e.g. incompatible data, systematic absences, etc., and the information supplied to the machine is in a simple form which is that often used by the crystallographer. The output from the data reduction programs, and also from the structure factor and least squares programs (SFLS) is suitable for input into the Fourier program for Patterson and electron density syntheses. In the case of symmetries higher than orthorhombic one must work with an appropriate sub-group which falls within the scope of the program, but here one would require to supply non-unique reflections and care must be taken where the origin of the sub-group is placed on the elements of lower symmetry of the super-group.

Information is presented to the program, and to the general SFLS program described below, by means of " directives." These are a combination of words (in English) and numbers, where appropriate, designed in the hope that they will be intelligible to crystallographers. As far as possible the program allows the information to be presented in any order, but where information is dependent upon other directives, interlocks are provided to ensure the correct order. Thus in the Fourier program, Fourier coefficients cannot be read into the machine until a knowledge of the space group has been supplied and then it is impossible to present an A and a B coefficient if the space group is centrosymmetric. This latter implies a standard setting of the space group. In this program many of the errors detected on input will be " error printed." The programme reads the space group number and self-adjusts for the standard setting of the space group specified in Vol. I of the International Tables (1952). A comparison between this system and an alternative method of specifying the symmetry elements is given later.

An example which illustrates the method of information presentation is given below (not all this information is essential, nor is the list comprehensive, and reference must be made to the detailed specification for further information):

TITLE

BUTYNE–IRON–CARBONYL. OBSERVED FOURIER
BASED ON 22 ATOMS, 1400 TERMS.
A.A.H./O.S.M./5/1/58.

SPACEGROUP 14.................... International Tables. i.e. $P2_1/c$.

DEFINE $X\ Z\ Y$.................... Cell orientation; indices $h\ l\ k$.

SECTION $Y = 0(1)20/40$ .... Sets limits to summation in any unit

RANGES $X = 0(1)30/60\ Z = 0(1)60/60$ multiple of 240ths.

UNITCELL 12·26 7·47 15·70 97·5 ...... $a\ b\ c\ \beta$ for monoclinic cell.

SELECT $A = (1)$.................... the first coefficient after the third index, here k, in the PLANES list is to be used as the real coefficient. (N.B. No ' B ' term can be specified as the space group is centrosymmetric).

SCALEFACTOR 10

PLANES
*0 0   *$h\ l$
2   −999   −1650 $k\ A_o\ A_c$.
4   −579   −564
6   −259   −216   Fourier coefficients which need not be integers.

x xxx xxx
*0 1
x xxx xxx
x xxx xxx
and so on for as many terms as are to be incorporated in the Fourier, terminating
x xxx xxx
x xxx xxx

FINISH

MAXIMUM DIGITS 4	Adjusts the layout of the output to
ROW SPACING 3	give a suitably sized rectangle.
START FOURIER...................	Kick-off command. Tests that all necessary information is present and commences calculation.

A number of programs for the calculation of structure factors have been written, some with associated least square refinements. For work with any of the two-dimensional plane groups a very complete program exists (Curtis, 1959) which permits least square refinement of positional and vibrational parameters of which the latter may be either isotropic or anisotropic. It is recognized that in two dimensions, the complete least squares matrix should usually be evaluated, and this is done. The size of the matrix formed depends upon the type of refinement requested. The reflection output is, as with all the SF programs which we list, suitable for re-input into the Fourier program for observed, calculated or difference syntheses.

For three-dimensional work a general SFLS program for all space groups exists. The methods employed in this program are closely similar to those used in an earlier SFLS program for the DEUCE computer described in another paper at this conference. The MERCURY program uses the higher capacity of the machine to allow 96 atoms in the asymmetric unit instead of 64 and also differs in that:

(1) The reflection data are stored inside the machine instead of being read in as they are required. This imposes a limit of about 6000 reflections on the data though this can be raised if need be by reverting to computing-off-tape methods. The program is also extended so that it can accept F^2 as well as $|F|$.

(2) The input and output of the program were altered so that they should be recognizable so far as possible without reference to any book of rules. This was because it was expected that most of the users of the MERCURY program would be crystallographers with little or no experience of high-speed computing, whereas the DEUCE program was designed for data preparation by the machine operators at the National Physical Laboratory.

(3) In view of the low speed of output on the standard MERCURY, the format of the structure factor output (as well as that of the data) was made variable so that only the information essential to the case in hand need be punched out. The output of the calculated structure factors can also be suppressed at any time in a refinement cycle, if it is only required for monitoring purposes.

There is no restriction on the orientation of the axes except in the hexagonal system. For such structures, for which symmetry related positions of the type $(y, y - x, z)$ occur, the unique axis must be c. This is because the symmetry routine does not decode $z - x$ and $y - z$. Since it has been found convenient to refer hexagonal data to orthogonal axes, an amendment to the program allows the structure factors put in and punched out to have indices for the orthohexagonal unit cell, while the atomic positions and symmetry relations are referred to the true hexagonal unit cell.

Atoms in special positions present a number of problems. Whenever a coordinate is fixed by symmetry, or a cross-term in the temperature factor is constrained to be zero, then the corresponding diagonal element of the normal matrix is zero (except for the influence of rounding errors). This leads to a singular matrix. The difficulty is overcome since the normal equations are solved by Gauss–Seidel iteration and the abnormally small diagonal element is recognized as an indication that no change should be made in the parameter concerned. In the tetragonal, hexagonal and cubic systems another difficulty appears. For a position of the type (x,x,z) the $x(= y)$ need not remain fixed. If now an attempt is made to refine x and y independently, a singular matrix results and the answers obtained may be meaningless. It was not felt to be justified to extend the main program to cover the variety of cases of this type which arise in three-dimensional work with anisotropic vibrations, and the practice adopted has been to write a short *ad hoc* amendment for each case. This alters the derivative calculations and copies the shifts in the parameters appropriately. The amendments have nearly all been small enough to require no special testing before the production run concerned. These provisions are rather similar to, but not quite so simple for the user as, those in the earlier two-dimensional program by Curtis.

In two respects the data tape for the three-dimensional program is longer than it might be. Firstly the atomic form factors are represented by linear interpolation in tables of 32 values rather than by exponential approximations with five coefficients. Secondly the symmetry relations are written out explicitly as algebraic expressions resembling those in International Tables rather than being selected from a stored list by a single space group number on the data tape. The decision to use tables for the form factors was based partly in disinclination to abandon a system which had proved highly successful on DEUCE, and partly on the greater ease with which crystallographers with no machine nearby, and no special knowledge of numerical analysis, can derive a suitable table for any form factor not previously available. The best fitting of an exponential series is a more subtle matter. Further the incorporation of the anomalous dispersion effect, at least in the real component, can be accomplished in a table of values, whereas the series method requires a complete re-evaluation of the coefficients save in the simplest case, that of a constant over the whole range. The case for writing out the symmetry relations in full is discussed below.

A choice of three different weighting schemes has been built into the program. These are:

(1) $\sqrt{w} = |F_o|/F_*$ if $|F_o| < F_*$, otherwise $\sqrt{w} = F_*/|F_o|$

(2) $\sqrt{w} = 1$ if $|F_o| < F_*$, otherwise $\sqrt{w} = F_*/|F_o|$

(3) $\sqrt{w} = [1/(1 + \{(|F_o| - b)/a\}^2)]^{\frac{1}{2}}$.

where F_*, a and b are constants set by the user before any cycle and where no special treatment is given to unobserved reflections. Other schemes can be added, or substituted for these (e.g. schemes in which special conditions are attached to those reflections for which $|F_o| = 0$). No provision has been made in the standard form of this program for weights to be specified for individual reflections. This facility of the DEUCE program was so little used that it did not justify the additional storage space which would have been required in MERCURY. Should increasing use of counter techniques for data collection lead to a more detailed knowledge of the relative reliability of individual reflections, the program can be modified to allow such a scheme, by storing less reflections or by lowering the precision with which $|F_o|$ is held (at present 19 bits and a sign). It is our experience that the weighting scheme employed is important, because we have found on several occasions that a change of weights has altered the atomic positions by as much as 0·02 Å and we suspect that too little attention has been given to this point in the past. Our usual practice is to investigate in detail the agreement between $|F_o|$ and $|F_c|$ as a check on the reasonableness of the system based on the initial internal estimates of reliability of the $|F_o|$. Changes based on such an analysis must, of course, be made with considerable caution.

The block diagonal approximation used (see Appendix) ordinarily provides fairly rapid convergence where there are fairly complete (*hkl*) data. There is always the risk, however, of instability with any program which does not calculate the full normal matrix and we certainly would not claim that this program could always be used safely without careful scrutiny of successive sets of shifts.

A typical set of directives is that shown below for the case of erythritol:

TITLE

ERYTHRITOL

UNITCELL 6·83 12·80 12·80 90 90 90	$a b c \alpha \beta \gamma$ for tetragonal ($I4_1/a$) cell,
1·542	rotated so that unique axis is a. λ for Cu radiation used in f_i tables.
SYMMETRY *	asterisk indicates centre at origin.
$X.Y.Z.$	Only 4 of 16 expressions needed
$X. - Y.1/2 - Z.$	because of this and I lattice.
$1/4 + X.3/4 - Z.1/4 + Y.$	
$1/4 + X.1/4 + Z.1/4 - Y.$	
*	asterisk indicates end of expressions.

FORMFACTORS

```
C
600 543 493 452 418 388 363 342    one hundred times
324 307 294 281 269 259 251 243    formfactors for carbon
236 224 214 206 199 193 188 184    and oxygen.
180 174 168 163 160 157 154 151
O
800 745 702 665 630 596 565 540
515 492 471 453 436 420 405 391
378 355 335 318 304 291 278 269
256 240 228 218 209 200 192 187
```

* . . . .   End of formfactors.

PRINT OBS CALC . . . .   Print terms for F_o and for F_c (and, by implication, ΔF) Fourier maps.

PARAMETERS $X\ Y\ Z\ B$ . . . .   Image of line in positions list.

SELECT $L\ F$ . . . .   Image of non*line in planes list.

WEIGHTS 3 400 0 . . . .

POSITIONS

```
C1  ·763  ·035  ·075  1·285
C2  ·113  ·018  ·003  1·285
O1  ·758  ·146  ·048  1·285
O2  ·175  ·012  ·105  1·285
```

* . . . .   End of atoms in LS.

* . . . .   End of atoms in SF.

SCALEFACTOR 1·00

PLANES
```
* 0 0
2 217
4 1326
x xxx
x xxx
(and so on for about 500 lines)
*8 5
5 116
```

FINISH . . . .   Ends planes list.

START . . . .   Order to begin calculation after checking that all essential directives have been read.

We now turn to the question of how much information the user should be expected (or permitted!) to give concerning the space group. It is clear that whilst some existing programs require the space group number only and others need a full list of equivalent positions, both methods work satisfactorily. The write-in-full method simplifies provisions for users to specify non-standard orientations of axes and functions other than the electron or vector density, e.g. the sine function for a generalized projection, but correspondingly complicates or prohibits the programming of checks against systematic absences. There is also the possibility of shortening the relations-list when all the atoms lie in special positions. One user, in this way, reduced the length of the list for Fm3m from 192 to 3. The user is also less likely to fall into the trap set by non-centrosymmetric space groups similar to $P2_12_12_1$, which has two formally similar origins not differentiated by the Hermann–Mauguin symbol alone. In these ways the system confers freedom on the user. On the other hand the space group number scheme transfers from the user to the programmer the onerous task of checking that any given space group is treated correctly. The greater tape-length and consequent input time of such a program are quite trivial disadvantages, but it is clearly not practicable to ensure that every space group routine works properly before release to trusting, impatient or critical users. While users who fail to punch the relations-list without error can hardly blame anyone else, they have seldom been prepared to be responsible for a critical test of a built-in routine for a " new " space group and may even fail to report a mistake if one is detected.

The Fourier and three-dimensional SFLS programs which we have described in some detail here are examples of machine-coded programs; the two-dimensional SFLS program is an excellent example of a sophisticated use of AUTOCODE supplemented by machine instructions. The use of AUTOCODE makes it possible for a given program to be modified for a different space group fairly readily (unless the adaptation involves a centro- to non-centrosymmetric transition, which is more complicated). Examples of this type of program include the isotropic and anisotropic least squares programs for $P2_1/c$, $P\bar{1}$ and $C2/c$.

(c) *Interpretation of Results*

Programs have been produced both for the analysis of intermediary results and also for certain operations on the final answers. The former include agreement analysis (see Appendix) and 19-point (or 27-point) interpolation for peak position. Programs also exist for locating hydrogen atoms in XH, XH_2 and XH_3 groups. The most important program so far in the final answer class is the distance-angle routine designed to list all interatomic distances less than a preset d_{max} (no two identical separations are punched) and all the angles between pairs of vectors which share one atom and which are both less than a_{max} in length. Symmetry relations and asymmetric unit only are required. The general program has the advantage that unusually short intermolecular contacts and similar features demanding special scrutiny are unlikely to be overlooked. A program has been produced to find the three-dimensional Fourier transform of any specified form factor. There is a program which determines the principal amplitudes and directions of vibration of an atom from its anisotropic temperature factor referred to the reciprocal axes, and another which will find principal vibration and libration axes and amplitudes for a rigid body at a centre of symmetry given the atomic temperature factors. The determination of the best least squares plane through a set of positions has been programmed.

(d) *Miscellaneous Programs*

The application of computers to direct methods of crystal analysis will be discussed by Woolfson in a separate communication to this meeting. At this point we merely note that he has adapted some of these methods to the MERCURY. To assist in the indexing of powder patterns a program exists which lists $\sin^2\theta$ (in order of increasing magnitude) together with appropriate indices.

COMPUTING SERVICES

Most of the British Universities with MERCURY installations organize computing services which are available to outside users at a standard rate of £75 per hour computing time. Whilst it is obviously better if a user can have access to tape editing equipment, tape preparation can usually be undertaken at a token fee. Some programs can be run very easily by operators, e.g. the Fourier program, but we find that it is rarely worthwhile to call for more than a single round of least squares refinement unless critical judgment can be applied to the results at once.

APPENDIX

We list here brief abstracts of the specifications of some programs for MERCURY.

(a) Machine

Ferranti MERCURY. 1024 words immediate access, plus 16,384 words on drums in standard machine. Input and output: 5-hole paper tape. Addition 180 μsec (floating point); multiplication 300 μsec (floating point); addition 60 μsec (10-bit fixed point). Coding by " conventional methods " or AUTOCODE. Arithmetical work essentially floating point. Graphical output of results possible. Standard commercial charge £75 per hour.

(b) Data reduction

(i) *General.* Input is intensity data from Weissenberg or oscillation photographs. Output is $|F_o|$, F_o^2 or MF^2 (with appropriate indices) where $M = (1/\hat{f})a \exp(-b \sin^c\theta)$ and $\hat{f}$, a, b and c are set on the data tape. Input can alternatively be F^2 instead of I. Scale and temperature factors, by Wilson's method, is available. Speed dominated by that of punch.

(C. K. Prout)

(ii) *General.* Input as in (i); output $|F|$ or F^2 with indices. However, can also produce, in addition to Wilson parameters, lists of unitary structure factors, and $\sin\theta/\lambda$ for each reflection. The number of regions into which the data is divided for the Wilson plot is adjustable, and an analysis of the reflections distributed over the total range is given. Output suitable for re-input to Fourier and SFLS programs.   (J. A. Bland)

(iii) *Layer Scaling.* Input is coefficients of observational equations for pairs of intersecting layers of F^2 data. Output is relative scale factors for layers derived by method of Rollett and Sparks, *Acta Cryst.* (1960), **13**, 273. Speed near that of punch.   (J. S. Rollett)

(iv) *Scaling and Averaging.* Input is F^2 data for layers on arbitrary scales normal to two axes and also scale factors. Output is sorted F^2 data, with multiple observations averaged, all on same scale. One axis can be given different weight from other. Speed near that of punch.   ((Miss) Lai T. F.)

(v) *Sorter.* Given a set of *hkl* data, will punch out a sorted set of data in suitable form for the Fourier or SFLS programs. Any number of coefficients may follow the third index on the input tape but only one coefficient is punched out. The indices may be interchanged in any desired way. Each *hkl* term uses 80 bits on the drum and there must be space for the whole of the data plus the largest layer of sorted data. All 510 free sectors can be used for these. Near speed of punch in all applications so far. (J. S. Rollett)

(c) Solution and refinement

(vi) *General Fourier Series.* Two- and three-dimensional. All triclinic, monoclinic and orthorhombic space groups and their projections. Maximum reflections depend on size of net, but approximately 5000 if non-centrosymmetric or 10,000 if centrosymmetric. Intervals in $n/240$ths where n is integral. Approximate time for 1000 reflections, 30 sections each 30×60 points: 60 minutes computing, 3 hours 45 minutes punching (this assumes 4 decimal digit numbers; up to 40% saving in time can be obtained if numbers are known to be less than this), if 33 characters/sec punch fitted. Output is sorted for ease in contouring, and can be output graphically. Input checked for consistency; multiplicity corrections included in program so that unique terms only required. Reflection input consists of one or more columns of Fourier coefficients, any pair of which may be added or differenced before being used as coefficient in Fourier series. A version exists which does not store the Fourier coefficients but computes from tape. The number of reflections is then limitless.   (O. S. Mills)

(vii) *Two-dimensional Least Squares.* SF and LS. All plane groups. About 500 reflections maximum. Variables: F_{obs} scale, atomic coordinates, individual isotropic vibrations, 3 anisotropic vibrations. Full matrix calculated (maximum parameters in any given cycle $\leqslant 85$). Up to 31 atoms in asymmetric unit. E.S.D. computed. Time per cycle of order 10–20 minutes. Output suitable for Fourier input. All atomic " special " positions can be dealt with. Can be used for neutron diffraction refinements. Details written up in AERE–T 3134.   (A. R. Curtis)

(viii) *Structural Factor and Least Squares* (SFLS). All space groups. Up to 6000 reflections, though this can be extended. Variables are F_o scale, atomic coordinates, six anisotropic vibrational parameters per atom (isotropic vibration parameters not refined). Chains of 3×3 and 6×6 matrices calculated, also 2×2 matrix for F_o scale. Up to 96 independent atoms for anisotropic refinement. Estimates of standard deviations not in present version. Cycle time for 1000 reflections, 10 independent atoms, centrosymmetric monoclinic space group, with anisotropic vibrations 35–40 minutes. Up to 16 chemical types of atom allowed, structure factor output optional.   (J. S. Rollett)

(ix) *SF and LS for Restricted Space Groups*. Separate AUTOCODE programmes for space groups $P\bar{1}$, $P2_1/c$ and $C2/c$. Each has different versions for isotropic and anisotropic refinement. (a) isotropic $P2_1/c$ can be dealt with either by the diagonal approximation, or by chains of 5×5 matrices (3 positional, vibrational and F_o scale parameters; the scale parameter is solved by overall 2×2 and each 5×5 reduced to 4×4 before solution). Maximum reflections depend upon number of atoms but 2000 planes, 22 atoms has been refined. E.S.D. from diagonal or inverted matrix diagonal elements as appropriate. Anisotropic version calculates chains of 10×10 matrices which are similarly reduced to 9×9 before solution (3 positional and 6 vibrational parameters). Time for 1000 planes, 10 atoms about 20 minutes (diagonal approximation), 35 minutes (5×5 matrices), and 50 minutes (anisotropic). Output suitable for input to Fourier program.   (O. S. Mills)

(x) *Full-matrix Least Squares for $P2_1/a$ only*. Unlimited reflections. Variables are F_o scale, atomic coordinates, 6 anisotropic vibrational parameters per atom. Up to 13 independent atoms (of 3 chemical types) in standard version. No estimated standard deviations in program. Special routines written to solve normal equations for particular cases. Cycle time, 7 atoms, 700 reflections, anisotropic vibrations, 2 hours.   (R. A. Sparks)

(xi) *Peak Positions*. Given 19 electron-density values nearest the maximum, finds the peak density and position by fitting a Gaussian ellipsoid. Where F_o, or $(F_o - F_c)$ map available in addition to F_o map, can apply both n-shift and back-shift rules. If the grid of the map is orthogonal, can also give integrated number of electrons and correction to isotropic temperature factor. Speed near that of punch.   (R. A. Sparks)

(xii) *Another program* for estimation of peak heights and positions from 27 point fitting is due to (Mrs.) J. M. Rowe.

(xiii) *Peak Shapes.* Given any form factor, produces the three-dimensional Fourier transform. Speed near that of punch.   ((Mrs.) M. M. Harding)

(xiv) *Hydrogen Positions.* Three separate routines to locate H atoms given bond distances, bond angles and heavier atom positions.

(a) XH groups. Given the positions of an atom and of three attached atoms, finds two positions for a fourth attached atom at a specified distance and making equal angles with the other three.

(b) XH_2 groups. Given the position of an atom and of two attached atoms, finds two positions for attached atoms at a specified distance and making equal and specified angles with the other two.

(c) XH_3 groups. Given the positions of four atoms, three of which are attached to the fourth, central one, finds two positions for atoms attached to a non-central atom. These are at a specified distance and all four angles between the skew lines in the system are equal. Near speed of punch.   (R. A. Sparks)

(xv) *Agreement Analysis.* Given F_o, F_c and indices, punches:

(a) $\Sigma\,|\,F_o\,|$, $\Sigma\,|\,F_c\,|$, $\Sigma\,|\,\Delta F\,|$ and R for specified ranges of F_o.

(b) $\Sigma\,|\,F_o\,|$, $\Sigma\,|\,\Delta F\,|$ and R for ranges of $\sin^2\theta$, and for each value of h, of k and of l. Near speed of punch.   ((Miss) Lai T. F.)

(d) Analysis of final results

(xvi) *Distance-angle Routine.* Input is:

(a) Unit cell, lattice type and lattice point equivalent position relations (for any of 230 space groups), d_{max} and a_{max}.

(b) Positions and name tags of independent atoms.

Output is all independent interatomic distances less than d_{max} and all independent angles between distances less than a_{max} which share an atom. Care is taken to ensure no distance or angle punched twice and that no distances to atoms in neighbouring unit cells missed. Limit of 16 atoms coordinating any given atom for angle calculation. Limits of 512 independent atoms and 2048 atoms in unit cell. Near speed of punch up to 100 independent atoms and 4-fold symmetry relation.   (R. A. Sparks)

(xvii) *Atomic Vibration Axes.* Given the vibrational parameters of an atom referred to the reciprocal axes (i.e. in the form $\exp - (\Sigma b_{ij} h_i h_j)$) finds the principal amplitudes of vibration and their directions. Near speed of punch.   (R. A. Sparks)

(xviii) *Molecular Axes.* Given the positions of a group of atoms and their weights, finds the axes of least and greatest inertia, and hence the best least squares plane through the group. Finds the distances of the atoms of the group from this plane and the coordinates of their projections on it. Can also find these coordinates for atoms which are not used in defining the plane. Near speed of punch. _   (R. A. Sparks)

(xix) *Molecular Vibration—Libration Tensors.* Given the position and vibrational parameters of a group of atoms forming a rigid body with a centre, finds parameters for molecular vibration and libration about axes through the centre.   (R. A. Sparks)

REFERENCES

Coding Methods

AUTOCODE

BROOKER, R. A. (1958). *The Computer Journal*, **1**, 15; 124.
BROOKER, R. A. (1959). *The Computer Journal*, **2**, xi.
BROOKER, R. A., RICHARDS, B., BERG, E. and KERR, R. H. (1959). " The Manchester Mercury Autocode System," The Computing Machine Laboratory, University of Manchester, May 1959.
BROOKER, R. A. (1959). *The Computer Journal*, **2**, 189.

PIG

Ferranti Mercury Computer. Programmers' Handbook. List CS 225 and Addendum No. 1.

Engineering

LONDSDALE, K. and WARBURTON, E. T. (1956). *Proc.I.E.E.* **103B**, Supplement 1–3, 174.
KILBURN, T., EDWARDS, D. B. G. and THOMAS, G. E., *ibid*, 247.
THOMAS, G. E., *ibid*, 483.
ROBINSON, A. A., NEWHOUSE, V. L., FRIEDMAN, M. J. and CARTER, I. P. V., *ibid*, 295.

Paper 10

A SUPERPOSITION METHOD AND PROGRAM FOR IMAGE-SEEKING PROCEDURES IN CRYSTALLOGRAPHY

by Robert A. Jacobson, Bruce R. Penfold and William N. Lipscomb

Departments of Chemistry: Harvard University, Princeton University
and the University of Minnesota

ABSTRACT

Sharpening of the Patterson function by the use of the gradient of the electron density as a starting function yields a sharply peaked function, which, when added to the usual Patterson function produces a higher degree of resolution of peaks than usual without false minima.

An IBM 704 program for the use of this function in evaluating the Buerger minimum function is described. Its application to the solution of several structures having no dominating heavy atoms has yielded some indication of the applicability of this method to the determination of complex structures.

INTRODUCTION

Image seeking as a method of obtaining a structure or partial structure from the Patterson function has been used, consciously or not, by various investigators almost as long as the Patterson function has been available. However, the formalization of this procedure, first by Wrinch[1] and later independently by many others, has resulted in its further development as a method of obtaining trial structures. In particular, the choice of whichever function is less at every point of the superposition, the minimum function of Buerger,[2] resulted in a significant reduction of background in successive superpositions. Finally, the greater resolution of new sharpening procedures[3] and the programming of this process in three-dimensional problems on high-speed digital computers[4] have further added to the power of these methods.

These methods are, of course, useful when heavy atoms are present, but probably find their greatest usefulness in structures having a large number of approximately equal atoms, especially when partial structures are known or can be guessed from available chemical methods. Furthermore, the fact that the crystal structure may be non-centrosymmetric is not, usually, a significant handicap, as it can become in other powerful methods. Moreover, further development of the method seems possible as the quality of data improves and the speed and capacity of high-speed computers improve.

Here we describe some sharpening procedures which have proved useful and some applications. A program in FORTRAN for the IBM 704 for the procedure of obtaining the minimum function is available. A FORTRAN program is also available for performing the preliminary sharpening operations.

APPLICATIONS OF GRADIENT SHARPENING

It is well known[5,6] that, owing to termination of Fourier series, the use of artificial exponential temperature factors tends to produce subsidiary minima around the maxima in a highly sharpened Patterson function. Moreover, these minima tend to shift and obscure neighboring peaks. We have established a physical basis for removing these minima, while still retaining the high degree of sharpening of the Patterson maximum for an interatomic vector.

Instead of the usual Patterson function $P(u) = a^{-1}\int_0^1 \rho(x)\rho(x+u)dx$, where ρ is the electron density, consider the derivative function $Q(u) = a^{-1}\int_0^1 \rho'(x)\rho'(x+u)dx$, where $\rho'(x) = d\rho(x)/dx$, and $\rho'(x+u) = d\rho(x+u)/dx$. This function gives a highly peaked maximum in Patterson space, but with subsidiary minima on either side. However, addition of some of the original Patterson function to the derivative function retains the sharpness of the maximum, and destroys the minima so that resolution of neighboring peaks is improved. The resulting function is

$$AP(u) + BQ(u),$$

where the ratio of B/A is chosen to remove the minima around peaks in the $Q(u)$ function.

In three dimensions

$$Q(u, v, w) = V \int_0^1 \int_0^1 \int_0^1 \nabla\rho(x\,y, z) \cdot \nabla\rho(x+u, y+v, z+w)dxdydz$$

$$= \frac{16\pi^2}{V} \sum_{hkl} \left(\frac{\sin\theta}{\lambda}\right)^2 |F_{hkl}|^2 \exp[2\pi i(hu + kv + lw)]$$

This general result can be obtained from the gradient operator

$$\nabla = a^*\partial/\partial x + b^*\partial/\partial y + c^*\partial/\partial z$$

in a non-orthogonal coordinate system. The empirical advantages of $(\sin\theta/\lambda)^2$ as a sharpening function have been noted before, but here we have established a physical basis for it, and have removed the subsidiary minima by adding the required amount of $P(u, v, w)$ to $Q(u, v, w)$. The appropriate ratio of B/A for the three-dimensional function is about 0·04, or slightly greater.

It must be expected that an increase in the resolution of a Patterson function, without the introduction of false detail or shifting of peaks will greatly facilitate the solution of trial structures by the use of superposition procedures. The initial choice of resolved peaks, whether or not they are single interactions, is a necessary, but not sufficient, requirement for a successful attack. Moreover, many superpositions are required, in complex structures, to obtain a recognizable molecular fragment, and hence it is quite important that any sharpening procedure should not appreciably shift the peaks of the Patterson function, for otherwise the correct structure will be lost.

These sharpening procedures, and subsequent application of the minimum function as computed in three dimensions on either the Remington Rand Univac Scientific 1103 or the IBM 704, have now been used in the structure investigations of cellobiose,[3] $(BH_2)_3[N(CH_3)_2]_3^7$, $(HCN)_4^8$ and $(PCF_3)_5^9$. In all of these studies this function was very helpful, but in the first two[3,7] it very probably meant the difference between success and failure. In the $(PCF_3)_5$ structure its greatest value was, probably, the enhancement of the $P \cdots P$ vectors because of the increased emphasis on the outer reflections by the $(\sin \theta/\lambda)^2$ factor.

In cellobiose[3] there are two molecules in the unit cell of symmetry $P2_1$. Hence, we found it best to search for a Harker peak of coordinates $(2x_i, \frac{1}{2}, 2z_i)$, and hence the location of the 2_1 axis is determined. All subsequent superpositions were then carried out in pairs on the symmetry-related peaks. Moreover, the chemical information that C–C distances of 1·5 Å and closest non-bonded $C \cdots C$ distances of 2·5 Å were expected was used to locate the peaks due to neighboring atoms. In each such attack five consecutive three-dimensional superpositions of the original vector map were made, and the minimum function computed after each superposition. After several false attacks, in which we obtained only parts of six-membered rings, we finally located in one consecutive set of five superpositions a complete six-membered ring, and its symmetry-related ring. The atoms then bonded directly to this ring were then found, and then an electron density map was found to yield nearly all of the remaining atoms of the structure. We wish to emphasize the importance of the initial choice of a resolved Harker peak, the subsequent use of symmetry-related peaks for the subsequent superpositions, the number of three-dimensional superpositions that may be required in a complex structure, the false starts which led us to pseudostructures having almost the same vector sets, and, finally, the great importance of the use of the chemical information.

We now give a summary of the program for the IBM 704, which is a further

128   R. A. Jacobson, B. R. Penfold and W. N. Lipscomb   [10]

development of our earlier program for the Remington Rand 1103. Modification of this program for computation in intervals of 60ths × 60ths × 60ths or 60ths × 30ths × 120ths is presently in progress.

REFERENCES

1. Wrinch, D. M. (1938). *Phil. Mag.* (7) **27**, 98.
2. Buerger, M. J. (1951). *Acta Cryst.* **4**, 531 .
3. Jacobson, R. A., Wunderlich, J. A. and Lipscomb, W. N. (1959). *Nature* **184**, 1719.
4. Rossmann, M. G., Jacobson, R. A., Hirshfeld, F. L. and Lipscomb, W. N. (1959). *Acta Cryst.* **12**, 530.
5. Waser, J. and Schomaker, V. (1953). *Rev. Mod. Phys.* **25**, 671.
6. Lipson, H. and Cochran, W. *The Determination of Crystal Structures*, London: Bell, 1953.
7. Trefonas, L. M. and Lipscomb, W. N. (1959). *J. Am. Chem. Soc.* **81**, 4435.
8. Penfold, B. R. and Lipscomb, W. N. (1960). *Tetrahedron Letters* No. 6.
9. Spencer, C. and Lipscomb, W. N. *Acta Cryst.* In press.

PATTERSON SUPERPOSITION PROGRAM

Summary

An IBM 704 program for evaluating the Buerger minimum function has been written in FORTRAN. The following is a general description.

Minimum requirements are an 8192-word core and six on-line tape units.

At present the program is restricted to computing the minimum function at intervals of 30ths × 60ths × 60ths, 30ths × 30ths × 120ths, 60ths × × 60ths × 60ths, or 60ths × 30ths × 120ths of the unit cell edges.

A prerequisite is a binary output tape from the Sly–Shoemaker Fourier program MIFR1. This binary tape is used as input for a preliminary part of the superposition program. The order of the unit cell blocks on this tape is critical.

Final output is in a coded form on a scale of 0 to 39, the number associated with each grid point being represented by a single Hollerith character. A complete section of a whole unit cell appears on one or two sheets of the printer.

The program can handle any symmetry which MIFR1 can handle. The only vector space groups concerned are, therefore, $P\bar{1}$, $P2/m$, $Pmmm$.

The point chosen for the superposition need not be a grid point. The program linearly interpolates.

The minimum function is computed for a full unit cell and output with the superposition point as origin.

Paper 11

MIFR1: A TWO- AND THREE-DIMENSIONAL CRYSTALLOGRAPHIC FOURIER SUMMATION PROGRAM FOR THE IBM 704*

by WILLIAM G. SLY† and DAVID P. SHOEMAKER

Department of Chemistry, Massachusetts Institute of Technology,
Cambridge, Mass., U.S.A.

ABSTRACT

MIFR1 is a very fast two- and three-dimensional Fourier–Patterson program for the IBM 704. At least 8192 words of core storage and at least three magnetic tape units are required. The instruction code must include STZ and CAD (CAC). A card-to-magnetic-tape unit and a tape-to-printer unit are required peripheral equipment. The program is available as a binary card deck with a manual of operating instructions. It is written in symbolic language (SAP), employs the Beevers–Lipson factorization, and virtually eliminates multiplication through table look-up. All space groups from triclinic through orthorhombic may be accommodated; a space group is specified by inclusion of special symmetry cards in the binary program deck, one such card being required for each symmetry element necessary to generate the space group. Other special cards are available to provide multiplicity corrections, fix the scale factor, permute the Miller indices to change summation order, change the coordinate grid spacing in one or more directions from 1/120 to 1/60 or 1/30, define the portion of the unit cell to be covered, and modify the output format if desired. Input is BCD magnetic tape prepared from properly sorted punched cards, one for each independent reflection. Input format can easily be varied, so that cards produced as output by a least-squares program may be accepted. Either a straight Fourier synthesis or a difference Fourier synthesis can be carried out, with appropriate control cards. Output consists of sheets printed under program control from BCD output tape, with 256 numbers in a 16 × 16 grid on each sheet. Limited format flexibility is provided to aid in direct contouring of the output sheets. The time required for calculating 30 sections, each with 30 × 60 points, for 1000 independent reflections in a centrosymmetric space group, is approximately 15 minutes for an 8192-word 704, but may be as little as 8 minutes for a 32768-word 704. The only limitation on number of input data is that Miller indices may not exceed 63 in magnitude when the grid spacing is 1/120, 31 when it is 1/60, or 15 when it is 1/30.

---

* Sponsored by the National Institutes of Health, Grant A2400, and the Office of Ordnance Research, Contract DA–19–020–ORD–4696. This work was done in part at the MIT Computation Center.

† Present address: Department of Chemistry, Harvey Mudd College, Claremont, California.

In sheer magnitude of the computational job involved the three-dimensional Fourier or Patterson calculation perhaps exceeds all other commonly encountered crystallographic computations, and ability to do this kind of calculation routinely and at acceptable cost on high-speed electronic computers has done at least as much as anything else to make possible such ambitious projects as determination of the atomic structure of proteins, not to mention the analysis of organic structures with fifty or more carbon atoms in the asymmetric unit.

The IBM 704 is one of the fastest and most powerful electronic digital computers in use today, and it is not surprising that many types of crystallographic computation have been programmed for it, not only once but several times. This is true of the (two- and) three-dimensional Fourier–Patterson calculation, as is shown by the following list of programs independently written for this machine:

S. BLOCK and J. R. HOLDEN (U.S. National Bureau of Standards and U.S. Naval Ordnance Laboratory). Requires 32768-word 704 (an older version operates in a 4096-word machine). Grid intervals of 1/60 or multiples. Written in FORTRAN.

L. BORN and E. HELLNER (Min. u. Petrogr. Inst., Kiel, Germany). Patterson functions, monoclinic or orthorhombic. 8192 core storage, three magnetic tape units, one magnetic drum unit (8192 words).

J. H. BRYDEN (U.S. Naval Ordnance Test Station, Calif.). 4096 core storage, four magnetic tape units. Data cards must be grouped according to form of trig. functions before loading; order within each group unimportant. Improved version being tested for IBM-709. Dr. Bryden is perhaps the first to write a successful three-dimensional Fourier program for the 704.

R. E. JONES, R. P. DODGE, and D. H. TEMPLETON (U. Calif., Berkeley). This program was written for the IBM 701, an ancestor of the 704.

W. G. SLY and D. P. SHOEMAKER (M.I.T., Cambridge, Mass.). MIFR1, here described.

R. G. TREUTING and S. C. ABRAHAMS (Brookhaven National Laboratories, Bell Telephone Laboratories). For 32768-word machine. Calculates the electron density on any one general plane.

A. ZALKIN (U. Calif. Rad. Lab., Livermore). FOURSUM, written in symbolic. May be used with FOURPRINT to print out the results, or FOURPLOT to obtain contoured plots with cathode-ray tube. FOURPRINT and FOURPLOT were written in FORTRAN. 8192-words core storage, four tape units. (CRT.) Grid intervals: multiples of ·0025. No limits on h, k, or l.

This list is possibly incomplete. It is not the purpose of this paper to evaluate or compare these programs; in many respects this can only be done by someone who has used a number of them. Instead it is the intent of this paper to describe the program MIFR1, with emphasis on the particular capabilities of the IBM 704 that suit it to this calculation.

The requirement of speed makes essential the Beevers–Lipson (1934) transformation of the trigonometric factor into cosine and/or sine products and factorization of the summation into three one-dimensional summations. Once this is accepted and a procedure has been formulated for obtaining and sorting into the appropriate order the coefficients of the triple products, the remainder of the calculation consists of carrying out the first, the second, and the third dimension summations (not necessarily in unbroken sequence). In each such one-dimensional summation it is necessary for each term (i) to determine the cosine or sine of an angle, (ii) to multiply it by the numerical coefficient (amplitude), (iii) to add the product to the existing partial sum, and (iv) to repeat this procedure for the next value of the space coordinate at the designated grid spacing, and continue until all required values of the coordinate have been accounted for.

All this might be done in a perfectly straightforward brute-force manner, say in FORTRAN language using floating-point arithmetic, but there exist several opportunities for improving computing efficiency. First, of course, the acceptance of a grid restricts the required angles to a number easily accommodated in a stored table, and a general cosine/sine sub-routine may be replaced by a fast table look-up. (This can, of course, be done in FORTRAN with subscripted variable notation.)

Further improvement in efficiency (beyond that obtainable by writing in symbolic or machine language instead of FORTRAN) is bought at some cost in precision, and requires careful balancing of the requirements of speed and precision in relation to the available high-speed storage capacity. It involves abandonment of floating-point arithmetic (to eliminate time-consuming floating-add operations) and the virtual abandonment of multi-plicative operations as such. The " multiplication " in step (ii) above is done by extension of the table look-up to include amplitude as well as angle, as in the procedures for Beevers–Lipson strips (Beevers and Lipson, 1934), M cards for IBM accounting machines (Schomaker, unpublished), etc. Storage must therefore be provided for a table, the size of which depends on (1) the smallest grid spacing demanded, (2) the desired numerical precision (in the absence of interpolation), (3) the degree of redundancy acceptable for the purpose of minimizing program complexity, and (4) the degree and frequency with which large amplitudes are broken up. In MIFR1 the smallest grid spacing is 1/120 cell edge, and for each amplitude a 121-place table covering one complete revolution is provided to reduce program complexity. Amplitudes are provided at intervals of 3 up to 63, at intervals of 64 up to 448, and at intervals of 512 up to 3584. Given amplitudes larger than 63 are broken up into two or three amplitudes as required, and the number of table look-ups is accordingly doubled or trebled. This procedure is, of course, akin to multiplication in principle but in this case is economical relative to use of multiplicative machine operations because (a) it is necessary to break up the amplitude only in a minor fraction of the terms, and (b) the burden of additional program steps required for the breakdown is largely shared among a large number of grid points. Any amplitude up to 4095 may be accommodated. The numbers in the table are the required products divided by three (as in the M-card system, to prevent increase in required numerical range in going from one dimension to the next) rounded to an integer. In MIFR1 the table occupies 2057 words of core storage, each word containing two tabular entries.

A particularly useful feature of the IBM 704, applicable to the repetition of the summing procedure (iv) for several grid points, is the presence of index registers and of indexable instructions. The frequency h is placed in modified form in the decrement of an indexing instruction. Thus, once the amplitude and frequency are selected the program " skips " through the table for successive grid points.

The limited precision imposed by the table look-up method as used in MIFR1 reduces the storage space necessary for a single sum (electron density) to less than half the 36-bit length of the 704 word. It is for this reason that the trigonometric tables are " packed " two entries per word; the same is true, moreover, of the block of third-dimension partial sums. Up to half the high-speed storage capacity of the computer is used for storing the third-dimension partial sums; thus the maximum number of grid points that can be accommodated in a single operation is 8192 in an 8192-word machine, or 32,768 in a 32,768-word machine. The use of half-word operations, as well as the necessity of considerable program compactness for use in an 8192-word machine, obviated the use of FORTRAN in writing MIFR1.

In this program the partial sums being developed in the calculation are stored in the machine, but the input data are read in as desired from a binary tape. When the grid interval is 1/120 in all three directions, a single pass of the binary input tape generates $1/8 \times 1/8 \times 2/8$ of the unit cell, amounting to 8192 grid points in an 8192-word machine. Additional blocks are obtained automatically by rewinding and rereading the input tape under the control of octant cards. The range of either the second or the third dimension, or both, obtainable with one pass of the input tape, may be doubled if a 32,768-word machine is used; at best this permits a time saving of about 50% over calculating the same volume of output with an 8192-word machine. Doubling or quadrupling the grid interval in a given direction doubles or quadruples the range covered, without affecting the number of grid points.

The binary input tape may contain a virtually limitless number of data, subject to the restriction that no index may exceed 63 (with a grid interval of 1/120). (In principle up to 10^6 different terms may be included without violating this restriction.) Machine storage space considerations required that this tape be prepared by a subsidiary program occupying the machine prior to the loading of the main Fourier program. The input program accepts a BCD tape prepared from punched cards, one for each independent reflection. For highest efficiency the cards should be sorted into a certain order of the Miller indices, ignoring sign. The input program takes full account of symmetry (triclinic, monoclinic and orthorhombic) without the necessity of additional programming. A novel feature is the handling of space groups by the inclusion of special symmetry cards in the binary program deck, one such card being required for each symmetry element required to generate the space group. Special cards are also available to provide multiplicity corrections. Coefficients for Miller indices differing in sign are properly combined and sorted inside the machine according to sine and cosine in the optimum manner. The coded output of the input program is written on to binary tape, one hundred coefficients per record.

As this binary tape is read in by the main program, admission of each term causes the sixteen first-dimension partial sums to be augmented by the appropriate Fourier terms until the second summation index is about to change. Input and first-dimension operations are then suspended and the 256 second-dimension partial sums are appropriately augmented, and the first-dimension sums are cleared. Input operations and first-dimension summation operations then resume. When the third index is about to change a special trigonometric table for the current value of the third index is prepared and the 8192 third-dimension partial sums are appropriately augmented, after which the first- and second-dimension sums are cleared and first-dimension summation is resumed. When the end of the input tape is sensed it is rewound, and the 8192 sums are separated from their half-word partners, converted to decimal, and written onto a BCD output tape for off-line printing under program control. The next octant control cards (if any) are then automatically read, and the next block calculated.

A limited degree of format flexibility permits, in many cases, the output sheets to be approximately similar in their proportions to the corresponding portion of the unit cell; in such cases the sheets may be contoured directly.

The resulting program is very fast, as may be seen from the following formula for estimation of the computing time for an 8192-word machine:

$$t = 0.6 + 0.67 \times B + N (0.0006 + 0.001 \times B \times C)$$

where

$t =$ running time in minutes from " LOAD CARDS " to final program stop;

$N =$ number of input data cards;

$C = 1$ if centrosymmetric, 2 if non-centrosymmetric;

$B =$ number of 8192-point blocks to be calculated ($=$ number of passes of the binary input tape).

Thus in a typical centrosymmetric case with 1000 coefficients where one-quarter of the unit cell is to be calculated in grid intervals of $1/120 \times 1/60 \times 1/30$, the number of blocks B is eight, and the estimated time is about

15 minutes. In a 32,768-word machine this can be cut to 7 or 8 minutes. The numbers in the output are integers ranging in magnitude from 0 through 4095, with either sign. The last digit is highly uncertain due to accumulated round-off errors.

There are several ways in which this program might be modified or augmented in order to make it more useful. We plan to write a routine similar to Zalkin's FOURPLOT to permit direct contoured plots to be photographed from the cathode-ray tube. Eventually we hope to adapt the program to the IBM 709 and 7090, and thereby obtain a further increase in speed. The minimum grid interval of 1/120 is not necessarily the optimum value for a 32,768-word machine; it can perhaps be changed to 1/200, and the permissible range of Miller indices changed accordingly.

It is worthy of note that Dr. Bruce Penfold (Harvard University) has written a Patterson superposition and vector search program that accepts the output of MIFR1. This has been successfully used.

REFERENCES

BEEVERS, C. A. and LIPSON, H. (1934). *Phil. Mag.* **17**, 855.
SCHOMAKER, V. Unpublished.

APPENDIX: INPUT MANIPULATIONS

We shall begin by discussing the mathematical expressions used, and their relation to the computational techniques employed.

The electron density may be written

$$\rho(x,y,z) = K[\sum_h \sum_k \sum_l A_{hkl} \cos 2\pi(hx + ky + lz)$$

$$+ \sum_h \sum_k \sum_l B_{hkl} \sin 2\pi(hx + ky + lz)] \tag{1}$$

where K is a scale factor ($2/V_c$ for the expression as written) and where the sum is taken over positive and zero values of all three Miller indices h, k, and l, and over negative values of at least two of them in the most general case (P1). The cosine and sine terms can be expanded as triple products of cosines and sines, and the summations can be factorised according to the scheme of Beevers and Lipson, so that the electron density may be written

$$\rho(x,y,z) = K \sum_l \{\sum_k [\sum_h (m_{hkl}A_{hkl}^{(1)} \cos 2\pi hx + m_{hkl}B_{hkl}^{(2)} \sin 2\pi hx) \cos 2\pi ky$$

$$+ \sum_h (m_{hkl}A_{hkl}^{(4)} \sin 2\pi hx + m_{hkl}B_{hkl}^{(3)} \cos 2\pi hx) \sin 2\pi ky] \cos 2\pi lz$$

$$+ \sum_k [\sum_h (m_{hkl}A_{hkl}^{(2)} \cos 2\pi hx + m_{hkl}B_{hkl}^{(1)} \sin 2\pi hx) \sin 2\pi ky$$

$$+ \sum_h (m_{hkl}A_{hkl}^{(3)} \sin 2\pi hx + m_{hkl}B_{hkl}^{(4)} \cos 2\pi hx) \cos 2\pi ky] \sin 2\pi lz\}$$

$$\tag{2}$$

where the summations need to be taken only over zero and positive values of the indices, m_{hkl} is a multiplicity factor, and

$$A^{(1)}_{hkl} = \quad A_{hkl} + A_{\bar{h}kl} + A_{h\bar{k}l} + A_{\bar{h}\bar{k}l}$$
$$A^{(2)}_{hkl} = - A_{hkl} - A_{\bar{h}kl} + A_{h\bar{k}l} + A_{\bar{h}\bar{k}l}$$
$$A^{(3)}_{hkl} = - A_{hkl} + A_{\bar{h}kl} - A_{h\bar{k}l} + A_{\bar{h}\bar{k}l}$$
$$A^{(4)}_{hkl} = - A_{hkl} + A_{\bar{h}kl} + A_{h\bar{k}l} - A_{\bar{h}\bar{k}l}$$

$$B^{(1)}_{hkl} = - B_{hkl} + B_{\bar{h}kl} + B_{h\bar{k}l} - B_{\bar{h}\bar{k}l}$$
$$B^{(2)}_{hkl} = \quad B_{hkl} - B_{\bar{h}kl} + B_{h\bar{k}l} - B_{\bar{h}\bar{k}l}$$
$$B^{(3)}_{hkl} = \quad B_{hkl} + B_{\bar{h}kl} - B_{h\bar{k}l} - B_{\bar{h}\bar{k}l}$$
$$B^{(4)}_{hkl} = \quad B_{hkl} + B_{\bar{h}kl} + B_{h\bar{k}l} + B_{\bar{h}\bar{k}l}$$

(3)

We have without loss of generality confined ourselves to positive and zero values of l, making use of the fact that

$$A_{\overline{hkl}} = \quad A_{hkl}$$
$$B_{\overline{hkl}} = - B_{hkl}$$

(4)

Equation (2) has been written in such a way that the order and grouping of summations and terms corresponds to the actual manner of operation of the program; the order in which individual terms are loaded on to the binary tape by the input program is that which is logically inferable from the equation. Thus, first all of the $A^{(1)}$ terms and $B^{(2)}$ terms (for all h), then all of the $A^{(4)}$ terms and $B^{(3)}$ terms, for the first k and the first l, are loaded; then the same for the next k, and so on through all k's for that l; then all of the $A^{(2)}$ and $B^{(1)}$, then all of the $A^{(3)}$ and $B^{(4)}$ for the first k and the same l are loaded; then the same for the next k, and so on through all k's for that l. Then l changes to the next value and the order with respect to h and k is repeated as before. This continues through all l, and the task of the input program is then complete.

This scheme brings together, for a given l value, all terms in which $\cos 2\pi l z$ appears, followed by all terms in which $\sin 2\pi l z$ appears. Likewise, within a given $\cos 2\pi l z$ group or $\sin 2\pi l z$ group and for a given k, all terms in $\cos 2\pi k y$ are grouped together, followed or preceded by all terms in $\sin 2\pi k y$. The order of the terms is otherwise unimportant. Each term is loaded on to the binary tape with the Miller indices coded according to cosine or sine. The main Fourier program regards a change from cosine to sine (or vice versa) in the k or l coded index as having the same status as a change in the magnitude of k or l respectively. Unnecessary changes back and forth between cosine and sine, for a given k or l value, are therefore undesirable, and are avoided in the scheme here described. An order deviating in any important way from that described above would not prevent the program from operating and yielding correct results, but would result in unnecessary repetition of second- or third-dimension summations and would lengthen, perhaps considerably, the time required for the entire calculation.

The above general expressions (equations 2 and 3) are applicable as given in the case of space group $P1$. For other space groups (with suitable choice of origin in the unit cell) the equations remain correct but certain of the coefficients $A^{(1)} \ldots B^{(4)}$ vanish by cancellation. We shall now discuss the manner in which this is brought about by those symmetry elements that may be present in triclinic, monoclinic, or orthorhombic space groups. These include two-fold rotation and two-fold screw axes parallel to the principal axes, and mirror planes and glide planes perpendicular to the principal axes. The following principles are applicable:

1. The A part of the structure-factor is symmetric with respect to inversion through the origin of coordinates, while the B part is antisymmetric. Thus A is symmetric and B antisymmetric with respect to simultaneous change in sign of all three Miller indices (equation 4).

2. If a two-fold rotation axis or a mirror plane passes through the origin of coordinates in the unit cell, or if a center of symmetry is present at the origin, both A and B are symmetric with respect to operation of that symmetry element, or to corresponding changes in the signs of the Miller indices. (Thus, a two-fold axis through the origin and parallel to the c axis makes A and B symmetric with respect to the simultaneous change in sign of h and k; a mirror plane through the origin perpendicular to c makes A and B symmetric with respect to change in the sign of l. A center of symmetry at the origin makes A and B symmetric with respect to the simultaneous change in sign of h, k, and l; since by rule (1) B must also be antisymmetric, it vanishes in this case.)

3. If (a) the two-fold axis is a screw axis or the plane is a glide plane, such that the operation contains a translational component of $1/2$ cell-edge in one or two directions, and/or (b) the axis or plane has positional coordinates in one or more directions that are $1/4$ cell-edge instead of zero, then A and B are symmetric with respect to the corresponding pure rotation or reflection (or corresponding changes in signs of the indices) if the sum of the Miller indices, corresponding to all of the directions in (a) and (b) is even, and antisymmetric if such sum of indices is odd.

4. For a d-glide plane passing through the origin, operation of which contains a translational component of $1/4$ in each of two directions, A and B are symmetric with respect to the corresponding pure reflection if *one half* the sum of the two corresponding Miller indices is even, and antisymmetric if it is odd.

A two-fold rotation axis parallel to the **a** direction will require $A^{(3)}$, $A^{(4)}$, $B^{(3)}$, and $B^{(4)}$ to vanish, by equations (3) and (4), since

$$A_{hkl} = A_{h\bar{k}\bar{l}} = \quad A_{\bar{h}kl} = \quad A_{\overline{hkl}}$$

$$A_{h\bar{k}l} = A_{hk\bar{l}} = \quad A_{\bar{h}\bar{k}l} = \quad A_{\bar{h}k\bar{l}}$$

$$B_{hkl} = B_{h\bar{k}\bar{l}} = - B_{\bar{h}kl} = - B_{\overline{hkl}}$$

$$B_{h\bar{k}l} = B_{hk\bar{l}} = - B_{\bar{h}\bar{k}l} = - B_{\bar{h}k\bar{l}}$$

$$\uparrow \qquad \uparrow \qquad \uparrow$$

Applicable rule: 2   1   2

A mirror plane normal to **a** will require $A^{(3)}$, $A^{(4)}$, $B^{(1)}$, and $B^{(2)}$ to vanish, since

$$A_{hkl} = A_{\bar{h}kl} = \quad A_{h\bar{k}\bar{l}} = \quad A_{\overline{hkl}}$$

$$A_{h\bar{k}l} = A_{\bar{h}\bar{k}l} = \quad A_{hk\bar{l}} = \quad A_{\bar{h}k\bar{l}}$$

$$B_{hkl} = B_{\bar{h}kl} = - B_{\bar{h}k\bar{l}} = - B_{\overline{hkl}}$$

$$B_{h\bar{k}l} = B_{\overline{hk}l} = - B_{hk\bar{l}} = - B_{\bar{h}k\bar{l}}$$

$$\uparrow \qquad \uparrow \qquad \uparrow$$

Applicable rule: 2   1   2

The simultaneous presence of these two symmetry elements automatically results in the exclusion of all the the B's, as is expected from the fact that these elements generate a center of symmetry at the origin.

The requirements of two-fold rotation and screw axes and mirror and glide planes in various directions and positions are summarized in Table 1.

As an example, let us consider space group $P2_1/c$, which contains a 2_1 axis at z, $x = 1/4,0$ and a c-glide at $y = 1/4$. For the axis, the presence of a translational component of $1/2$ in the y direction, and the coordinate $z = 1/4$, require us to examine the index-sum $k + l$:

	$k + l$ even	$k + l$ odd
Required to vanish:	$A^{(2)}$, $A^{(4)}$,	$A^{(1)}$, $A^{(3)}$,
	$B^{(2)}$, $B^{(4)}$.	$B^{(1)}$, $B^{(3)}$.

For the glide plane, the coordinates $y = 1/4$ and the translational component of $1/2$ in the z direction again require us to examine the sum $k + l$:

	$k + l$ even	$k + l$ odd
Required to vanish:	$A^{(2)}$, $A^{(4)}$,	$A^{(1)}$, $A^{(3)}$,
	$B^{(1)}$, $B^{(3)}$.	$B^{(2)}$, $B^{(4)}$.

K

Thus, in this space group all of the B's vanish whether $k + l$ is even or odd; this corresponds to the fact that the two symmetry elements generate a center of symmetry at the origin. The surviving terms for a given set of Miller indices are therefore

$$A^{(1)}.\cos 2\pi hx.\cos 2\pi ky.\cos 2\pi lz + A^{(3)}.\sin 2\pi hx.\cos 2\pi ky.\sin 2\pi lz$$

when $k + l$ is even, and

$$A^{(2)}.\cos 2\pi hx.\sin 2\pi ky.\sin 2\pi lz + A^{(4)}.\sin 2\pi hx.\sin 2\pi ky.\cos 2\pi lz$$

when $k + l$ is odd.

This scheme, which permits the effects of symmetry elements to be considered individually, has proven to be a very convenient one for computer application. The present program is designed to handle any combination

TABLE 1

VANISHINGS DUE TO SYMMETRY
ELEMENTS

		Required to vanish	
		Appropriate index-sum even	Appropriate index-sum odd
2-fold rotation or screw axis parallel to:	a	$\begin{cases} A^{(3)}, A^{(4)}, \\ B^{(3)}, B^{(4)}. \end{cases}$	$A^{(1)}, A^{(2)},$ $B^{(1)}, B^{(2)}.$
	b	$\begin{cases} A^{(2)}, A^{(4)}, \\ B^{(2)}, B^{(4)}. \end{cases}$	$A^{(1)}, A^{(3)}$ $B^{(1)}, B^{(3)}.$
	c	$\begin{cases} A^{(2)}, A^{(3)}, \\ B^{(2)}, B^{(3)}. \end{cases}$	$A^{(1)}, A^{(4)},$ $B^{(1)}, B^{(4)}.$
Mirror or glide plane perpendicular to:	a	$\begin{cases} A^{(3)}, A^{(4)}, \\ B^{(1)}, B^{(2)}. \end{cases}$	$A^{(1)}, A^{(2)},$ $B^{(3)}, B^{(4)}.$
	b	$\begin{cases} A^{(2)}, A^{(4)}, \\ B^{(1)}, B^{(3)}. \end{cases}$	$A^{(1)}, A^{(3)},$ $B^{(2)}, B^{(4)}.$
	c	$\begin{cases} A^{(2)}, A^{(3)}, \\ B^{(1)}, B^{(4)}. \end{cases}$	$A^{(1)}, A^{(4)},$ $B^{(2)}, B^{(3)}.$

of the eight triple products of cosines and sines. The program reserves certain words in storage as indicators as to whether or not the corresponding terms (triple trigonometric products) are to be included in the sum; each is equal to one if the term is to be included, zero if not. Provision is made for independent routines, corresponding to individual symmetry elements, to be introduced into the program (simply by including special cards in the program deck). The program sends control to each of these in turn. Each forms and examines the appropriate combination of Miller indices and stores zeros in the words corresponding to terms that must vanish (ones having been stored in these words initially). Only those terms that have survived when all of the symmetry routines have been consulted will be further processed and loaded on to the binary output tape.

Paper 12

AN IBM 704 PROGRAM FOR INTERPRETING THE RESULTS OF CRYSTAL STRUCTURE REFINEMENTS

by WILLIAM R. BUSING and HENRI A. LEVY

Chemistry Division, Oak Ridge National Laboratory*
Oak Ridge, Tennessee

ABSTRACT

A program is described which computes various functions of the atomic co-ordinates and anisotropic temperature factor coefficients, such as interatomic distances, bond angles, principal axes of thermal motion, etc. If information on the standard errors of the parameters is available in the form of a variance-covariance matrix, the program also computes the standard error of each calculated function.

INTRODUCTION

Although the crystal structure parameters which are most conveniently refined by least squares or Fourier methods are the atomic coordinates and anisotropic temperature factor coefficients, it is usually not easy to interpret the chemical significance of these quantities themselves. Of greater interest are various functions of these parameters such as the interatomic distances, bond angles, principal axes of thermal motion, etc. It is also desirable to have available an estimate of the standard errors of these quantities. The purpose of this paper is to describe an IBM 704 computer program which may be used to obtain this information. This program may be used independently, reading all input data from cards, or it may be used in conjunction with the least squares refinement program OR XLS, in which case much of the input is taken from the output magnetic tape of a least squares cycle.

Input to the program includes the structure refinement parameters, the unit cell parameters, symmetry information, and a list which defines in detail the specific functions to be computed. The calculation of standard errors is optional, but if it is to be included information about the errors of the structure parameters must be supplied in the form of a variance-

---

*Operated for the U.S. Atomic Energy Commission by Union Carbide Corporation.

covariance matrix, and estimates of the unit cell parameter errors may also be provided.

The program has been written to calculate fifteen different kinds of functions which are listed in Table 1, and it has also been arranged to facilitate the addition of new types of functions which the user may wish to program. For this purpose many sub-routines for performing vector and matrix arithmetic are available and some of these are listed in Table 2. The mathematical methods of computing these quantities will be discussed in more detail below.

ERROR CALCULATION

The quantities f which this program computes are functions of the cell parameters a_k and of n basic structure parameters p_i which include the independent position and thermal parameters. A sub-routine is provided for each kind of function to be computed.

The standard error in a specific function f is given by

$$e = (e^{'2} + e^{''2})^{1/2}.$$

Here
$$e^{''2} = \sum_{i=1}^{n} \sum_{j=1}^{n} (\partial f/\partial p_i)(\partial f/\partial p_j) V_{ij}$$

is the contribution of the structure parameters to the error, and V_{ij} are the elements of the variance-covariance matrix for these parameters. The contribution of the cell parameter errors, $e^{'2}$, is given by a similar expression.

The partial derivatives are computed numerically according to expressions of the type

$$\partial f/\partial p_i = (f^{'} - f)/\Delta p_i$$

where $f^{'}$ is the value of f computed after adding an increment Δp_i to the parameter p_i. The increment Δp_i is assigned the value $0 \cdot 01 \, V_{ii}^{1/2}$. The derivatives $\partial f/\partial a_i$ are computed similarly. This method of derivative calculation allows the incorporation of constraints among atomic parameters, such as those arising from symmetry, in a simple and convenient way. All non-basic parameters needed for evaluation of the functions (for example, a coordinate of a symmetry-constrained atom) are evaluated from the basic parameter set. This evaluation is repeated, for the derivative computation, after each increment Δp_i has been added to p_i. Provision is made for the user to establish any special constraints at the proper point in the program.

Before computing the derivative with respect to a particular parameter the program makes two tests to avoid unnecessary calculations. The first test prevents the computation of derivatives with respect to parameters with zero error, such as a constant coordinate of an atom in a special position or a cell parameter which is fixed by symmetry. The second test bypasses the calculation of derivatives with respect to parameters not involved in the function in question. This test requires that there be associated with each function sub-routine a preliminary sub-routine which designates the specific parameters involved in each calculation.

FUNCTION EVALUATION

Each quantity to be calculated is defined in the input to the program by a sequence of instruction integers. The first of these selects the function sub-routine to be used, and the remaining integers specify the atoms involved or provide other information needed by the function sub-routine.

The fifteen types of functions which are included in the program are described briefly in Table 1. Although all of these function sub-routines are written to compute only a single specified quantity, and the error calculating

TABLE 1

Types of Functions which have been Programmed for Computation by the Function and Error Program

Single-valued functions	Multiple-valued functions	
1 One interatomic distance.	101 Distances (less than d_{max}) between all atoms of one specified symmetry position and all those of another. The two symmetry positions may be the same.	201 Distances (less than d_{max}) between all atoms in the basic symmetry position and all atoms in all symmetry positions of eight cells.
2 The angle defined by three atoms.		
3 The angle between normals to planes each defined by three atoms.		
4 The difference between two interatomic distances. The difference between two angles each defined by three atoms.		
6 The sum of several angles each defined by three atoms		
7 The r.m.s. thermal displacement of an atom along its rth principal axis.	107 Same as function 7 computed for $r = 1, 2,$ and 3.	207 Same as function 107 computed for each kind of atom.
8 The angle between the rth principal axis of thermal motion of one atom and a vector defined by any two atoms.	108 Same as function 8 computed for $r = 1, 2,$ and 3.	208 Same as function 108 computed for each kind of atom.

TABLE 1—*continued*

Single-valued functions	Multiple-valued functions	
9 The r.m.s. components of thermal displacement along the rth principal axis of one atom projected on a vector defined by any two atoms.	109 Same as function 9 computed for $r = 1, 2,$ and 3.	209 Same as function 109 computed for each kind of atom.
10 The angle between the rth principal axis of thermal motion of one atom and the ith axis of a cartesian co-ordinate system defined by the positions of specified atoms.	110 Same as function 10 computed for nine combinations of r and i.	210 Same as function 110 computed for each kind of atom.
11 The r.m.s. component of thermal displacement along the rth principal axis of one atom projected on the ith axis of a cartesian coordinate system defined by the positions of specified atoms.	111 Same as function 11 computed for nine combinations of r and i.	211 Same as function 111 computed for each kind of atom.
12 The r.m.s. component of thermal displacement of one atom in the direction of a vector defined by any two atoms.		
13 The r.m.s. radial thermal displacement of an atom.		
14 Interatomic distance averaged over thermal motion. One atom is assumed to ride on the other.		
15 Interatomic distance averaged over thermal motion. The two atoms are assumed to move independently.		

scheme is designed on this basis, a scheme is provided for the evaluation of more than one quantity with a single sequence of instructions. These multiple-valued functions are also listed in the table. In these cases the program automatically modifies the sequence of integers for each of the several quantities to be computed so that the task of preparing this instruction input is reduced.

To simplify the programming of the various functions a number of sub-routines have been included in the program and some of these are listed in Table 2. The operation of the first two of these will be briefly described. Each atom involved in a function is defined by three integers a, s, and c of the instruction sequence. Sub-routine ATOM produces the triclinic coordinates of atom (a, s, c) by selecting from the parameter table the coordinates of the

ath kind of atom, transforming them with the sth of the symmetry transformations provided, and finally making a cell translation according to c which specifies one of the eight cells about the origin. Sub-routine BETA makes a similar selection and transformation to store the 3×3 matrix of the anisotropic temperature factor coefficients of the specified atom.

In the evaluation of the various functions it has been found convenient to make use of matrix arithmetic and vectors referred to a general triclinic coordinate system. For example, the length of a vector $\mathbf{v}$ is computed as $l = (\tilde{\mathbf{v}}\mathbf{g}\mathbf{v})^{1/2}$ using sub-routines to perform the arithmetic. The sub-routine STOAA is available to store the 3×3 matrix $\mathbf{g}$, where $\mathbf{g}_{ij} = \mathbf{a}_i \cdot \mathbf{a}_j$, the scalar product of two lattice vectors. For the determination of the principal axes of thermal motion the eigenvalues and eigenvectors of the matrix $\beta\mathbf{g}$ are found. The mean square thermal displacement of an atom with anisotropic temperature factor coefficients β in the direction of a vector $\mathbf{v}$ is calculated as

$$(1/2\pi^2)\,(\tilde{\mathbf{v}}\mathbf{g}\beta\mathbf{g}\mathbf{v})/(\tilde{\mathbf{v}}\mathbf{g}\mathbf{v})$$

Similarly the mean square radial thermal displacement is evaluated as $(1/2\pi^2)$ trace $(\beta\mathbf{g})$. Other calculation methods are described briefly in Table 2.

OUTPUT

The output of the program includes a general heading which describes the type of function being computed such as " Distance between two atoms, Ångströms." This heading is put out each time the type of function is changed. Then for each computed quantity there is put out the specific description of the atoms involved in terms of the integers a, s, and c for each. On the same line is printed the numerical value of the function, the computed standard error, and the error computed without considering the errors of the unit cell parameters. The last is included so that the relative importance of the cell errors can be determined.

TABLE 2

ARITHMETIC SUB-ROUTINES USED BY THE FUNCTION SUB-ROUTINES AND AVAILABLE FOR USE IN PROGRAMMING NEW FUNCTIONS.

ATOM	Obtains the coordinates of an atom, given the parameter table and the integers a, s, and c which specify the kind of atom, the symmetry transformation, and the unit cell translation.
BETA	Obtains the 3×3 matrix of the anisotropic temperature factor coefficients, given the parameter table and the integers a and s which specify the kind of atom and the symmetry transformation.
STOAA	Stores the 3×3 metric tensor $\mathbf{g}$ given the unit cell parameters.
STOBB	Stores the 3×3 reciprocal metric tensor $\mathbf{g}^{-1}$ given the unit cell parameters.
MM	Multiplies two 3×3 matrices.
MV	Multiplies a vector by a 3×3 matrix.

VM   Multiplies a 3 × 3 matrix by a transposed vector.

VV   Multiplies a vector by a transposed vector to produce a scalar.

VMV   Multiplies a vector by a 3 × 3 matrix and then by a transposed vector to produce a scalar.

DIFV   Performs vector subtraction.

COSVV   Computes the cosine of the angle between two vectors. Let **u** and **v** be vectors referred to the triclinic coordinate system and let ϕ be the angle between them. Then

$$\cos \phi = \tilde{\mathbf{u}}\mathbf{g}\mathbf{v}/(\tilde{\mathbf{u}}\mathbf{g}\mathbf{u}\tilde{\mathbf{v}}\mathbf{g}\mathbf{v})^{\frac{1}{2}}.$$

ARCCOS Computes ϕ in degrees given $\cos \phi$.

NORM   Stores a vector **w** which is normal to two given vectors **u** and **v** where all vectors are referred to the triclinic coordinate system. The expression used is $\mathbf{w} = \mathbf{g}^{-1} \mathbf{w}'$ where

$$w'_i = u_j v_k - u_k v_j, \; i \neq j \neq k.$$

EIGVAL Computes the three eigenvalues, $\lambda^{(r)}$, of a given 3 × 3 matrix **W**. The sub-routine solves the cubic equation $| \mathbf{W} - \lambda \mathbf{I} | = 0$ in analytical form.

EIGVEC Computes an eigenvector **v** of the matrix **W** given an eigenvalue $\lambda^{(r)}$. If $\mathbf{W}' = \mathbf{W} - \lambda^{(r)}\mathbf{I}$ then $v_j =$ cofactor W_{ij} where i is taken as 1, 2, or 3 to avoid a nul vector.

TRACE   Computes the trace of a 3 × 3 matrix.

Paper 13

LEAST SQUARES REFINEMENT PROGRAMS FOR THE IBM 704

by WILLIAM R. BUSING and HENRI A. LEVY

Chemistry Division, Oak Ridge National Laboratory*
Oak Ridge, Tennessee

ABSTRACT

Crystallographic least squares programs for the IBM 704 are summarized and the program OR XLS is described in some detail. The relative merits of full matrix least squares and the diagonal approximation are discussed.

The authors find themselves in the difficult situation of being asked to discuss the various crystallographic least squares programs available for the IBM 704 computer, when, in fact, they are really familiar with only one of them—their own. This means that detailed descriptions of other programs would possibly be erroneous, and that comparisons between them might be prejudiced. To avoid these pitfalls we have decided to devote most of this paper to a description of our own program with the hope that persons familiar with the others will contribute their remarks to the discussion.

The available IBM 704 least squares programs are individually summarized in the Appendix. The earliest of these is Sayre's NY XR1 which has been superseded by Hatch's NY XR2† and by Vand and Pepinsky's extensively modified version, PS XR3 (Vand and Pepinsky, 1959). These three programs use the diagonal approximation to the least squares refinement and provide for isotropic temperature factors on the individual atoms. A program written by MacIntyre (1959) refines structure parameters including anisotropic temperature factor coefficients using diagonal least squares. The program OR XLS which was prepared by the present authors (Busing and Levy, 1959) uses the full matrix for least squares refinement (with the observational equations linearized) and permits the adjustment of either isotropic or anisotropic temperature factor coefficients. A similar program written by Hamilton (private communication) is limited to two-dimensional refinements.

---

*Operated for the U.S. Atomic Energy Commission by Union Carbide Corporation.

†Descriptions of these programs are available from IBM, New York.

The principal distinguishing features of OR XLS are then the use of the full matrix and the choice of the form of the temperature factors. The program permits refinement based on either the structure factor or its square. Any number of scale factors may be adjusted, and either X-ray or neutron scattering factors may be used. The program requires a standard error to be assigned to each observation for weighting purposes, but provision is made for these standard errors to be calculated by an extra section of code according to any scheme selected by the user. The user is completely free to select the parameters to be varied.

The program is divided into five segments primarily to conserve memory space for storing the matrix of normal equations. The first segment is a data processor which writes the observations on magnetic tape together with the interpolated values of the X-ray scattering factors and other pertinent information about each reflection. Segment two is the main structure factor segment which produces a magnetic tape with the derivatives corresponding to each observation. Segment three then reads this magnetic tape and stores the matrix of normal equations in the core memory. Segment four inverts this matrix and segment five computes the corrections to each parameter. Control is then returned to segment two for output of the corrected parameters.

The program computes structure factors and their derivatives using the expressions for space groups $P1$ or $P\bar{1}$. Symmetry information is provided to produce the various symmetry positions. Instead of transforming the coordinates, however, the equivalent transformations of the indices are made.* Special positions which require only that certain parameters be fixed are easily treated. When special positions require certain relationships between two parameters, an extra section of code must be supplied by the user to establish these constraints. In this way any symmetry situation can be accommodated rigorously.

Since the matrix of normal equations is symmetric only the $n(n + 1)/2$ non-equivalent elements of a matrix of order n are stored. The matrix inverter uses the method of Lagrange† which takes advantage of the symmetry, and a storage scheme has been devised so that the inversion is performed entirely in the fast memory using only n storage locations in addition to those occupied by the matrix. On completion of the process the inverse matrix has replaced the original matrix in the memory. In this way 120 variables can be accommodated in an 8192-word memory or 251 in a 32,768-word machine.

---

*This method has been developed from ideas presented by R. J. Prosen, ACA Meeting, French Lick, Indiana, June, 1956.

†See, for example, TURNBULL and AITKEN, *An Introduction to the Theory of Canonical Matrices* Blackie and Son, Ltd., London and Glasgow (1932), pp. 85–86.

The time required for inverting a matrix is 3·6 minutes for $n = 100$. This high speed is attained by the use of single precision floating-point arithmetic throughout the inversion process, a procedure which may be subject to the criticism* that it is possible for the accumulation of round-off error to invalidate the inversion of large matrices. It should be remembered, on the other hand, that such difficulties are the most pronounced for poorly conditioned matrices, and that these are produced by the least squares procedure only when the parameters are not strongly determined by the observations. Numerical tests of the procedure have been made using typical crystallographic least squares matrices of orders 57 and 113. Let an error matrix X be defined by $X = AB - I$ where A is the original matrix, B is the supposed inverse, and I is the identity matrix. The values of max $| X_{ij} |$ were computed and in each of the two cases found to be 2×10^{-5}, or very small compared to unity. Further encouragement can be derived from the fact that since the least squares refinement is an iterative procedure any error introduced in one cycle will tend to be corrected on the next. It is this fact, of course, which makes the diagonal approximation give correct results.

In conclusion, it is probably desirable to discuss the relative merits of the diagonal approximation and of full matrix least squares. The feeling of those who have used the full matrix method is that it usually leads to convergence with less difficulty than does the diagonal method. In general, about three cycles of the latter are required for each one of the former. On the other hand, the computer time required for the full matrix method goes up rapidly with the size of the problem and for problems of fifteen atoms, or so, exceeds that required for the diagonal approximation even though fewer cycles are required. The full matrix method, however, yields a more accurate estimate of the standard errors (Sparks and Trueblood, 1958) and, furthermore, provides information on the covariances between parameters which is needed if the standard errors of bond distances and angles are to be correctly estimated. It would seem that no single decision can be made in favor of either method, and that perhaps a suitable compromise between them will have to be used for the large problems of the future.

APPENDIX

Program Abstracts

*NY XR*2. Structure factor least squares. Subprogram must be prepared for each space group. Possible variables: scale factor, coordinates, individual atom isotropic temperature factor coefficients. Diagonal least squares with intra-atomic cross terms included for non-orthogonal space groups. Approximate time for one standard cycle,* isotropic: 3 min. Weighting scheme: equal, general, or min $(1, 100/F_o^2)$.

*PS XR*3. Structure factor least squares. Any space group. Possible variables:

---

*A standard cycle is taken as 1000 observations on a centrosymmetric monoclinic structure with ten atoms in the asymmetric unit.

scale factor, coordinates, individual atom isotropic temperature factor coefficients. Diagonal least squares with intra-atomic cross terms included for non-orthogonal space groups. Capacity: 106 atoms with 8 k memory, 128 for 16 k or larger memory. Approximate time for one standard cycle, isotropic: 3 min. Weighting scheme: equal or $1/f_i$. Special features: automatic control of damping factor.

Program of W. M. Macintyre. Structure factor least squares. Subprograms available for all triclinic, monoclinic, orthorhombic, and tetragonal space groups. Possible variables: scale factor, coordinates, individual atom anisotropic temperature factor coefficients. Diagonal least squares with cross terms between scale factor and temperature factor coefficients. Approximate time for one standard cycle, anisotropic: 14 min. Weighting scheme: general.

OR XLS. Structure factor least squares. Any space group. Possible variables: several scale factors, neutron scattering factors, coordinates, overall or individual atom isotropic temperature factor coefficients, or individual atom anisotropic temperature factor coefficients. Full matrix least squares. Capacity: 120 variables with 8 k memory or 251 variables with 32 k memory. Approximate time for one standard cycle, isotropic: 10 min anisotropic: 43 min. Weighting scheme: general. Special features: refinement based on F or F^2; arbitrary selection of parameters to be varied.

REFERENCES

BUSING, W. R. and LEVY, H.A. (1959). CF Memo 59–4–37, Oak Ridge National Laboratory, Oak Ridge, Tennessee, April, 1959.

MACINTYRE, W. M. (1959). *Acta Cryst.* **12**, 761.

VAND, V. and PEPINSKY, R. (1959). Report No. GI 52, The Groth Institute, Pennsylvania State University, University Park, Pennsylvania, October, 1959.

SPARKS, R. A. and TRUEBLOOD, K. N. (1958). ACA Meeting, Milwaukee, Wisconsin, June 1958.

Paper 14

COMPUTATION OF MADELUNG SUMS
AND CRYSTAL ENERGIES

by DAVID H. TEMPLETON and QUINTIN C. JOHNSON

Lawrence Radiation Laboratory and Department of Chemistry
University of California, Berkeley, California

ABSTRACT

A strategy is outlined for the calculation of the Madelung constant according to Bertaut's method and the crystal energy with repulsion treated as a simple power dependence on distance. A program is described which permits these calculations to be done conveniently and rapidly with the IBM 704 computer.

If one understands in sufficient detail the forces between atoms, then in principle one can calculate the thermodynamic properties of arbitrary structures, or, conversely, one can predict the structure which would be thermodynamically most stable. For the crystalline materials that we call salts, the force between a pair of atoms is well approximated by a term which is just the Coulomb force for a pair of point charges plus a second term which is strongly repulsive at short distances and ineffective at long distances. The potential energy of the crystal is calculated by adding the potential energies associated with these two terms for every pair of atoms in the crystal.

The Madelung sum, U_c, is:

$$U_c = - e^2 A/L = \sum_{i \neq j} e_i e_j / r_{ij}, \qquad (1)$$

where e is the charge of the electron, L is a standard distance (often chosen as the nearest neighbor distance, r_o), A is the Madelung constant corresponding to this choice of L, e_i is the charge of an ion, and r_{ij} is the distance between two ions. In this sum, attention must be paid to the number of terms of each kind so that one gets the energy for a definite quantity of material, for example one mole. One wishes to have the limit of the sum as it extends to neighbors at very large distances. However, this sum is convergent only by cancellation of positive and negative contributions, each of which increases without limit, and therefore the series must be terminated properly. Except for this conditional convergence, this sum would be a relatively prosaic job for a fast electronic computer.

The short-range term includes the specific chemical effects, and its treatment depends on the nature of the problem. For salts consisting of monatomic ions which are isoelectronic with rare gases, interesting and useful results can be obtained with a simple repulsive potential proportional to some high negative power of the distance:

$$u_{ij} = B_{ij}/r_{ij}{}^n, \tag{2}$$

where B is characteristic of the kind of atoms involved. With a potential of this simplicity, the calculation of repulsion energy presents no special problems.

At Berkeley these calculations have been made by hand and with a variety of IBM computers, including the CPC (card programmed computer), the 650, and the 704. The strategy which has been developed will be discussed in terms of a 704 program which was completed early in 1960.

THE MADELUNG SUM

We have been interested in problems involving various symmetries and with variable parameters. Enormous accuracy is not required, but it is essential to know the order of magnitude of the accuracy and especially to avoid convergence blunders. It is desirable to have a program which can be used for new problems without programming changes and with a minimum of new data. These considerations have controlled the choice of strategy for the Madelung sum.

We use the method of Bertaut (1952, 1953) as elaborated by Templeton (1955) and Jones and Templeton (1956) for spherical charge distributions whose densities are a linear function of the radial coordinate. The Madelung constant is:

$$A = \frac{(g - Q)L}{RZ} \sum_j (z_j)^2 - \frac{\pi R^2 L}{ZV} \sum_h |F|^2 \phi \tag{3}$$

$g = 26/35$
$Q = $ a correction for termination of the h series
$L = $ standard distance
$R = $ an arbitary distance less than half
        the nearest neighbor distance
$Z = $ molecules per unit cell
$z_j = $ charge number (with sign)
        of an atom
$V = $ volume of unit cell
$h = $ magnitude of reciprocal vector $\mathbf{h}$
$F = \sum_j z_j \exp(2\pi i\, \mathbf{h}.\mathbf{x}_j)$
$\phi = 288\, (\alpha \sin \alpha + 2 \cos \alpha - 2)^2 \alpha^{-10}$
$\alpha = 2\pi hR$

The sums over j include all atoms in the unit cell. The sum over h includes all reciprocal lattice vectors in a sphere of arbitrary radius. The series termination correction depends on the radius of this sphere as follows, according to a statistical theory:

Maximum α	Q
2π	0·00030
3π	0·000090
4π	0·000012
5π	0·0000057

Other values of Q are listed by Jones and Templeton. Experience has shown that Q is reliable to 20 per cent or better in most cases. Thus termination at 2π yields accuracy better than 0·1 per cent with Q neglected and better than about 0·02 per cent if the correction is made.

THE 704 PROGRAM

The program for the 704 computer was written in Fortran language for a machine configuration of 32K core storage. Approximately 30 per cent of this storage is used. No attention has been given to economy of storage, and such large storage capacity is not an intrinsic requirement of the strategy described here. One magnetic tape is used, for writing output. On-line printing is permitted by a sense switch, but is relatively time-consuming.

The program can be loaded as a deck of about 300 binary cards followed by a dozen or more cards which describe the data for the specific problem in alphabetic and decimal-numeric characters. The program loads the data, prints them as an identification of the problem, and then distinguishes between crystal systems. Triclinic problems are not provided for. Rhombohedral problems must be set up in hexagonal coordinate systems, and, like hexagonal problems, are considered by the machine as if they were monoclinic. One-fourth of reciprocal space is considered in the h sum for monoclinic (and hexagonal) problems; otherwise only one-eighth is considered. Appropriate multiplicity factors are applied to give the result for the complete sphere.

The atomic positions have been loaded as coordinates of the atoms of the asymmetric unit, together with a code for the lists of equivalent positions. Coordinates are generated and printed for all atoms in the unit cell. A list of the shorter interatomic distances, up to a specified limit, is calculated and printed. The program chooses $R = 0·495\ D$, where D is the shortest distance in this list.

The Madelung constant is calculated according to equation (3), with series termination at a value of α specified by the input data. The charge structure factors F are calculated as if the structure were triclinic. A routine scans reciprocal space along rows, working outward in both directions from the point nearest the origin until vectors are found which lie outside the termination sphere. When F is zero, the program skips the calculation of ϕ. The calculation of the Madelung constant is the slowest step of the internal program.

The repulsive terms are calculated according to equation (2) with neglect of neighbors of a particular kind at distances greater than a specified distance. The exponent in (2) need not be integral. The answers are printed.

If another set of data cards follows, the program proceeds to the new problem, saving the program-loading time.

Typical running times, with off-line printing and with series termination at $\alpha = 2\pi$, are 80 sec to load the program, plus 10 sec for rutile, 70 sec for brookite, and 130 sec for corundum. On-line printing adds about 70 sec to each problem. The running time depends mainly on the number of atoms in the unit cell and the symmetry. Rutile is tetragonal with 6 atoms per unit cell. Brookite is orthorhombic with 24 atoms per unit cell. Corundum is rhombohedral, with 30 atoms in the hexagonal unit cell.

APPLICATIONS

An application of these methods, described elsewhere (Templeton, 1957), is the determination of the positions of oxygen and fluorine in YOF, where they could not be distinguished with X-rays. These calculations were carried out with a more specialized program and the IBM 650.

It is anticipated that the present 704 program may be modified to calculate first and second derivatives of the energy with respect to variation of parameters, but at the present writing this has not been done. Such modification would permit automatic refinement to the structure of minimum energy according to an arbitrary choice of interaction parameters.

More complicated functions could be used for the repulsive potential with little increase in running time.

Many Madelung constants have now been calculated with this program and will be published elsewhere.

Acknowledgment

This research was supported by the U.S. Atomic Energy Commission. We thank the staff of the Computer Center of the University of California for their cooperation.

REFERENCES

BERTAUT, F. (1952). *J. phys. radium* **13**, 499.
BERTAUT, F. (1953). " Ferroelectric and high dielectric crystals: Contribution to the theory of fields, potentials and energies in periodic lattices," U.S. Air Force Report AD–22696, July, 1953 (unpublished).
JONES, R. E. and TEMPLETON, D. H. (1956). *J. Chem. Phys.* **25**, 1062.
TEMPLETON, D. H. (1955). *J. Chem. Phys.* **23**, 1629.
TEMPLETON, D. H. (1957). *Acta Cryst.* **10**, 788.

L

Paper 15

X-RAC AND DIGITAL COMPUTING METHODS

by R. PEPINSKY, J. VAN DEN HENDE and V. VAND

Crystal Research Laboratory and The Groth Institute,
The Pennsylvania State University, University Park, Pa., U.S.A.

Introduction

The development and use of electronic digital and analogue computers in the past decade has altered many aspects of crystallography. Due to the explosive growth in computer development, numerous and often intricate calculations are no longer the prime bottleneck in the solution of crystal structures, as was the case until the late forties. Machines have proved to be so valuable that a modern laboratory simply cannot operate without access to them. The availability of high-speed calculating devices has become the critical problem in most crystallographic laboratories.

Availability and usefulness is determined by several factors: the amount of computing time required, coupled with the time of programming and other preparation, and the cost of use of the machine; the location of the computer with respect to the laboratory; the ease of handling of the machine; the machine's reliability; and ease of interpretation of the output produced.

Concerning problems of availability of large-scale machines

A limited budget very often proves to be the limitation in any research project. Thus economy of computer operation is of primary importance. Even though the speed of electronic digital computers has increased by several orders of magnitude, the rental or purchase costs of current high-speed digital machines tend to very large figures. The ratio of cost to speed does become increasingly advantageous; but as crystallographic techniques advance and machines improve, problems of increasing complexity are examined, and refinements of structures are pressed to increasing degrees of precision and detail.

There is no question but that the future of crystallographic computing lies with general-purpose high-speed transistorized machines. Improvements in manufacturing methods, increasingly great competition between commercial sources, and of course advances in electronic design, tend to ameliorate economic limitations. Analogue computers will tend to disappear *per se*;

154

but analogue-to-digital input and digital-to-analogue output devices will retain importance for certain classes of problems.

This is the second Conference with the present title to be held in crystallography; the first, at the (now) Pennsylvania State University, occurred ten years ago. In 1950, no completely electronic automatic sequence digital machines were available. It was not until about 1955 that the IBM 704 machine, the first of the large-scale commercial devices in America adequate for larger crystallographic problems, could be utilized by workers in our field. The 704 is now an obsolete computer, in part because it is a thermionic tube machine, and in part because its immediate successor from IBM, the 709, had improved storage features, faster circuitry, and hence much greater computing capacity. The major development in machine design has of course been occasioned by the introduction of transistorized circuitry. The IBM 7090, the Philco TRANSAC, the Bendix G–20 and the Control Data Corporation 1604 are among contemporary large-scale commercially-available American computers. All are completely solid-state machines.

With the advent of these, used 704 and 709 machines are now within the economic reach of some university research centers; and some American universities are wise enough to purchase them. The economic disadvantage of these older machines is their maintenance cost. The excellent 709 can now be obtained by universities for about $350,000; but the annual cost of maintenance by a trained IBM crew begins at about $50,000, and climbs each year. Although purchase costs will decrease for tube computers in the next few years, maintenance costs will increase. From a glance at developments since 1955, no one should be eager to predict what a third Conference on computing methods in crystallography, in 1970, will involve—other than to say that what we report now will in 1970 appear about as ancient as Egypt.

Crystallographers are not the elect among contemporary scientists. Unless they are associated with large industrial or federally-supported laboratories in America, they must beg time on large-scale machines where they can find it. Our own Crystal Research Laboratory is blessed with an arrangement with the U.S. Atomic Energy Commission, whereby about 10 hours of IBM 704 time is available to us each month. Without this arrangement, our work would be impossible. But it would be equally impossible if it were not for the support we have had, since 1947, from the Office of Naval research, for the construction and operation of a special-purpose electronic analogue machine for crystal-structure computations: X–RAC (with its associated machine S–FAC).

Some remarks on X–RAC

X–RAC is an anomaly among computers. Operative since late 1948, X–RAC is still by far the fastest and most economical instrument available for two or three-dimensional Fourier synthesis, with visual presentation of accurate contour maps. It has operated essentially without significant failure for a dozen years. A careful study has shown that X–RAC is more economical and, even so, capable of greater accuracy for its special purposes, than any digital machine yet on the market. When utilized for observations of structure-factor phase changes on a two-dimensional Fourier map, it is perfectly safe to say that no digital machine will *ever* approach its combined speed and accuracy. It has survived two great revolutions in general computer development, and is perhaps the only large special-purpose machine with so long a record of full operation which still possesses such advantages over the largest property-programmed digital machines.

The operational features of X–RAC were extensively described in the 1950 Conference book, and of course there is no need to repeat the description here. (Some reprints of the 1950 X–RAC chapter are available, although the complete Conference volume is out of print.) A contour map is produced in one second, once Fourier coefficients are inserted in the machine; and this rate could easily be increased if it were necessary. The circuitry has never been described in the press. The plans were offered to European crystallographers as early as 1951, in case the decision was reached to duplicate the machine in some center or centers; and funds could have been made available from America to support construction in Europe. I have always felt that more wisdom should have been exerted, in selecting an experienced electronics man with crystallographic interests, to advise British crystallographers of the possibilities inherent in the basic X–RAC design. How many man-years of dull computations and contour-map delineation would probably have been avoided, if bad advice had been avoided!

Certain improvements have been made in X–RAC circuitry, since the machine was last described in 1950. The entire presentation oscilloscope system has been re-worked or replaced, so that today both the photographic and viewing cathode-ray systems provide very sharp and beautiful contour patterns. A few of these are reproduced in Paper [28], page 273. The entire S–FAC system, for computation of two-dimensional structure factors, has been re-designed and re-constructed. The combined use of these associated machines is marvellously powerful. As a training device for young crystallographers, they are unsurpassed.

Both machines operate on full schedule, on our own and a few outside problems. I do not believe that more than a half-dozen days a year, since 1950, have been taken out of this operating schedule for component replacement or maintenance. Test procedures are so simple that any difficulties are almost immediately noticeable; and circuits are generally repaired in a few minutes when this proves necessary. This is of course a tribute to Mr. Paul Jarmotz, who has been in charge of circuit and other component construction and maintenance during the life of these machines.

No special volumes on X–RAC, and no series of papers, have been pressed into the general literature, since the 1950 report. One volume, entitled *X–RAC Operation Manual*, has been issued, chiefly for the use of operators and users. A volume describing the design and operation of the earlier model of S–FAC has also been issued. S–FAC circuitry is particularly ingenious; and at the request of the supporting contracting agency, patents have been taken out on some aspects of the electronics. An example of the generally useful electronic designing here is a circuit which provides electrometer-tube action, but by utilizing an old-fashioned, inexpensive 6AK5 miniature pentode with a new type of grid circuit.

It is interesting that a majority of electron tubes presently operating in X–RAC were installed in Alabama in 1947 and 1948, and survived the transfer of the computer to Pennsylvania in 1949! This speaks well for the conservative mode of operation of these tubes, due to proper circuit and overall design.

Der Untergang des X–RACs

In time, X–RAC—as it now stands—will become of decreasing importance in crystal analysis; new methods of structure determination, plus lower cost and increasing speed of digital machines, will lead to this end. We could today build a machine with fully digitalized (punched-card or paper-tape) input; or we could build an even more accurate version of X–RAC, with larger capacity and rather simplified circuitry; and this could be done at much less cost than was required for our one and only model. We could couple X–RAC and S–FAC intimately to a large electronic digital general-purpose machine, and build the most powerful device for structure analysis for which crystallographers could hope. We have not done so chiefly for lack of funds: most of Office of Naval Research contract funds available to us in the past decade have gone into operation, maintenance and use of the machines as they stand, in X-ray and neutron diffraction studies of the structural mechanisms responsible for certain classes of physical properties, and in biochemical molecular structure studies; and our thinking has had to be directed to these and other basic matters.

There is one further difficulty, in the matter of support for the development of a new version of a special-purpose computer. Already in 1946 the decision had been made in most quarters, that the future of computing lay with digital machines. Funds for the support of the development of X–RAC were provided in the face of this trend, thanks to the wisdom of Dr. Mina Rees and others in our Office of Naval Research. Today, unless a sizeable analogue machine can be considered as a possible general input or output device for a large-scale general-purpose digital computer, it has small power to attract funding. Under conditions in America, where the constructional techniques for large digital machines rest in industrial hands, input and output systems are tied to commercial realms as well. One does not play with the " innards " of large digital devices, in university laboratories. Such computers are too much in demand for computing purposes. Until this condition alters, due to the appearance of a plethora of obsolete machines on the market, development work for specialized ends will remain chiefly under industrial control, or within the province of very large federal laboratories.

Computing facilities available to us

My purpose here is to describe the place of X–RAC and S–FAC in the computing procedures presently applied within our laboratory: and I will describe an output device for a digital machine which will simulate some of the features of X–RAC.

X–RAC and S–FAC are components in our laboratory, in combined analogue and digital facilities. Small-scale punched-card facilities are available within the Groth Institute, under support of the Directorate of Solid State Sciences of the Air Force Office of Scientific Research, Air Research and Development Command. These include standard and special IBM Card Punches and a Verifier, a 407 Accounting Machine, a Reproducing Punch, a Sorter, and several Cardatype Machines with Arithmetic Units. An Interpreter and other small-scale machines are available in the University Computing Center, which also contains an IBM 650 machine. (Since the rental costs of the 650 are excessive to us, we made no use of that machine.) Through support of the Atomic Energy Commission, we have use of the IBM 704 machine with 32K-word core storage, at the New York University Computing Center. Additional IBM 704 time has been available to us, in the past, in various industrial laboratories, and particularly at the General Motors Research Center near Detroit and the Curtiss–Wright Research Laboratory at Quehanna, Pa. We presently anticipate availability of time on an IBM 7090 machine at another industrial installation.

The digital computing needs of the Groth Institute are desperately great; and we are attempting to solve them through acquisition of a large-scale digital machine directly within the Institute. A library of programs and data on magnetic tapes for the 704 machine is maintained in the Groth Institute, along with a file of over two million IBM cards containing crystallographic data. This library is rapidly increasing, and will exceed six million cards within the coming year. Special, highly-effective small-scale machine methods have been developed in the Institute to retrieve data from these massive card files. The IBM SHARE Library is available to us at New York University.

General computing processes

The general course of a standard X-ray or neutron analysis is as follows:

A. The intensity data are collected. This is now beginning to be accomplished on the excellent single-crystal automatic diffractometer and analogue computer, SCADAC, constructed by us and described elsewhere. Neutron scattering data are collected on the automatic diffractometers by the Penn State Guest Group at the Brookhaven National Laboratory. These diffractometers are also described elsewhere.

B. Intensity data are corrected for Lorentz and polarization factors and absorption by IBM 704 programs. The scale factor may be roughly determined by Wilson's method.

C. Another 704 program computes one-dimensional Patterson function summations, for introduction into X–RAC. The 704 printouts are arranged exactly as are the coefficients on the X–RAC panels. An IBM 407 program for these one-dimensional summations has been developed also, and is used when the analyst concerned does not wish to wait for a scheduled visit to the 704 in New York; the 407 computations are then done in the Groth Institute. Three-dimensional Patterson maps are then computed on and photographed from X–RAC.

D. In case of non-centrosymmetric structures containing anomalous scatterers, the $P_s(u)$ function is computed similarly, using a 704 program followed by X–RAC computations.

E. The Patterson map is interpreted by standard methods, including image-seeking. The $P_s(u)$ function is interpreted by the methods described in the paper by Okaya and Pepinsky to this Conference. Where necessary, statistical methods are applied for determination of some phases.

F. Coordinates obtained from E are tested on S–FAC, in two-dimensional projections. Three-dimensional coordinates are then utilized for a 704 computation of structure-factor phases, and one-dimensional summations (for an X–RAC three-dimensional electron density computation) are calculated immediately thereafter on the 704. The printouts are again arranged just as the coefficients are required on X–RAC panels.

G. The three-dimensional electron density approximation is computed on X–RAC, and new atomic coordinates are obtained. S–FAC is used on two-dimensional projections for further testing.

H. Cycles E, F and G are repeated, until the phases are established and the structure fairly well determined. The scale factor is refined somewhat in this process.

I. The coordinates are refined, along with the scale factor and other parameters, using the least square approximation method, on the 704, with or without differential-synthesis weighting. Interatomic distances are calculated on the 704, as well.

Paper 16

THE OPTIMAL SHIFT METHOD FOR THE REFINEMENT OF CRYSTAL STRUCTURES

by A. Niggli,* V. Vand and R. Pepinsky

Crystal Research Laboratory and The Groth Institute
College of Chemistry and Physics, The Pennsylvania State University
University Park, Pa., U.S.A.

ABSTRACT

When $m < n$, the least squares method is inapplicable for the refinement of sets of m equations with n unknowns. As in the initial stages of crystal structure refinement it may be advantageous to concentrate on a small set of the most important structure factors only, a refinement method is described which is suitable for such applications. The method is a rational extension of intuitive methods, such as those of shifting atoms according to Bragg–Lipson charts; it is related to the relaxation method in applied mathematics.

Introduction

Crystal structures are, as a rule, refined either by the Fourier method or by the least squares method in one of its many forms—the full matrix inversion, the diagonal approximation, steepest descents, the difference synthesis, etc. However, the least squares method is applicable only when the problem is overdetermined, i.e. when there are more equations available than unknowns; this is usually the case in the final stages of a crystal structure refinement.

On the other hand, in the initial stages of refinement it is often advantageous for various reasons, to concentrate on a few most important structure factors only, such as those of which the phases are known, or which have the greatest weights (large absolute values and small angles θ). The problem then becomes underdetermined, and the least squares method can no longer be applied. However, intuitive methods, such as shifting the atoms according to Bragg–Lipson charts, are in reality solutions of such underdetermined sets of equations; they are often used by crystallographers with success.

It was found desirable, in connection with a Monte Carlo program for testing random crystal structures, to develop a method for the solution of

---

* Permanent address: Institut für Kristallographie und Petrographie, Eidg. Techn. Hochschule, Sonneggstr. 5, Zürich 6, Switzerland.

the underdetermined problem, and at the same time to bring this method, intuitive in origin, on a rational basis so that it can be programmed for a high-speed computer. Thus a new method, named the *optimal shift method*, has been developed. This proves to be distinct from, but related to the least squares method; it is, in fact, complementary to the least squares approach.

Statement of the problem in its simplest form

Let $F(u_1, u_2, \ldots, u_n)$ be a function of n unknown variables u_i, where $i = 1, \ldots, n$. Let F_c be the value of F calculated from a set of assumed parameters u_i. It is desired to vary the u_i by adding to them Δu_i in such a way that

$$F_c(u_i + \Delta u_i) = F_o,$$

where F_o is a given (e.g. observed) value of the function. Let us also assume that within the range Δu_i the function F can be expanded into a Taylor series

$$F_o = F_c + \sum_i (\partial F/\partial u_i) \Delta u_i + \ldots, \tag{1}$$

and that the higher terms can be neglected. Then, writing ΔF for $F_o - F_c$, we obtain one linear equation for the n unknown Δu_i's:

$$\sum_i (\partial F/\partial u_i) \Delta u_i = \Delta F.$$

This has an infinity of solutions; but by adding further conditions, a unique solution for the Δu_i can be obtained.

The obvious choice of such a condition is to change those u_i most which have the greatest effect on the change of F, and not to change those u_i which do not exert any influence on the value of F; this is exactly what is done in the intuitive refinement method. Expressed mathematically, we require Δu_i to be proportional to $\partial F/\partial u_i$ for all values of i.

We have thus n additional conditions:

$$\Delta u_i = K (\partial F/\partial u_i), \ i = 1, \ldots, n, \tag{2}$$

where K is an as yet undetermined proportionality constant. Substituting into (1) for Δu_i,

$$\sum_i (\partial F/\partial u_i) . K (\partial F/\partial u_i) = K \sum_i (\partial F/\partial u_i)^2 = \Delta F,$$

we obtain an equation for K:

$$K = \Delta F / \sum_i (\partial F/\partial u_i)^2.$$

We have thus reduced the original problem to one equation with one unknown, K. Substituting in (2) for K, we finally obtain the equations for the Δu_i's:

$$\Delta u_i = \Delta F (\partial F/\partial u_i) / \sum_j (\partial F/\partial u_j)^2. \tag{3}$$

If F is taken to be the structure factor of atoms with coordinates u_i, these are the basic equations for the *optimal shifts* of the atoms.

Equation (3) superficially resembles that of the least squares or steepest descent method; but the sum in the denominator is taken over the n variables j and not over the set of equations. Note that if the individual scales measuring the u_i are changed, e.g. by the equations $u_i = k_i u_i'$, and if the k_i are different for different i, then the absolute values of the shifts change to

$$\Delta u_i = \Delta F k_i^2 (\partial F / \partial u_i) / \sum_j (k_j^2 \partial F / \partial u_j)^2.$$

This arbitrariness of the result can be eliminated by introducing another condition for the k_i: that the n-dimensional space in which the u_i are measured should be isotropic, i.e. the expectations of the magnitudes of errors Δu_i should be the same in all directions.

Application to centrosymmetrical crystal structures: Space group $P\bar{1}$

Taking the simplest centrosymmetrical space group $P\bar{1}$, the function is now the structure factor for N atoms per asymmetric unit,

$$F(hkl) = 2\sum_i^N f_i \cos \phi_i. \tag{4}$$

Here $\phi_i = 2\pi(hx_i + ky_i + lz_i)$; h, k, l are the Miller indices, x_i, y_i, z_i are the fractional coordinates and f_i the individual scattering factor of the i-th atom.

If the trial coordinates are obtained from a random number generator (cf. paper [27] by V. Vand and A. Niggli), then the fractional coordinates are isotropic. If, however, the refinement is started from an atomic model measured in Å, the metric coordinates are to be taken as isotropic; if the fractional coordinates are taken as isotropic, then the following formulae are obtained:

The partial derivatives of the structure factor (4) are

$$\partial F / \partial x_i = -4\pi h f_i \sin \phi_i.$$

Using formula (3) for the optimal shifts, we obtain

$$\Delta x_i = -h\Delta F f_i \sin \phi_i / 4\pi(h^2 + k^2 + l^2) \sum_j f_j^2 \sin^2\phi_j, \tag{5}$$

with similar equations for Δy_i and Δz_i.

If the metric coordinates are taken as isotropic, the denominator contains

$$(h^2/a^2 + k^2/b^2 + l^2/c^2) = 4 \sin^2\theta/\lambda^2,$$

and the formula (5) becomes

$$a\Delta x_i = -\lambda^2 h\Delta F f_i \sin \phi_i / 16\pi a \sin^2\theta \sum_j f_j^2 \sin^2\phi_j, \tag{6}$$

where a, b, c are the three constants of a (nearly) orthogonal cell.

In a problem involving many atoms the formula (6) may be simplified still further by substituting in the denominator the average value $\frac{1}{2}$ for the $\sin^2\phi_j$:

$$a\Delta x_i = -\lambda^2 h\Delta F f_i \sin \phi_i/8\pi a \sin^2\theta \sum_j f_j^2,$$

or for equal atoms

$$a\Delta x_i = -\lambda^2 h\Delta F \sin \phi_i/8\pi a \sin^2\theta . f . N, \qquad (7)$$

where N is the number of atoms per asymmetric unit. However, it is doubtful whether formula (7) has any advantage over formulae (5) or (6), as $\sin \phi_i$ values have to be calculated anyhow.

The refinement of a structure may now proceed by arranging the observed set of structure factors according to some *weighting scheme*, and then taking the reflections one at a time, starting with that of the greatest weight, and applying the formula for the optimal shifts; this approach corresponds to the relaxation method in applied mathematics. When the shifts are large, the set of structure factors and weights have to be recalculated after one or a small number of shifts.

The order in which the structure factors are to be taken is suggested by formula (7). Obviously one should take that reflection first which causes the largest total shift given by

$$\sum_i \Delta u_i^2 = a^2\Sigma\Delta x_i^2 + b^2\Sigma\Delta y_i^2 + c^2\Sigma\Delta z_i^2;$$

this corresponds to removing the heaviest strain first in the relaxation method. Using formula (7), we obtain

$$\sum_i \Delta u_i^2 = \lambda^2(\Delta F)^2/32\pi^2\sin^2\theta f^2 N.$$

It can be seen that, neglecting constant terms (as we are interested in the relative weights only), the structure factors should be taken in the order of decreasing weights

$$W = |\Delta F|^2/f^2\sin^2\theta;$$

since the order of weights is not affected by taking the square root, we can as well use the expression

$$W = |\Delta \hat{F}|/\sin \theta,$$

where $\hat{F} = F/f$ is the sharpened structure factor.

In formula (5), $\Delta F = F_o - F_c$; therefore for proper evaluation, the signs of both F_o and F_c have to be known. The refinement would then converge to the correct structure, subject only to the limitation of neglecting the higher terms in the Taylor expansion. If the sign of F_o is not known, it is, as usual, given the sign of F_c:

$$F_o = \text{sg}(F_c) |F_o|.$$

If this sign assignment is incorrect, improper shifts of the atoms might result which, in certain cases, may delay or even prevent a convergence to the correct structure; i.e. the refinement may be trapped in one of the false minima of the disagreement factor R, corresponding to an incorrect stable combination of signs. The optimal shift method thus converges only when the trial structure is close enough to the correct structure, so that there are enough correct signs of the most important structure factors to assure a correct convergence. This situation is well known in crystallography, and common to all refinement methods.

Formula (5) has been tried out in several calculations of test structures. If the sign of F_o was correct, it adjusted F_c to F_o with remarkable efficiency, even for comparatively large Δx. The neglect of higher terms in the Taylor series does not lead to difficulties; the main problem is always that of our ignorance and incorrect assignment of signs or phases to the F_o's.

There remains an interesting possibility: when $|F_c| > |F_o|$, the value of $sg(F_c)|F_o| - F_c$ always has the correct sign but sometimes the wrong magnitude, even when $sg(F_o) \neq sg(F_c)$. It is thus possible to take for the refinement only those structure factors for which $|F_c| > |F_o|$. If this is done throughout the refinement, *all* the shifts would be made in the correct directions, although sometimes, when the signs of F_o and F_c are opposite, they would be smaller in magnitude than they should be. It thus appears that, if sufficient reflections were available, and if the refinement continued for a sufficiently long time, the trial structure would be bound to refine towards the correct one, and the phase problem would be solved.

Some additional help could be obtained by taking any three mutually independent reflections with greatest weights, say (100), (010) and (001), and assigning to them the signs of the F_c's; this is equivalent to the free choice of 8 origins in the space group $P\bar{1}$. Then the choice of the remaining reflections can be governed by the condition $|F_c| > |F_o|$. When beginning the refinement of whatever model, statistically 50% of the structure factors should fulfil this condition; but as the refinement proceeds, the residuals of the class of reflections worked on will decrease in preference to the other class of reflections, and in some cases the refinement may end with a wrong structure and with no more reflections left fulfilling the above criterion. However, if an unlimited set of structure factors is available, and if there are no rational dependence between the coordinates, there should always be some reflections which can continue the refinement.

It is to be noted that the above principle can equally well be applied to the least squares and the difference Fourier synthesis methods. Tests are being made to ascertain how much their radius of convergence is thereby increased.

Application to non-centrosymmetric crystal structures: Space group $P1$

By using the appropriate structure factor expressions instead of (4), formula (5) or its equivalent can easily be derived from the general equation (3) for any space group. As an example, we have for the structure factor in space group $P1$

$$| F |^2 = A^2 + B^2 \text{ with } A = \Sigma f_i \cos \phi_i,$$
$$B = \Sigma f_i \sin \phi_i, \tag{8}$$

and for its partial derivatives

$$\partial | F | / \partial x_i = (A . \partial A / \partial x_i + B . \partial B / \partial x_i) / | F |,$$

where

$$\partial A / \partial x_i = - 2\pi h f_i \sin \phi_i,$$
$$\partial B / \partial x_i = + 2\pi h f_i \cos \phi_i.$$

Thus we obtain for isotropic rectangular coordinates

$$a \Delta x_i = - \lambda^2 h | F | \Delta | F | f_i (A \sin \phi_i - B \cos \phi_i) /$$
$$/ 8\pi a \sin^2\theta \Sigma_j f_j^2 (A \sin \phi_j - B \cos \phi_j)^2; \tag{9}$$

knowledge of the phases is necessary for the computation of A and B used in this formula.

Generalization to more than one equations

If m equations in n unknowns are given, then, after neglecting the higher terms in the Taylor series, these can be written as

$$\Sigma_i (\partial F_k / \partial u_i) \Delta u_i = \Delta F_k, \, k = 1, \dots, m. \tag{10}$$

In the conditions (2) the derivatives are replaced by linear combinations of derivatives:

$$\Delta u_i = \sum_{p=1}^{m} K_p (\partial F_p / \partial u_i). \tag{11}$$

By substituting in (10),

$$\Sigma_i (\partial F_k / \partial u_i) \Sigma_p K_p (\partial F_p / \partial u_i) = \Delta F_k,$$

and changing the order of summation, we obtain

$$\Sigma_p K_p \Sigma_i (\partial F_k / \partial u_i) \, (\partial F_p / \partial u_i) = \Delta F_k. \tag{12}$$

Let

$$\Sigma_i (\partial F_k / \partial u_i) \, (\partial F_p / \partial u_i) = a_{kp};$$

then

$$\sum_{p}^{m} K_p a_{kp} = \Delta F_k, \, k = 1, \dots, m \tag{13}$$

represents m linear equations for the m unknown K_p's, which can be solved by standard methods. Once the K_p have been calculated, they are substituted into (11), and thus all the Δu_i can be computed.

Diagonal approximation to the optimal shift method

In some applications, such as crystallographic equations, the coefficients a_{kp} of the equation matrix are usually small for $k \neq p$, as compared to the a_{kk}. This is caused by the fact that the derivatives contain trigonometric functions which are as likely to be positive as negative, whereas their squares are always positive. If the non-diagonal terms a_{kp} are neglected, we obtain from (12)

$$K_p \sum_i (\partial F_k / \partial u_i)^2 = \Delta F_k,$$

from which it follows that

$$\Delta u_i = \sum_k^m [\Delta F_k (\partial F_k / \partial u_i) / \sum_j^n (\partial F_k / \partial u_j)^2].$$

This equation closely resembles the one of the least squares method, except that the summation in the denominator is taken over j from 1 to n.

An analysis of particular examples has been made for various values of m and n. It appears that for $m = n$, all three methods of the optimal shift, least squares and the direct solution of $n \times n$ equations, give the same result. For $m < n$, the least squares method is inapplicable, whereas the optimal shift method gives good results, and for $m > n$ the inverse is true. The optimal shift method thus does not replace the least squares method, but is complementary to it.

Application of the optimal shift method

An IBM 704 program has been written for the application of the optimal shift method to the space group $P\bar{1}$, for the present; it is in process of being tested. For structures of 10 atoms and 60 reflections, the program takes time of the order of a few seconds per refinement cycle, but it is hoped to reduce this time in the future (the speed of the IBM 704 computer is 24 μsec per addition).

The following procedure has been found generally effective: first of all, normalized (sharpened) structure factors $\hat{F}_o$, corresponding to a point atom structure, are obtained; in order to save computing time, the test program does not provide any scattering curves or temperature factors. In the next step, weights for these structure factors are computed according to the formula

$$W' = |\hat{F}_o| / \sin \theta, \tag{14}$$

as reflections with large W' are also likely to have large W according to (15). For N atoms in the asymmetric unit, a set of about $6N$ structure factors having the greatest weights W' is then selected. It contains the strongest low-order reflections; including missing reflections with $F_o = 0$ does not seem to be advantageous.

Trial models are now obtained, e.g. from a random number generator (cf. the paper by V. Vand and A. Niggli), but in general any models can be read in if their coordinates are punched on cards; even a combination of both these procedures may be used by reading in known parts of the structure and keeping them fixed throughout the whole refinement, whereas the unknown parts are generated at random. For a trial structure to be tested, the structure factors $\hat{F}_c$ corresponding to the set of the $\hat{F}_o$'s is then calculated, and after proper scaling the discrepancies $\Delta\hat{F}$ are computed. Once these are known, new weights are calculated for the whole set, according to the formula derived in the section " application to centrosymmetrical crystal structures,"

$$W = |\Delta\hat{F}|/\sin\theta. \tag{15}$$

By looking for the highest values of these weights W, a subset of the structure factors showing the most serious discrepancies is now selected; its optimal size turns out to be determined by the condition that if the whole set contains $6N$ structure factors, it should contain about $\sqrt{(6N)}$ ones. Handling such subsets at a time corresponds to block relaxation in the relaxation method. The optimal shift method is then applied to the subset, either by solving the $\sqrt{(6N)}$ equations simultaneously according to (13), or by $\sqrt{(6N)}$-times applying formula (5) or (6) to one reflection at a time; in the latter case, after every step structure factors and weights are recalculated for the subset only, and the structure factor with the greatest weight W is always taken for the next adjustment.

Once the subset is worked over, the structure factors of the whole set are recalculated and rescaled; a disagreement factor R is then computed and compared to the earlier value of R. If the improvement makes it seem worthwhile, new weights are computed, a subset is again selected, and a new cycle of refinement is initiated. If, on the other hand, the refinement is not to be continued, the final value of R is examined in order to accept or reject the particular model tested. If accepted, particulars are printed out; in any case, the program reads in or generates the next structure model to be tested. The accepted models are judged by the crystallographer and may be refined further by standard methods, using all the structure factors.

Note

After submitting this paper for publication, we had an opportunity to see a private communication by J. Gillis (Weizmann Institute of Science, Rehovoth, Israel). For his " iterated difference synthesis " an equation is given which somewhat resembles our equation (3); however, it is based on a summation of the numerator over the Miller indices (as in the least squares treatment), and the denominator is replaced by an adjustable constant.

We are grateful to Dr. D. Rogers for drawing our attention to this.

Acknowledgments

We are grateful for support of this research under Contracts N6onr–26916 with the Office of Naval Research, AF 49(638)–416 with the Directorate of Solid State Sciences of the Air Force Office of Scientific Research (ARDC), AT(30–1)–1516 with the U.S. Atomic Energy Commission, and Grant No. A–228 from the National Institute of Health. IBM 704 calculations have been accomplished at the New York University Computing Center, with support of the Atomic Energy Commission.

M

Paper 17

COMPARISON OF VARIOUS LEAST SQUARES REFINEMENT TECHNIQUES

by Robert A. Sparks

Department of Chemistry, University of California,
Los Angeles, and
Oxford University Computing Laboratory

ABSTRACT

The convergence properties of the least squares method as used in several computing laboratories are investigated. It is found that the methods employed by Cruickshank, Rollett, Mills and Curtis lead to convergence for the refinement of anthracene and that various acceleration devices can greatly speed this convergence. It is also shown that by storing the observational equations it is possible to get nearly the same parameter shifts as would be obtained from the full matrix method but without actually forming this full matrix. For problems with a large number of parameters, this method can lead to a great saving of computer time.

A recommended least squares program is described. This program involves storage of the observational equations, calculation of the same blocks of the normal equations matrix that are used by Cruickshank and utilization of the conjugate-gradient acceleration device.

INTRODUCTION

The least squares method as applied here will be formulated in the following way. The function ϕ is to be minimized with respect to the atomic position and temperature parameters and over-all scale factor, this last quantity being applied to the calculated structure factors. Thus,

$$\phi = \sum_h w_h(F_{o_h} - G \mid F_c \mid_h)^2$$

where for a structure factor with index h, w_h is the weight of the observation, F_{o_h} is the observed amplitude, $\mid F_c \mid_h$ is the theoretical amplitude, and G is the scale factor. $\mid F_c \mid_h$ is a function of the position and temperature parameters and can be written as follows:

$$\mid F_c \mid_h = \sqrt{A_h^2 + B_h^2}$$

$$A_h = \sum_{i=1}^{m} f_i e^{-T_i} \cos 2\pi(h.r_i)$$

$$B_h = \sum_{i=1}^{m} f_i e^{-T_i} \sin 2\pi(h.r_i)$$

$$T_i = h^2(B_{11})_i + k^2(B_{22})_i + l^2(B_{33})_i + hk(B_{12})_i + hl(B_{13})_i + kl(B_{23})_i$$

where m is the total number of atoms in the unit cell, r_i is the vector whose elements are the position parameters of the ith atom, f_i is the scattering factor of the ith atom, and the six $(B_{jk})_i$'s are the temperature parameters for the ith atom, which is assumed to be vibrating ellipsoidally.

Since $G \mid Fc \mid_h$ is not a linear function of the independent parameters, it is expanded in a Taylor's series about a point in parameter space which is an approximate solution to the minimization of ϕ. If all but first order terms are neglected, the resulting expression is linear in terms of the increments of the independent parameters, and these equations may then be solved in a least squares fashion. The resulting increments are then added to the initial set of parameters, the $G \mid Fc \mid_h$ expanded about the new point in parameter space, and the resulting equation solved for the new increments. This process is repeated until the resulting increments are negligible.

Computionally this technique can be very time-consuming. Each iteration requires the formation and solution of a set of linear equations, the order of which is equal to the number of independent parameters involved. For large problems it is found that the formation of the equations is the most time-consuming step. For example, for anthracene (a 64-parameter problem) three-fourths of the iteration cycle of Mercury is used in this process. Thus, if the matrix representation of the observational equations for the kth iteration is

$$M_k x_k = c_k$$

then the normal equations are produced by the following matrix operations:

$$A_k = M_k^T M_k \tag{1}$$

$$b_k = M_k^T c_k. \tag{2}$$

If m is the number of observations and n the number of independent parameters, then M_k is a matrix containing $m \times n$ elements, c_k has m elements, A_k has $n \times n$ elements, and x_k and b_k have n elements each. Most workers have modified the above technique, gaining speed but sacrificing some accuracy on each iteration. It is the purpose of this paper to discuss various schemes now used and several which have been proposed.

Two simplifying procedures are immediately obvious: (1) If the set of simultaneous equations for the kth iteration is represented by

$$A_k x_k = b_k \tag{3}$$

then one can substitute for the matrix A_k some matrix B_k which is a good approximation to A_k but requires much less time to form. (2) The matrix A_1 can be substituted for each successive A_k, thus requiring the formation of only one such matrix.

SUBSTITUTION OF B_k FOR A_k

If the linear approximation to $G \mid F_c \mid_h$ were exact, then the matrix A_k would not change on successive iterations (the subscript k on the matrices will be dropped for the remainder of this discussion). It is obviously possible to get close enough to the solution for this approximation to be nearly correct. The problem then reduces to a simple linear one which has been described by Kunz (1949) and Boedwig (1956, pp. 125–181). Let the shifts actually calculated for the kth iteration be

$$y_k = B^{-1}b_k.$$

Then the new right-hand sides of (3) will become

$$b_{k+1} = b_k - Ay_k$$

The new set of shifts will be

$$y_{k+1} = B^{-1}b_{k+1} = y_k - B^{-1}Ay_k = [I - B^{-1}A]y_k = [I - B^{-1}A]^k y_1$$

Thus, the process will converge if and only if all the eigenvalues of

$$I - B^{-1}A$$

are between plus one and minus one.

From the nature of the least squares problem, A must be positive-definite (that is, there exists a matrix M such that $A = M^T M$). If B and hence B^{-1} is also positive-definite, then the eigenvalues of $[I - B^{-1}A]$ must be greater than minus one (see Appendix).

It is also possible to replace B^{-1} by ηB^{-1} where η is some scaling constant (this procedure is the familiar partial shift rule); then the process will converge if the eigenvalues of

$$I - \eta B^{-1}A$$

are between plus one and minus one. This situation can always be guaranteed by choosing a positive-definite B and an appropriately small value for η.

There is one other very important advantage to having B positive-definite and in addition symmetric. It is possible to reformulate the linear problem to one which is very well-conditioned (meaning the new matrix has a narrow eigenvalue spectrum) and which again is a system of linear equations where the matrix is positive-definite and symmetric. Thus, if

$$Fy = d \tag{4}$$

is the matrix representation for these well-conditioned equations, then

$$F = (N^T)^{-1}AN^{-1}$$
$$y = Nx$$
$$d = (N^T)^{-1}b$$

where $B = N^T N.$

To form F, y, and d, one must first obtain the matrix N from the matrix B. A convenient way to form N and a proof that F is positive-definite and symmetric is given in the Appendix. The importance of this reformulation lies in the fact that such a set of well-conditioned equations can be rapidly solved to very good approximation by well-known iterative techniques.

THE ADVANTAGE OF SAVING THE OBSERVATIONAL EQUATIONS

The weakness of the above arguments is the assumption that A_k does not change on successive iterations. Unfortunately, to compare existing methods this assumption is necessary. It is possible, however, to devise a routine which will solve the truly linear system of equations (3) with very nearly the same accuracy as the full matrix method but which would be far less time-consuming because the matrix A_k would never be formed.

Thus, if B_k is a good approximation to A_k and can be formed with relatively few operations, then

$$x_k = B_k^{-1}b_k + [I - B_k^{-1}A_k]B_k^{-1}b_k + [I - B_k^{-1}A_k]^2B_k^{-1}b_k$$
$$+ [I - B_k^{-1}A_k]^3B_k^{-1}b_k + \dots \quad (5)$$

If the absolute values of the minimum and maximum eigenvalues of $[I - B_k^{-1}A_k]$ are small, then the process will converge rapidly and x_k will be well approximated by only a few terms. Calculation of each successive term involves a multiplication of a vector by $[I - B_k^{-1}A_k]$. This can most easily be performed in the following succession of steps.

$$(1) \quad s = M_k r$$
$$(2) \quad t = M_k^T s$$
$$(3) \quad v = B_k^{-1}t$$
$$(4) \quad w = (r - v)$$

Steps 1 and 2 will be by far the most time-consuming and involve a total of $2mn$ multiplications. Formation of the unique part of A_k would require $n(n + 1)m/2$ multiplications. Thus, very roughly $1 + [(n + 1)/4]$ terms of the series (5) could be calculated in the time necessary to form A_k. Reformulation of the problem to that of equation (4) will not change this argument. In addition the acceleration devices which will be discussed later can be used here and will greatly diminish the number of terms needed for a good approximation of x_k. The disadvantage of this method is that the mn elements of the matrix M_k must be stored in the computer and for moderately large problems must be placed in a large auxiliary store such as magnetic tape. Prior to forming the matrix A_k, Busing and Levy (1959) actually do store M_k on magnetic tape in their IBM 704 least squares program. The

IBM 709 has the added advantage that this matrix can be brought into the high-speed store with no loss of computing time.

POSITIVE–DEFINITE AND SYMMETRIC APPROXIMATIONS

Three methods for choosing B so that it is guaranteed to be positive-definite and symmetric will be described here.

(1) The diagonal of B is set equal to the diagonal of A. All other elements of B are made zero. Since the diagonal elements of A are always positive, it is obvious that this approximation leads to a positive-definite B.

(2) Square blocks along the diagonal of B are set equal to the corresponding blocks of A. All other elements of B are made zero. The blocks are chosen so that all (9×9 blocks) or most (3×3 blocks for position parameters, 6×6 blocks for temperature parameters) of the intra-atomic off-diagonal elements of A are included in B. It is easy to show that each of these blocks is symmetric and is formed by a multiplication of a matrix by its transpose; thus, B is positive-definite.

(3) It has been found (Trueblood (1954), Sayre (1956), Cromer (1957), Rossman and Lipscomb (1958), Vand and Pepinsky (1958), and others) that neglecting the cross-terms between scale factor and temperature factors can lead to bad shifts (usually over-shifts) in these parameters. A square block to correct for this effect would be of the order $6N + 1$ where N is the number of independent atoms. Such a B matrix would take nearly as long to form as would the matrix A.

Several fairly simple techniques have been employed; only one of these leads to a symmetric positive-definite matrix. This method (originally proposed by V. Schomaker) is that used by D. W. J. Cruickshank on the Pegasus computer at Leeds. The technique is to introduce an overall temperature factor. The B matrix then consists of a 2×2 block connecting overall temperature and overall scale factors, and blocks of 3×3 and 6×6 or 9×9 for the atomic parameters. The overall scale factor is obtained from the two equations in two unknowns. The individual temperature factor shifts are obtained from a linear combination of three sets of shifts: (1) those shifts obtained from the atomic parameters equations, (2) the overall-temperature factor shift obtained from the two equations for scale and temperature factor, and (3) the overall-temperature factor shift obtained by neglecting all (including scale factor – temperature factor) off-diagonal elements. If these shifts are called U_1, U_2, and U_3 respectively (the last two being expanded into anisotropic terms), the shift actually used by Cruickshank is

$$U = U_1 + U_2 - U_3$$

It can be shown that this method does lead to a positive-definite and symmetric matrix (see Appendix).

OTHER APPROXIMATIONS

Several other methods have been employed or postulated which in general do not have the features of those already discussed. We will consider just four of these: (1) the method used by J. S. Rollett on the Mercury at Oxford, (2) a method proposed by A. R. Curtis and O. S. Mills (1959), (3) a method proposed by V. Schomaker and J. Waser, and (4) a supposedly logical but quite unsuccessful method devised by the author.

(1) The method of J. S. Rollett is the same as the one used by D. W. J. Cruickshank except that U_1 alone is used for the shifts in the anisotropic temperature parameters.

(2) The method of A. R. Curtis and O. S. Mills is to calculate (in addition to the 2×2 block) all the terms connecting the scale factor with all other parameters. After obtaining the overall scale factor shift from the 2×2, the other blocks of equations are solved using this scale factor shift.

(3) The method suggested by V. Schomaker and J. Waser is to obtain derivatives for one independent atom while calculating structure factors; solve the resulting nine equations in nine unknowns; correct the calculated structure factors forming a new set of nine equations for the next independent atom and so forth. After the last atom parameters have been adjusted in this way, the scale factor is corrected by the same procedure followed by a new adjustment of the first atom parameters, etc. Given that the matrix A does not change during this procedure, the method is a generalization of the Gauss–Seidel method for solving a system of linear equations. This method has been shown to converge without a shift factor for any positive-definite matrix (Reich, 1949). Calculation of derivatives and formation of the 9×9 blocks is no more time-consuming than any other method treated here. However, both the old atom contribution and the new atom contribution must be calculated to be able to revise the calculated structure factors; thus, this process takes about twice as long as a normal structure factor calculation.

(4) Because of the large correlation of the scale factor with other parameters, it was felt that a good B matrix could be formed by choosing from the matrix A 9×9 blocks for the independent atoms and all the elements in the row and column corresponding to the scale factor parameters. However, this method turned out to be the poorest one investigated.

SUBSTITUTION OF A_1 FOR A_k

This process is much more difficult to analyze than the substitution of an approximate B_k for A_k because of the very large range of choice of starting parameters. Actually one would think that any chemically reasonable starting point (no overlapped atoms) should lead to a matrix not much different from the final matrix. The reasoning involved is that the matrix elements are sums taken over all of reciprocal space and hence it should not greatly matter where a given independent atom was placed in real space. Unfortunately, the sums are weighted according to the observations and indeed if there is a large number of absent reflections, a large part of reciprocal space would not be included at all. It has been shown that the latter effect (absent reflections) does lead to an enhancement of cross terms which would otherwise be expected to be small (Sparks, 1958).

Since A_1 must be positive-definite and symmetric, the same considerations mentioned above would be applicable here.

ACCELERATION DEVICES

Almost everyone who has ever written an automatic least squares routine has found it necessary to apply some sort of partial shift rule not only to prevent divergence but to speed convergence. Since these rules are empirical and therefore rather difficult to analyze, we shall be concerned here only with optimum partial shifts—the optimum constant being obtained from a know-ledge of the minimum and maximum eigenvalues of $B^{-1}A$. The vector of shifts on successive cycles will tend to become more and more aligned along the dominant eigenvector (that is, the eigenvector corresponding to the eigenvalue of largest magnitude of the matrix $I - \eta B^{-1}A$). If η is chosen too small, the vector with minimum eigenvalue will dominate; if too large, the vector with maximum eigenvalue will dominate. Thus, the optimum shift factor, η_{op}, is given by

$$1 - \eta_{op}\lambda_{max} = -1 + \eta_{op}\lambda_{min}$$

$$\eta_{op} = \frac{2}{\lambda_{min} + \lambda_{max}}$$

where λ_{min} and λ_{max} are respectively the minimum and maximum eigenvalues of $B^{-1}A$.

If the optimum shift factor, η_{op}, is chosen and the vector of shifts is aligned along the minimum eigenvector (the worst possible situation), the successive shifts will always be in the same direction and will decrease very slowly. To insure that the last set of parameters is in error by a vector whose magnitude is no greater than ϵ, then the last set of shifts must be a vector with magnitude less than

$$\delta = \frac{\eta_{op}\lambda_{min}\epsilon}{1 - \eta_{op}\lambda_{min}} = \frac{2\lambda_{min}\epsilon}{\lambda_{max} - \lambda_{min}}$$

If we define μ such that

$$\mu = \frac{\delta}{\epsilon} = \frac{2\lambda_{min}}{\lambda_{max} - \lambda_{min}}$$

then μ is a measure of the rate of convergence of any given approximation. Another measure is the maximum number of cycles P_1 required to reduce the magnitude of the error vector to one one-hundredth of the initial error vector. Again the worst situation is along either the minimum or maximum eigenvector.

$$(1 - \eta_{op}\lambda_{min})^{P_1} = 10^{-2}$$

$$P_1 = - 2/\log_{10}\left(\frac{\lambda_{max} - \lambda_{min}}{\lambda_{max} + \lambda_{min}}\right).$$

So far we have been considering a simple situation where just a fraction of the shift called for is actually applied. It is possible to improve the situation by taking a linear combination of the current and immediately preceding shifts. Thus, if the applied shift for the kth cycle is

$$z_k = \alpha y_k + \beta z_{k-1} \text{ (where } y_k \text{ is the shift actually calculated)}$$

then two constants α and β must be used. A. R. Curtis (1959) has shown that the optimum values for α and β are

$$\beta = \left[\frac{(\lambda_{max})^{1/2} - (\lambda_{min})^{1/2}}{(\lambda_{max})^{1/2} + (\lambda_{min})^{1/2}}\right]^2$$

$$\alpha = \frac{4}{[(\lambda_{max})^{1/2} + (\lambda_{min})^{1/2}]^2}$$

(see Appendix). The measure of convergence, P_2, for this system will be defined similarly to P_1. Thus,

$$P_2 = - 2/\log_{10}\left[\frac{(\lambda_{max})^{1/2} - (\lambda_{min})^{1/2}}{(\lambda_{max})^{1/2} + (\lambda_{min})^{1/2}}\right]$$

(see Appendix).

The acceleration devices discussed so far have involved some shift factors which must be estimated by guesses as to what the maximum and minimum eigenvalues of $B^{-1}A$ are. The only requirement is that the real part of the eigenvalues be positive. It is possible to devise systems in which the shift factors are obtained from operations on the successive shift vectors. Two techniques will be described: (1) the gradient method (proposed for the crystallographic problem by V. Schomaker and J. Waser, 1958), and (2) the conjugate-gradient method (developed by M. R. Hestenes and E. Stiefel, 1952). Both of these methods require that the problem be transformed to the form of equation (4) which means that a positive-definite B must be chosen.

(1) The gradient method is very closely related to the technique proposed by Vand and Pepinsky (1958); unfortunately, the matrix that they chose is not symmetric and the analysis becomes quite difficult for the Vand and

Pepinsky case. The algorithm for the system of equations $Fy = d$ is for n cycles:

$$y_o = 0;$$
$$r_o = d$$

$$\left.\begin{array}{l} \alpha_k = r_k^T r_k / r_k^T F r_k \\ r_{k+1} = r_k - \alpha_k F r_k \\ y_{k+1} = y_k + \alpha_k r_k \end{array}\right\} \text{For } k = 0 \text{ to } n$$

Forsythe (1956) has conjectured that the gradient method tends to make the shift vector become a linear combination of the maximum and minimum eigenvectors. In this event the convergence rate will be identical to P_1.

(2) The conjugate-gradient method has the advantage that it will give the correct solution after n iterations where n is the number of independent parameters. The algorithm is

(1) $y_o = 0$

(2) $r_o = d$

(3) $\alpha_o = r_o^T r_o / r_o^T F r_o$

(4) $r_1 = r_o - \alpha_o F r_o$

(5) $y_1 = y_o + \alpha_o r_o$

(6) Solve the following two equations in two unknowns for α_k and β_k

$$\left.\begin{array}{l} \left\{\begin{array}{l} \alpha_k(r_k^T F r_k) - \beta_k(r_k^T r_k) = 0 \\ \alpha_k(r_{k-1}^T F r_k) + \beta_k(r_{k-1}^T r_{k-1}) = r_{k-1}^T r_{k-1} \end{array}\right\} \\ (7) \; r_{k+1} = -\alpha_k F r_k + \beta_k r_k + (1 - \beta_k) r_{k-1} \\ (8) \; y_{k+1} = \alpha_k r_k + \beta_k y_k + (1 - \beta_k) y_{k-1} \end{array}\right\} \text{For } k = 1 \text{ to } n$$

Unfortunately, for the conjugate-gradient method, there is no conjecture corresponding to the Forsythe one for the gradient method.

NUMERICAL RESULTS

In order to provide a quantitative comparison of the different approximations discussed here, we took for A the final matrix in a series of full matrix least squares cycles in the refinement of visually estimated data for anthracene (a 64 parameter problem) (Mathieson, Robertson and Sinclair, 1950; Sparks, 1958).* Different B matrices were then formed according to the above prescriptions and the maximum and minimum eigenvalues of $B^{-1}A$ were obtained. These together with η_{op}, μ, P_1, and P_2 are listed in Table 1. In

---

*Anthracene was a logical choice, since without doubt more computer time has been spent on this one structure than on any other investigated.

TABLE 1

Approximation	Maximum eigenvalue	Minimum eigenvalue	η_{op}	μ	P_1	P_2	P_3
1. Diagonal	4·91	0·071	0·36	0·029	160	19	18
2. Block Diagonal: 1 × 1 for scale factor; 9 × 9 for atom parameters	2·62	0·124	0·73	0·099	49	11	9
3. Cruickshank Method: 9 × 9 blocks for atom parameters	1·91	0·30	0·90	0·37	15	6	6
4. Rollett Method: 9 × 9 blocks for atom parameters	1·83+0·08	0·30	0·94	0·39	14	6	
5. Curtis–Mills Method: 9 × 9 blocks for atom parameters	1·96	0·30	0·88	0·36	15	6	
6. Gauss–Seidel Method	1·07	0·24	1·53	0·58	11	5	
7. Bordered Block Diagonal: 9 × 9 for atom parameters; scale factor row and column included	1·87	− 0·939					
8. Block Diagonal: Scale factor removed; 9 × 9 blocks for atom parameters	1·89	0·30	0·91	0·38	15	6	
9. Bonded Block: Scale factor removed; 9 × 9 diagonal blocks for atom parameters; 9 × 9 off-diagonal blocks; connecting bonded atoms	1·67	0·45	0·94	0·74	9	4	
10. A poor but chemically reasonable trial structure; full matrix	3·37	0·29	0·55	0·19	27	8	

addition to those approximations already mentioned, we have calculated the eigenvalues for a 9 × 9 block-diagonal approximation after eliminating the scale factor as a parameter. Also investigated was a 9 × 9 block-diagonal approximation with the scale factor removed and with off-diagonal blocks between chemically bonded atoms included. These two approximations have no practical use (since in a practical problem the scale factor cannot be eliminated as a parameter). They are included here only to point out the effect of scale factor and bonded atom correlations.

Also included in Table 1 is the convergence factor, P_3, which for the conjugate gradient method is defined in the same manner as P_1. The numerical values of P_3 are the largest number of cycles necessary to reduce the error vector by a factor of 10^2 for something over one hundred random right-hand sides for each of the three methods investigated.

Finally, an initial chemically reasonable trial structure for the anthracene molecule led to a matrix A_1 and the maximum and minimum eigenvalues for $A_1^{-1}A$ were obtained and are listed in Table 1. This trial structure makes all carbon–carbon bonds equal to 1·39 Å, all carbon–hydrogen bonds equal to 1·0 Å, all angles equal to 120°. The molecule was placed on a center of symmetry. The carbon atoms would have to move from 0·10 to 0·55 Å to give the correct structure. The R value for this trial structure is 89%.

DISCUSSION OF THE NUMERICAL RESULTS

Throughout this paper we have assumed that the matrix A is not changing from cycle to cycle. In analyzing the numerical results, one must keep in mind the fact that only in the later stages of refinement is A approximately constant.

It would appear (compare approximations 1, 2, and 10 of Table 1) that using on each successive cycle the same full matrix which was obtained from a poor trial structure is better than using either the diagonal or block-diagonal approximations. (It is assumed that the diagonal or block-diagonal matrices are formed during each cycle.) One must consider, however, how long it takes to form the original full matrix as opposed to forming successive diagonal or block-diagonal matrices. On Mercury, approximately 5·5 64-parameter diagonal least squares cycles could be performed while one full matrix was being generated and inverted. About 3·2 9 × 9 block-diagonal least squares cycles could be performed in the same time. Once the full matrix is formed and inverted, a subsequent cycle will take about the same length of time as the diagonal least squares cycle and about 0·56 of the time needed for the block-diagonal least squares cycle. In any case it seems that a calculation of one full matrix for a 64-parameter problem is certainly better than a diagonal and probably better than a block-diagonal approximation.

The three closely related methods of Cruickshank, Rollet and Curtis–Mills (approximations 3, 4 and 5 of Table 1) are all significantly better than the block-diagonal method (approximation 2) and they require almost no extra computing time. It is interesting to note that they are all nearly equivalent to eliminating the scale factor as a parameter (approximation 8). Except for the desirable features (positive-definite and symmetric) of the Cruickshank method there seems to be little to choose among these three methods.

The bordered block-diagonal and bonded-block approximations (approximations 7 and 9) illustrate the importance of interatomic cross-terms in the normal equations. Because of the absence of a large number of reflections from the anthracene data, the cross-terms between interatomic temperature factors are non-zero (Sparks, 1958).

The Gauss–Seidel method (approximation 6) appears to be the best of all those tried. However, for the 64-parameter problem about $1 \cdot 6$ cycles of the Cruickshank, Rollett, or Curtis–Mills methods can be performed in the time necessary for one cycle of Gauss–Seidel. Thus, there is probably little to choose among any of these methods. It is interesting that the optimum shift factor for the Gauss–Seidel method is greater than one—a result which is consistent with this method when used in the other applications.

Clearly there is an advantage to using the acceleration devices (compare P_1, P_2 and P_3 columns of Table 1), the most sophisticated [the Curtis device (P_2) or the conjugate-gradient technique (P_3)] being the best. The conjugate-gradient method has the very great advantage that no shift factors must be guessed at. However, it does require that the problem be transformed into that of equation (4) which makes for a somewhat complicated algorithm, but which does not take much additional time.

RECOMMENDED METHOD

The method which seems to have the most advantages is that which is used by Cruickshank coupled with the conjugate-gradient method. In order to avoid the annoying linear approximation, it is recommended that a series such as (5) should be formed, especially in the early stages of refinement. This method is currently being programmed for the IBM 709. The detailed algorithm is given in the Appendix. Thus, using this technique for anthracene it should be possible to obtain a set of shifts which would differ from the full matrix shifts by less than one per cent in $0 \cdot 65$ of the time required for the full matrix cycle. It is hoped that this recommended method will be even more advantageous for larger problems where the production of the full matrix becomes extremely prohibitive. Unfortunately, for larger problems the eigenvalues will have a larger spread and the numbers P_1, P_2 and P_3 shown in Table 1 will increase.

Acknowledgments

I wish to acknowledge very helpful discussions with K. N. Trueblood, J. S. Rollett, D. W. J. Cruickshank, O. S. Mills, A. R. Curtis, J. Waser, and especially V. Schomaker. The calculations were performed on SWAC at the University of California at Los Angeles and on Mercury at Oxford University. This work was supported in part by the National Science Foundation of the U.S.A., the U.S. Office of Naval Research, the U.S. Office of Ordnance Research, and the U.S. Air Force Office of Scientific Research and the Nuffield Foundation.

APPENDIX

The matrix definitions which are used here can be found in any standard matrix algebra text (a good one is *Computational Methods of Linear Algebra*, by V. N. Fadeeva, 1959).

THE EIGENVALUES OF $B^{-1}A$ ARE POSITIVE

If B and hence B^{-1} are positive-definite, a non-singular matrix N can be found such that

$$B = (N^{-1})(N^{-1})^T$$

$$B^{-1} = N^T N$$

then, $$B^{-1}A = N^T N M^T M.$$

$B^{-1}A$ has the same eigenvalues as the matrix F ($B^{-1}A$ and F are similar) where F is defined as

$$F = (N^{-1})^T (B^{-1}A) N^T$$
$$= N M^T M N^T$$
$$= (M N^T)^T (M N^T)$$

Since F is positive-definite, it and $B^{-1}A$ have positive eigenvalues. F is also symmetric.

CURTIS ACCELERATION METHOD

Let the applied shift for the kth cycle be

$$z_k = \alpha y_k + \beta z_{k-1}$$

where y_k is the shift actually calculated. Assume z_k is an eigenvector of $B^{-1}A$ with eigenvalue equal to λ. Assume

$$z_k = r z_{k-1}$$

where r is a constant. Then,

$$rz_{k-1} = \alpha y_k + \beta z_{k-1}$$

$$y_k = \left(\frac{r-\beta}{\alpha}\right) z_{k-1}.$$

Since

$$y_{k+1} = y_k - B^{-1}Az_k,$$

then

$$r\left(\frac{r-\beta}{\alpha}\right) z_{k-1} = \left(\frac{r-\beta}{\alpha}\right) z_{k-1} - r\lambda z_{k-1}$$

$$r^2 + r(-\beta + \alpha\lambda - 1) + \beta = 0.$$

It is desired to minimize the magnitude of r for the worst cases (where λ equals λ_{min} or λ_{max}). To minimize the roots of the above equation for these situations

$$(-\beta + \alpha\lambda_{min} - 1)^2 - 4\beta = 0$$

$$(-\beta + \alpha\lambda_{max} - 1)^2 - 4\beta = 0$$

From these two equations

$$\beta = \left[\frac{(\lambda_{max})^{1/2} - (\lambda_{min})^{1/2}}{(\lambda_{max})^{1/2} + (\lambda_{min})^{1/2}}\right]^2$$

$$\alpha = \frac{4}{[(\lambda_{max}^{1/2} + (\lambda_{min})^{1/2}]^2}$$

$$r = \beta^{1/2}$$

FORMATION OF THE SQUARE ROOT OF A MATRIX

Let the elements of B (order n) be b_{ij} and the elements of N be n_{ij} where i is the row number and j is the column number. If

$$n_{ij} = 0 \text{ for } i > j$$

$$n_{11} = \sqrt{b_{11}}$$

$$n_{ij} = b_{ij}/n_{11}; \ j = 2, n$$

$$n_{ii} = \sqrt{b_{ii} - \sum_{l=1}^{i-1} n_{li}^2}; \ i = 2, n$$

$$n_{ij} = (b_{ij} - \sum_{l=1}^{i-1} n_{li}n_{lj})/n_{ii}; \ i = 2, n; \ j = i + 1, n;$$

Then $B = N^T N$ and N is upper triangular.

CRUICKSHANK METHOD

Let one more parameter (the isotropic temperature factor, B) be added to the observational equations. Each row of the resulting matrix will then have one more element which can be obtained from the other elements in that row since

$$w\left(\frac{\partial G\,|\,F_c\,|}{\partial B}\right) = w\sum_{i=1}^{N}\frac{\partial G\,|\,F_c\,|}{(\partial B_{11})_i}(S_{11}) + \frac{\partial G\,|\,F_c\,|}{(\partial B_{22})_i}(S_{22}) + \frac{\partial G\,|\,F_c\,|}{(\partial B_{33})_i}(S_{33}) +$$

$$+ \frac{\partial G\,|\,F_c\,|}{(\partial B_{12})_i}(S_{12}) + \frac{\partial G\,|\,F_c\,|}{(\partial B_{13})_i}(S_{13}) + \frac{\partial G\,|\,F_c\,|}{(\partial B_{23})_i}(S_{23}).$$

where

$$\frac{\sin^2\theta}{\lambda^2} = h^2 S_{11} + k^2 S_{22} + l^2 S_{33} + hk S_{12} + hl S_{13} + kl S_{23}$$

and N is the number of independent atoms (it is assumed that the parameters of all the atoms are being refined.) Assume that A, x, and b are bordered by zeros in the following manner and let the second element of x be the scale factor shift

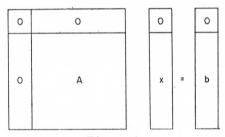

Diagram 1

The new normal equations are then

$$Cx = D^T b$$

$$C = D^T A D$$

where the elements of the matrix D (order $n + 1$) are ones for the second through $(n + 1)$th diagonal elements, the numbers S_{jk} in the first column (in positions corresponding to the temperature parameters), and zeros elsewhere. From the matrix C 9×9 diagonal-blocks are chosen for the atom parameters and a 2×2 diagonal-block for the scale and overall temperature parameter. Let the elements of the 2×2 block be s_{11}, s_{12}, s_{22}, and s_{21} and the elements of the inverse of this block be s_{11}^{-1}, s_{12}^{-1}, s_{22}^{-1}, s_{21}^{-1}.

Let the matrix R be made up of the 2×2 block, P, and the inverses of the 9×9 blocks where

$$P = \begin{bmatrix} s_{11}^{-1} - \dfrac{1}{s_{11}} & s_{12}^{-1} \\ s_{21}^{-1} & s_{22}^{-1} \end{bmatrix}$$

Then, the applied shifts are

$$y = DRD^T b$$

and thus, for the Cruickshank method

$$B^{-1} = DRD^T.$$

B^{-1} is a $(n + 1)$th order matrix with first row and column equal to zero. Let the matrix W have $w_{22} = \sqrt{s_{22}^{-1}}$, $w_{21} = s_{12}/w_{22}$ upper triangular 9×9 diagonal-blocks obtained (by the method of the last section) from the 9×9 blocks of the matrix R, and all other elements equal to zero. Then,

$$R = W^T W.$$

Thus, B^{-1} has no negative eigenvalues and has one zero eigenvalue because of the zero row and column. If this row and column are deleted, the resulting matrix (order n) is positive-definite.

RECOMMENDED METHOD

The following technique is the method which is currently being programmed for the IBM 709. For each trial structure perform the following operations.

(1) Calculate structure factors and the observational equation matrix, M. At the same time form the right-hand side vector, b, the 2×2 block for overall temperature factor and scale factor, and 9×9 blocks for the atom parameters.

(2) Form the matrix R and hence W (see the two preceding sections for the definition of R and W and the method of obtaining W from R).

(3) Form $N = WD^T$. Delete the first row and column which are all zeros. N will then be upper triangular and of order n.

(4) Form

$$r_o = Nb$$

$$y_o = 0$$

N

(5) Form

$$s_o = N^T r_o$$

$$t_o = M s_o$$

$$v_o = M^T t_o$$

$$w_o = N v_o$$

$$\alpha_o = r_o^T r_o / r_o^T w_o$$

(6) Form

$$r_1 = r_o - \alpha_o w_o$$

$$y_1 = y_o + \alpha_o r_o$$

(7) Perform the following operations for $k = 1$ to p until for the pth cycle $|y_{p+1} - y_p|$ is less than some previously chosen ϵ:

(a) Form

$$s_k = N^T r_k$$

$$t_k = M s_k$$

$$v_k = M^T t_k$$

$$w_k = N v_k$$

(b) Solve the following two equations for α_k and β_k

$$\alpha_k(r_k^T w_k) - \beta_k(r_k^T r_k) = 0$$

$$\alpha_k(r_{k-1}^T w_k) + \beta_k(r_{k-1}^T r_{k-1}) = r_{k-1}^T r_{k-1}$$

(c) Form

$$y_{k+1} = \alpha_k r_k + \beta_k y_k + (1 - \beta_k) y_{k-1}$$

$$r_{k+1} = -\alpha_k w_k + \beta_k r_k + (1 - \beta_k) r_{k-1}$$

(8) Obtain the parameter shifts x from

$$x = N^T y_{p+1}$$

(9) Add the parameter shifts to the last set of parameters.

REFERENCES

BOEDWIG, E. (1956). *Matrix Calculus.* Interscience, New York.
BUSING, W. R. and LEVY, H. A. (1956). Oak Ridge National Laboratory Report. Number 59–4–37.
CROMER, D. T. (1957). *J. Phys. Chem.* **61**, 254.
CURTIS, A. R. (1959). Private communication.
FADEEVA, V. N. (1959). *Computational Methods of Linear Algebra.* Dover Publications, New York.
FORSYTHE, G. E. (1956). Private communication.
HESTENES, M. R. and STIEFEL, E. (1952). *J. Res. Natl. Bur. Stand.* **49**, 409.
KUNZ, K. S. (1949). Proc. Computation Seminar, 37.
MATHIESON, A. MCL., ROBERTSON, J. M. and SINCLAIR, V. C. (1950). *Acta Cryst.* **3**, 245.

REICH, E. (1949). *Ann. Math. Stat.* **20,** 448.
ROSSMANN, M. G. and LIPSCOMB, W. N. (1958). American Crystallographic Association Meeting, Milwaukee.
SAYRE, D. (1956). Private communication.
SCHOMAKER, V. and Waser, J. (1958). Private communication.
SPARKS, R. A. (1958). Thesis, U.C.L.A.
TRUEBLOOD, K. N. (1954). Private communication.
VAND, V. and PEPINSKY, R. (1958). American Crystallographic Association Meeting, Milwaukee.

Paper 18

CRYSTALLOGRAPHIC CALCULATIONS ON SWAC AND THE IBM 709*

by R. A. SPARKS, M. M. BLATTNER, C. L. COULTER, and
K. N. TRUEBLOOD

Department of Chemistry, University of California,
Los Angeles.

ABSTRACT

I. SWAC

SWAC, built by U.S. National Bureau of Standards and University of California, Los Angeles, with aid of U.S. Office of Naval Research. 256-word Williams Tube memory (512 word magnetic core soon), 8192 word magnetic drum. 37-bit words. Input and output on IBM collator and reproducer or tabulator. Fixed point. Add time, 64 μsec; multiply 368 μsec. Machine language programs. 4-Address machine. Not available commercially.

SF–DS Program. All space groups, any number of reflections, scale F_0, individual isotropic or 6 anisotropic vibration parameters. Limit for SF about 1000 atoms isotropic, 200 atoms anisotropic. Limit for DS 20 atoms. E.S.D.'s not computed. SF time including card input and output about 20–50 msec per atom-position-reflection, depending upon whether isotropic or anisotropic and upon fraction time given to input and output. DS time comparable.

SF–LS Program. All space groups, any number of reflections, positions, scale factor, 6 individual anisotropic vibration parameters. Full matrix limit 7 atoms anisotropic, 15 atoms isotropic; chains of 6 × 6, 3 × 3, limit 56 atoms; miscellaneous others. E.S.D.'s and correlation coefficients for full matrix. Recycle any parameters desired, with any specified fraction of shifts. Time per cycle including card input and output about 0·25 sec per atom-position-reflection for 6 × 6, 3 × 3 chains, about 0·4 sec per a–p–r for 64 × 64 matrix. Can calculate SF's for atoms not included in LS.

Fourier Program. Two and three-dimensional; observed, calculated, or difference. All space groups, any number of reflections. Input or output on cards. Intervals 120ths along no more than one axis, 60ths or 30ths along any. About 1 hour needed for 54,000 points, 1000 unique reflections. Part of SF–DS program.

Other Programs. (a) Sharpen and modify F^2 data in any of several ways, remove origin peak from Patterson if desired; (b) distances and angles, only as called for; (c) least squares plane (as eigenvalue problem); (d) Weissenberg data-

* This work was supported in part by the United States Air Force under Contracts No. AF 18(600)–857 and No. AF 49(638)–719 monitored by the Air Force Office of Scientific Research of the Air Research and Development Command.

processing; (e) Wilson plot; (f) calculation of principal axes and mean-square displacements for vibration ellipsoids; (g) least squares fit of peaks to 10-parameter Gaussian ellipsoid; (h) miscellaneous minor programs.

II. IBM 709

The IBM 709, manufactured by International Business Machines Corporation U.S.A.

Storage. 32,768-word magnetic-core storage, two or four 4096-word magnetic drums, up to 48 magnetic-tape units.

Input–Output. Magnetic tape, 3 card readers, 3 card punches, 3 printers, cathode-ray tube recorder.

Speed. Basic machine cycle of 12 μsec, most fixed operations take 2–3 machine cycles. Fixed multiply 2–20 cycles and built-in floating point operations take 2–17 machine cycles. Single address machine.

Programming Languages. Fortran, FAP (essentially machine language), or others, depending upon the assembly system used.

Advantages. Three index registers, indirect addressing, input–output handled independently of calculations, very versatile instruction structure.

Availability. The machine we have used is not available, but others are; cost is not known.

Programs Available. Only a few routines have been completed and tested. The structure factor routine takes about 7–8 msec per atom-position-reflection with anisotropic temperature parameters plus a few minutes for loading and preliminary symmetry operations. Thus, a calculation for the typical 1000-reflection 10-atom monoclinic structure requires a little less than 10 minutes. A typical monoclinic least squares routine (R. A. Sparks' method) or Fourier should take approximately one-third to one-half hour per cycle. Various minor routines have been written.

I. SWAC

The use of SWAC for crystallographic calculations has already been described (Sparks *et al.*, 1956) and we shall mention here only changes during the past four years. The computer itself is currently being modernized. Magnetic core storage of 512-word (eventually 1024-word) capacity will replace the Williams-tube high speed memory, with a consequent gain of more than a factor of two in basic add time (to 32 μsec or less). The word length is still 36 bits plus sign. Four-address logic will be retained, with a planned increase in the number of available instructions from 13 to about twice that number. Input and output are still on punched cards but high-speed magnetic tape units will be added. Since input–output and drum commands probably now consume between 30 and 50% of our computing time, the high-speed tape should permit significant cuts in the times of our programs.

The chief addition to our SWAC programs during recent years has been a full-matrix least squares routine. Because of the limited size of the computer, the largest matrix which can be handled is 64 × 64. Consequently, for general ellipsoidal vibration parameters, the limit is 7 atoms (9 × 7 plus 1 parameters), although structure-factor calculations can be included for almost any additional number; for individual isotropic temperature factors, 15 atoms can be refined. Some experience with this program will be described elsewhere in this volume. A few other routines have also been added; the more important of these are mentioned in the abstract and do not merit further comment.

II. IBM 709

The IBM 709 is a data-processing system designed to be considerably more efficient, especially with respect to input and output operations, than older computers of comparable speed. It consists of at least two computers, coordinated through a central processing unit (C.P.U.) and operating

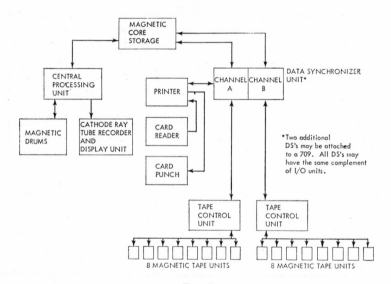

FIG. 1

(usually) in parallel. The computer which handles all of the calculations not having to do with the input or output of information is called the " main frame," and is directly connected to the central processing unit. Input and output operations are handled by one to three smaller computers, called data synchronizer units (D.S.U.). Each D.S.U. is made up of two data synchronizer channels (D.S.C.), and each D.S.C. controls eight magnetic tape units. In addition a printer, card reader, and card punch may be attached to one channel of each D.S.U. Figure 1 illustrates the flow of information in the 709 data-processing system. The high-speed memory consists of a maximum of 32,768 words (35 bits plus a sign) of magnetic core storage; some machines with one-half or one-fourth this capacity memory are also available. The main frame and the D.S.U.'s have independent access to the high-speed memory, as shown in Fig. 1, within certain limits. The main frame is a single address digital computer with a 12 μsec machine cycle. Most fixed point operations take 2–3 machine cycles, fixed multiply 2–20 cycles, and built-in floating point operations take 2–17 machine cycles. There are three index registers attached to the main frame, and most instructions are indirectly addressable, thus effectively providing an additional index register which need never be cleared or stored. There are more than 180 instructions for the main frame, of which about 100 are instructions connected with input and output. Included are a number of extremely useful instructions such as those to convert numbers from binary to binary-coded decimal or vice versa, and those to provide extensive manipulation of the various registers in the machine. The input–output components attached to the main frame include four sense-lights (programmer controlled), six sense-switches (operator controlled), two or four 4096-word magnetic drums, and a cathode-ray tube display unit and recorder. In addition, the input–output components controlled by the D.S.U. are available. The D.S.U.'s are small computers capable of transmitting information to or from core storage, from or to the input–output units attached to them. There are 15 commands to govern the behavior of the D.S.U.'s. Up to three D.S.U.'s may be attached to a given machine, thus allowing 6 input–output components to be operating simultaneously and independently, and giving a maximum of 48 magnetic tape units, 3 printers, 3 card readers and 3 card punches per machine.

The time taken for most 709 calculations is a function of the programming efficiency and the speed of the arithmetic unit of the machine rather than of the speed of the input and output units. We have recently finished programming some general crystallographic routines for the IBM 709 associated with the Western Data Processing Center at the University of California, Los Angeles, and will discuss these and such routines as are presently being coded. Because of the complexity of this system, very few programs are ever coded in actual machine language on the IBM 709; each machine is operated within the framework of an assembly system such as FORTRAN, SOS (Share Operating System), SCAT (Share Compiler–Assembler Translator), 9AP (9 Assembly Program), FAP (Fortran Assembly Program), etc. The assembly program used at W.D.P.C. is Fortran Load and Go, in connection with FAP. This enables the programmer to code his programs in either Fortran or FAP (very similar to the SCAT system) or mixtures thereof; most large routines are written as a series of subroutines connected with a Fortran main program. Each of the subroutines may be assembled and checked out separately, and the assembly program takes care of relatively addressing the various programs and coordinating them.

Most small crystallographic routines are coded in FORTRAN, using, where applicable, subroutines distributed through the SHARE system. Large programs, particularly those involving logical operations (e.g. symmetry operations), have thus far been coded in FAP with a FORTRAN main program to handle some arithmetic operations and input–output.

A structure factor program has been written for all space groups, using separate symmetry subroutines for space groups through orthorhombic, for tetragonal space groups, for cubic space groups, and for hexagonal or trigonal space groups. The f_i calculation is handled in a subroutine as a three-point interpolation from any specified short stored f-table, and the temperature factor exponential is also handled by a subroutine. It takes about 7–8 msec per atom-position-reflection, or about 10 minutes for a typical monoclinic crystal with 1000 reflections and six anisotropic B_{ij}'s per atom. A two-dimensional Fourier program is already operative and a three-dimensional Fourier routine is presently being completed. It will calculate two Fouriers (an observed and a calculated or difference) at once, and the total time for a typical monoclinic crystal for structure factors and Fourier summations should be about one-half hour. The present routine will not be able to give sections parallel to any arbitrary plane, although this feature may be added later. The least squares procedure which will be used is that recommended by Dr. R. A. Sparks elsewhere in this volume. It will allow the adjustment of position parameters, one scale factor per atom, one isotropic B per atom or six anisotropic B_{ij}'s per atom, an overall scale factor, and an overall temperature factor; any of these parameters which are independent may be varied. The time per cycle is not known, but one-third to one-half hour is a rough estimate for one cycle for a typical monoclinic crystal with 1000 unique reflections. Because the full matrix is not calculated, the time per cycle will go up only about as the number of atoms rather than as its square.

Some smaller, auxiliary routines have also been written. These include a routine for generating the weighted sum of the residuals of the structure factors as a function of the position of a molecule of known structure and specified orientation in the plane group *pgg*, a routine for generating the Buerger Minimum Function M_2 from a Patterson synthesis, a routine for calculating the standard deviation of the electron density from the F_o and F_c data, and a routine for analyzing the temperature factors of a molecule in terms of the diagonalized translation and oscillation tensors of the molecule. In addition, Dr. Gus Palenik of the U.S. Naval Ordnance Test Station, China Lake, California, is writing a number of routines for the IBM 709. At this time he has programs for calculating a two-dimensional Fourier synthesis, a full-matrix least squares refinement of at least 120 independent parameters, interatomic distances, a three-dimensional sharpened

Patterson synthesis, and Lorentz, polarization, and Tunell corrections for Weissenberg data. All of his programs are written in FORTRAN; by the end of the summer of 1960 he expects to have others available as well, including a three-dimensional Fourier program.

In summary, one must conclude that the IBM 709 is a remarkably versatile data-processing system from a crystallographic point of view. Its size and speed make it (and machines like it) particularly attractive for working with large molecules, and with large-scale statistical or other approaches to the phase problem.

We are indebted to the staffs of Numerical Analysis Research and the Western Data Processing Center on this campus for their cooperation in providing computing facilities to us, and to the United States Office of Naval Research for their partial support of SWAC. Our work has been supported in part by the United States Air Force under Contracts No. AF 18(600)–857 and AF 49(638)–719, monitored by the Air Force Office of Scientific Research of the Air Research and Development Command.

REFERENCES

SPARKS, R. A., PROSEN, R. J., KRUSE, F. H. and TRUEBLOOD, K. N. (1956). *Acta Cryst.* **9**, 350.

Paper 19

THE MANCHESTER UNIVERSITY MUSE COMPUTER, AND FUTURE CRYSTALLOGRAPHIC POSSIBILITIES

by O. S. Mills

Department of Chemistry, University of Manchester

INTRODUCTION

The machine described in this paper will be the latest of a series of digital computers which have been designed in the laboratories of the Department of Electrical Engineering of the University of Manchester. The machine which will be installed at Manchester will be called MUSE and is being designed by a team of Ferranti Ltd. and University engineers led by Professor T. Kilburn. The machine will be available commercially, marketed by Ferranti Ltd., and will then be known as ATLAS. The commercially available machines will differ from MUSE only by variations in peripheral equipment and storage capacity.

A GENERAL DESCRIPTION OF MUSE

The applications to crystallographic calculations of two of the machines which have been designed in this University and which have also been available commercially, viz. the Ferranti Mark I (and Mark I*) and the MERCURY, have been described (Ahmed and Cruickshank, 1953; Mills and Rollett, 1960). The main differences between these machines, as far as the user was concerned were

    (i) the increased speed, roughly a factor of ten times,

    (ii) the replacement of 40–bit fixed point arithmetic by floating point arithmetic (30–bit argument and 10–bit exponent) and

    (iii) the increase in size of the immediate access store from 256 to 1024 words.

In the MUSE computer, further developments of this kind have continued and a number of novel and important features incorporated. These further developments are discussed in the following sections.

194

(i) Basic word length and programming facilities

Forty-eight bits will comprise a WORD. These bits may be used to hold a single floating point number, or an instruction or two half-words.

Floating point numbers will consist of 40 bits argument, i.e. 39 bits and sign digit, and 8 bits exponent (octal base). This arrangement permits an accuracy of about 1 in 10^{11} with a range of $8^{\pm 127}$, i.e. $10^{\pm 115}$. Whilst this is clearly more than adequate for all crystallographic calculations which are likely to be carried out in the foreseeable future, it is worthwhile noting that additional accuracy can be obtained, if needs be, as the single accumulator will consist of 79 bits argument and 8 bits exponent.

In addition to the accumulator, there will be 128 B–lines, some of which will be used for special purposes, in which fast fixed point arithmetic and logic can be carried out. Each B-line will consist of 24 bits, i.e. a half-word, so that arithmetic therein will be performed modulo 16,777,216. Fixed point arithmetic can also be performed in the accumulator (40 bits) but it is doubtful whether there will be much call for this method of working for crystallographic purposes with its attendant crop of scaling difficulties.

Programmes will be presented to the machine either by conventional coding schemes or by a system of AUTOCODE. In the former method, instructions may be decoded into a single machine instruction or into a jump instruction which leads to fixed sub-routines which will be permanently available inside the machine, i.e. incapable of being overwritten. These instructions which involve the use of these permanently programmed sub-routines located in the fixed store of the machine will be called extracode instructions. The programmer need not, and probably will not, know whether he is dealing with a single machine instruction or a composite extracode instruction. A few constants will be available in the fixed store, the greater part of which contains machine-controller programmes.

The 48 bits of an instruction will be divided into groups of 10, 7, 7, 24. These refer to function, B-line, B-line and address so that basically the machine can operate, without modification, on a store size of 2^{20} words, the remaining 4 bits are used for special purposes. The provision of two B-addresses permits double B-modification of some instructions and operation of pairs of B-lines on one another.

(ii) Storage

One of the major headaches which besets a programmer who tackles any large problem with present day machines is that of multi-level (usually two) storage. Thus it becomes of paramount importance that he arrange for the right numbers to be in the correct location in the immediate access store at the right time; further, since transfers from drum, or tape, to immediate access store are relatively time consuming, these transfers must be minimized.

There are two ways of reducing the inherent waiting time which occurs when calling for data from the drum, or returning information to it. One is to optimum programme so that the drum is always (in theory) in the right position just at the right time, and the other is to perform other, perhaps unrelated, calculations whilst waiting. If the problem does not contain such additional sidetracks the solution is to run one or more programmes apparently simultaneously, i.e. adopt a system of programme sharing. Programme sharing is an important aspect of MUSE. In addition, time will also be saved as calculations can proceed whilst the actual transfer is taking place as well as during waiting time. However, the larger problem, that of two-level integration, still remains and it is proposed to tackle this problem in a novel way. Alternative methods include increasing the size of the immediate access store but this is an expensive palliative at £10 per word and will not be adopted on MUSE. The order code will, however, allow for an increase of immediate access store should anyone prefer this method to that described below.

The main storage system of MUSE will consist physically of two stores; one of these will be a fast ferrite core store with an effective access time of less than 1 μsec and will contain 16,384 words. There will also be additional storage in the form of magnetic drums and magnetic tape. However, the drum and core stores will not need to be regarded at different levels but the combined units will represent, to the user, the main store. During programming, the immediate access store will not be referred to explicitly, although in fact all accumulator and B-line operations will involve its use. Each drum unit will hold 24,576 words and MUSE will have four such drums. The logical design of the machine will allow for a maximum of 2^{20} words in this main store and the make-up of this store can be varied in other versions of ATLAS according to customers' requirements. It should be noted that the capacity of the immediate access store alone is equal to that of the auxiliary drum store of the standard MERCURY and thus all the current programmes which utilize the MERCURY fully, e.g. the S.F.L.S. and Fourier synthesis programmes referred to elsewhere, will be capable of execution without any drum transfers.

In the one-level store concept, problems will be programmed in terms of locations, symbolic or fixed, in the combined immediate access and drum store. When the programme is obeyed, space in the immediate access store will be allocated to these locations according to the frequencies with which any given block of addresses is used. When an address which is not currently in the immediate access store is called for, that block of 512 words in the latter store which, in the " opinion " of a " supervisor " programme, is least likely to be used in the immediate future is written up onto the drum and the appropriate block which contains the address referred to brought from the drum into the vacant place in the immediate access store. Thus it will be apparent that all the locations in the combined store, from the machine viewpoint, must be imagined as being symbolic addresses. In order to reduce waiting time during the write-to-drum phase involved in this procedure, the block of numbers in the immediate access store will not be written to a fixed location on the drum, but to the first unallocated space in time on the drum. A record of this floating location, and of all similar ones, will be kept. The " supervisor " programme which will control these operations will be kept in the fixed store mentioned earlier; this programme will maintain a record of the previous drum transfers in any programme and will use this history as a basis for the decision of which block will be written on to the drum whenever a new block is required. This supervisor programme will be more efficient over its choice of drum transfers than any but the best human programmer exercising continuous care, quite apart from the saving in mental effort involved. From the foregoing, it will be seen that the programmer will not normally be required to arrange for anything other than one-level working, the " supervisor " deciding how best the immediate access store can be allocated. Nevertheless it will still be possible for a programmer to have direct control over drum transfers should this be imperative.

When more than one programme is present in the machine at any one time, the supervisor programme will be responsible for ensuring that each programme uses separate blocks of addresses even though they may bave been written as though they actually used the same addresses. One resultant feature of multi-programme use is that a programme which took five minutes on one day might take twenty-five on the next day! Another feature of the machine will be the use of time-division to enable the computer to control the simultaneous use of a number of peripheral equipments of vastly varying response times. In this way it will be possible for such input/output mechanisms as paper tape readers and punches, magnetic tape decks, flexowriters, line-printers, etc. to operate at the same time. The available peripheral equipment will be discussed later.

(iii) Speed

The machine will be a parallel-operating machine of the single address type with a basic addition time (for floating point operation) of approximately 1 μsec. The logical design of the arithmetic unit allows for operations, which involve physically distinct parts of the mill, to take place independently and therefore it is misleading, if not impossible, to quote times for individual arithmetical operations. A greater insight into the practical operating speed can be obtained by consideration of the times of typical " loop " operations which frequently occur.

In the following example we consider the formation of a scalar product. The central loop of this calculation requires the following operations:

$A' = \mathbf{x}_1$ Set accumulator equal to coefficient of vector 1

$A' = A . \mathbf{x}_2$ Multiply accumulator by coefficient of vector 2

$A' = A + S$ Add in partially accumulated total

$S' = A$ and return to working dump;

test   count, test and repeat as required.

This will take approximately 7·5 μsec on MUSE. The corresponding time on MERCURY would be 780 μsec. This factor of about 100 times as fast as MERCURY on arithmetic instructions of the type normally encountered, coupled with the much lower frequency of drum transfers will mean that many refinements and Fourier calculations which now take of the order of 2–3 hours per cycle, can be performed in about 1 minute.

(iv) Peripheral equipment

The logical design for dealing with peripheral equipment allows for up to 256 such devices. These can be distributed over such mechanisms as punched paper tape readers, tape punches, card readers and punches, parallel printers, Xerox printers, flexowriters, graphical outputs, magnetic drums and magnetic tape decks. The number and variations of these which will be fitted to any ATLAS will be decided by the future use of the machine and by price! The MUSE installation will be equipped with the following:

> 4 paper tape readers (300 characters/sec),
> 4 paper tape punches (60 characters/sec),
> 1 card reader,
> 1 card punch,
> 1 parallel printer (120 characters/line at 10 lines/sec),
> 4 flexowriters (with additional off-line printers),
> 1 graphical output,
> 4 magnetic drums (24,576 words capacity),
> 8 magnetic tape decks.

Paper tape input/output will normally be on a 7-hole parity-check system. However, it will also be possible to read 5-hole tapes, some of which may have been produced for the MERCURY computer (see later), and the output, whilst it will be basically 7-hole, can also be adjusted as required for existing 5-hole equipmennt, though this clearly will reduce the flexibility of the arrangement.

There will be eight channels for magnetic tapes, each capable of holding four tape decks. It is expected that each of the magnetic tape decks will deal with blocks of 1024 words reading and writing at 11,250 words per deck per sec. Such transfers will be accompanied by a checksum control. Each tape can hold approximately 3,000,000 words.

A further form of input which it is hoped to supply on MUSE will be an automatic device capable of accepting typescript or even hand printed symbols.

APPLICATION TO CRYSTALLOGRAPHIC USE

The main features of any machine which are immediately examined by a potential crystallographic user are size, speed, ease of programming and availability. In the previous paragraphs sufficient information has been given to enable the trained programmer to assess the machine in the light of his own problems. The following notes will merely touch, therefore, briefly on the highlights of some future applications.

The enhanced speed clearly represents another step forward of immense value to the subject. Those problems which can, at the present time, be regarded as of moderate complexity, i.e. up to about 20–25 atoms, on which the bulk of crystallographic effort will undoubtedly be spent during the next ten years, will be capable of very rapid refinement; roughly a minute or so per cycle should suffice. Large scale data processing can be run simultaneously with other problems and the fast input/output will reduce time on this to reasonable fractions of the total. Fouriers involving approximately 6000 terms, e.g. insulin, which requires about 30–35 minutes a section on MERCURY, would need less than 10 seconds per section. As already mentioned earlier, those problems which can be run on MERCURY can be run on MUSE without drum transfers. The speed limit on MUSE does not now seem to be serious to crystallographers during the next decade.

It is useful to consider the maximum size of least-squares problem which can be treated when the full matrix is formed. If only the upper triangular matrix of the normal equations is stored, together with the right hand sides, the minimum number of locations required for storage is $\frac{1}{2}N(N + 3)$ where N is the total numbers of parameters. If we consider the drum portion of the main store, then the maximum number of parameters which can be treated is 441, so that it will just be possible to refine a 50 atom problem in this way on MUSE. The 16-drum version of ATLAS will, similarly, take a 100 atom problem. Such refinements should still be relatively fast. No account has been taken of magnetic tape storage in these arguments; its use would increase the number of parameters still further, but at a cost of speed. The MUSE storage will allow about 110 atoms to be refined isotropically. The size is roughly that of vitamin B_{12}.

The use of machines of this size and capacity should permit more ambitious automatic treatment of results. Quite apart from the further extension of direct methods, more can be done in the machine scanning of electron density and vector maps. Provided that three consecutive sections of a three-dimensional map can be held in the machine at once, then peak detection and listing can be made simple and automatic. Arrangements would have to be provided for peaks which are pronouncedly non-spherical and no Fourier map need be examined by the crystallographer, or indeed even printed, unless it is specially required. The drum storage alone would permit such searches to be carried out on sections of cell edge roughly 35 Å where the net interval is every 0·2 Å.

Mention has been made earlier of the main types of coding conventions. The order-code of the conventional method, i.e. the basic and extracode instructions, will be very comprehensive and should prove convenient in use. Perhaps even more interesting is the further development by R. A. Brooker of a method of communication with the machine. Users of MERCURY, and professional programmers of other machines, will be familiar with the methods of AUTOCODE whereby instructions are punched in a form designed to be readily understood by the programmer without specialized machine knowledge. A master programme then translates and complies the user's programme in terms of machine instructions. Excellent as such a system has proved itself to be, it still suffers from drawbacks which prevent its complete, or even near complete, divorce from the machine itself. Thus whilst the organization of routines within the programme are effected by AUTOCODE itself, communication between the two levels of storage must be programmed by the user save in the matrix routines and some specialized sub-programmes. One further difficulty must exist, that of convention, i.e. the user must write his instructions in a language recognizable by AUTO-CODE. The same difficulty will apply to any machine language, universal or otherwise, which is insisted upon by a programme unless that programme is inherently a learning programme. With ATLAS and MUSE both these difficulties can be removed, the two-level difficulties as described earlier and the communication problem by the extension of AUTOCODE, which will be capable of interpreting programmes written in any self-defining structure language.

The so-called ATLAS AUTOCODE is a proposal for instructing the machine in a combination of declarative and imperative sentences. The declarative sentences describe how each instruction is to be recognized and translated in terms of less complex instructions and ultimately into basic machine instructions. From about 100 basic forms it will be possible for every user to build his own personal AUTOCODE. It is not expected that the hierarchy of instruction definition will be presented each time to the machine; instead there will probably be a general language which can be supplemented, as required, for particular problem areas. The scheme shows an admirable lack of restriction to any particular problem-oriented language. One immediate result of this system will be that programmes which already exist in the MERCURY AUTOCODE language will be acceptable to the machine.

Acknowledgments

The author thanks the members of the Department of Computer Engineering and Computing Machine Laboratory for valuable discussions.

REFERENCES

AHMED, F. R. and CRUICKSHANK, D. W. J. (1953). *Acta Cryst.* **6**, 765.

EDWARDS, D. B. G., LANIGAN, M. J. and KILBURN, T. (1960). " Ferrite Magnetic Core Memory Systems with Rapid Cycle Times " *Proc.I.E.E.*, Part B, **107** (to be published).

KILBURN, T. (1959). " MUSE." Symposium on Large Machines, Proc. of the Unesco International Conference on Information Processing, June 1959. Oldenbourg Press Munich.

KILBURN, T., EDWARDS, D.B.G. and ASPINALL, D. (1959). " Parallel Addition in Digital Computers; A New ' Fast-Carry ' Circuit." *Proc.I.E.E.*, Part B, **106**, 464.

KILBURN, T., EDWARDS, D. B. G. and ASPINALL, D. (1960). " A Parallel Arithmetic Unit using a Saturated Fast-Carrying Circuit " *Proc.I.E.E.*, Part B, **107** (to be published).

KILBURN, T. and GRIMSDALE, R. L. (1960). " A Digital Computer Store with very Short Read Time," *Proc.I.E.E.*, Part B, **107** (to be published).

MILLS, O. S. and ROLLETT, J. S. (1960). " Programming and Crystallographic Applications of the Ferranti Mercury Computer." These Proceedings, Paper No. 9.

O

Paper 20

STRUCTURE FACTOR ALGEBRA AND STATISTICS

by E. F. Bertaut

Laboratoire d'Electrostatique et de Physique du Métal, Institut Fourier,
Place du Doyen Gosse, Grenoble, France

SOMMAIRE

On considère la statistique des facteurs de structure en laissant les coordonnées fixes et en variant les vecteurs de l'espace réciproque. Dans ce but on définit des "facteurs de structure d'ordre supérieur p." On montre d'une manière générale que la fonction génératice de cumulants est linéaire dans ces facteurs. Des relations classiques entre moments et cumulants sont valables entre moments des facteurs de structure ordinaires et les "facteurs de structure d'ordre p." On donne des applications au cas d'une, de deux et de trois variables.

SUMMARY

Statistics of structure factors with fixed coordinates and variable reciprocal vectors are considered. For this purpose "structure factors of higher order p" are defined. A general proof is given that the cumulant generating function is linear in these factors. Classical moment-cumulant relations are valid between moments of ordinary structure factors and the "structure factors of order p." Applications are given for the uni-, bi- and trivariate case.

INTRODUCTION

The structure factors $F(\mathbf{h}_k)$, Fourier transforms of the electronic density, depend on the atomic coordinates $\mathbf{x}_j (j = 1, \ldots, t)$ and on the reciprocal vectors $\mathbf{h}_k (k = 1, \ldots, m)$. Their statistics may be envisaged from two different points of view. One may, for instance, keep the reciprocal vectors fixed and vary the coordinates according to some plausible law of positional probability[1]. One may also consider the coordinates as fixed and vary the reciprocal vectors. By this latter method Sayre[2], Cochran[3,4], Hauptmann and Karle[5,6], and the author[7,8] have established relations between structure factors and averages of structure factor products with the help of straight-forward algebra. Recently, Hauptmann and Karle[9] have examined the question by the technique of "new joint probability distribution functions."

In this paper we investigate the problem again by means of classical mathematics, i.e. moment and cumulant calculations. We only consider the centrosymmetrical case. In the first part we recall the properties and definitions of moment and cumulant generating functions (abbreviated m.g.f. and c.g.f.). Considerable simplification is achieved by using the fact that moments and cumulants of trigonometrical structure factors may be linearized[10, 11]. Our method is complete in the sense that no useful relation can be overlooked. In the second part we establish relations for the uni-, bi- and trivariate case. The practical value of the higher moment approximation of Hauptmann and Karle[9] is also discussed.

PART I

DEFINITIONS

Use will be made of normalized structure factors $E(\mathbf{h})$ defined by

$$E(\mathbf{h}) = F(\mathbf{h})/(\langle \, | \, F(\mathbf{h}) \, |^2 \, \rangle)^{\frac{1}{2}} \qquad (1.1)$$

These structure factors are obtained from experimental data as described in references[12, 13]. The analytical form of $E(\mathbf{h})$ may be written

$$E(\mathbf{h}) = \sum_{j=1}^{t} \phi_j \xi_j(\mathbf{h}), \qquad (1.2)$$

where

$$\phi_j = f_j(\mathbf{h})/(\langle \, | \, F(\mathbf{h}) \, |^2 \, \rangle)^{\frac{1}{2}} \sim Z_j/(\sum_{j=1}^{t} n_j Z_j^2)^{\frac{1}{2}}, \qquad (1.3)$$

$$\xi_j(\mathbf{h}) = \sum_{s=1}^{n_j} \exp(2\pi i \mathbf{h} . \mathbf{C_s r_j}). \qquad (1.4)$$

$\xi_j(\mathbf{h})$ is the usual trigonometric structure factor, $f_j(\mathbf{h})$ the atomic form factor, ϕ_j a " modified " atomic factor, Z_j the number of electrons on the atom j. The summation in (1.4) is over the n_j equivalent positions of atoms j. $\mathbf{C_s}$ is the symmetry operator of the group. The summation in j (1.2) is over the atoms in the asymmetric unit cell. Atoms are always labelled by the index j $(j = 1, 2, \ldots, t)$, reciprocal vectors by the index k $(k = 1, 2, \ldots, m)$. $E(\mathbf{h_k})$ will be written E_k as long as there is no confusion.

MOMENT AND CUMULANT GENERATING FUNCTIONS

The m.g.f. $\mathcal{M}$ is defined by

$$\mathcal{M}(u_1, \ldots, u_m) = \langle \, \exp(u_1 E_1 + \ldots u_m E_m) \, \rangle,$$

$$= \Sigma \mu_{p_1 p_2 \cdots p_m} u_1^{p_1} u_2^{p_2} \ldots u_m^{p_m}/(p_1! p_2! \ldots p_m!) \qquad (1.5)$$

$\mu_{p_1...p_m}$ is a moment or order $p = p_1 + p_2 ... + p_m$ defined by

$$\mu_{p_1...p_m} = \langle E_1^{p_1} E_2^{p_2} ... E_m^{p_m} \rangle = \lim_{u_k \to 0} \frac{\delta^p \mathcal{M}}{\delta u_1^{p_1} \delta u_2^{p_2} ... \delta u_m^{p_m}} \qquad (1.6)$$

The functions E_k are linear in the $\xi_j(\mathbf{h_k})$ so that (1.5) may be written as

$$\mathcal{M}(u_1, ..., u_m) = \langle M_1 M_2 ... M_t \rangle \qquad (1.7)$$

where

$$M_j = \exp \sum_{k=1}^{m} u_k \phi_j \xi_j(\mathbf{h_k}) \, (j = 1, 2, ..., t) \qquad (1.8)$$

We suppose that between coordinates $x_j y_j z_j (j = 1, 2, ..., t)$ there is no rational dependence so that the average of the product (1.7) is equal to the product of averages $\langle M_j \rangle$. We abbreviate

$$\mathcal{M}_j = \langle M_j \rangle, \qquad (1.9)$$

so that

$$\mathcal{M}(u_1, ..., u_m) = \mathcal{M}_1 \mathcal{M}_2 ... \mathcal{M}_t. \qquad (1.10)$$

Define functions K_j by

$$K_j = \log \mathcal{M}_j. \qquad (1.11)$$

We have the result

$$\mathcal{M}(u_1, ..., u_m) = \exp K(u_1, ..., u_m), \qquad (1.12)$$

with

$$K = K_1 + K_2 + ... + K_m. \qquad (1.13)$$

The introduction of K has the advantage that functions belonging to different atoms occur additively. That is, the difficult handling of products of functions belonging to different atoms is avoided.

If K is written

$$K(u, ..., u_m) = \Sigma \kappa_{p_1 p_2 ... p_m} u_1^{p_1} u_2^{p_2} ... u_m^{p_m} / (p_1! p_2! ... p_m!), \qquad (1.14)$$

the relation between the $\kappa_{p_1 p_2 ... p_m}$ and $\mu_{p_1 p_2 ... p_m}$ is that between cumulants and moments. K (1.14) is called the cumulant generating function[14, 15].

MOMENTS AND CUMULANTS

We shall now be concerned with the formal expressions of $\mathcal{M}_j$ and K_j (belonging to the atom j).

Moments. $\mathcal{M}_j$ (1.8), (1.9) is expanded as a sum of polynomials $\sigma_{p;j}/p!$ of order p

$$\mathcal{M}_j = \sum_{p=0}^{\infty} \sigma_{p,j}/p!, \qquad (1.15)$$

where

$$\sigma_{p;j} = \left\langle \left(\sum_{k=1}^{m} u_k \phi_j \xi_j(\mathbf{h_k}) \right)^p \right\rangle$$

$$= \phi_j^p \sum_{p_k} u_1^{p_1} \ldots u_m^{p_m} m_{p_1 \ldots p_m} / (p_1! \ldots p_m!) \quad (1.16)$$

We have introduced here the moments

$$m_{p_1 \ldots p_m} = \left\langle \xi^{p_1}(\mathbf{h}) \ldots \xi^{p_m}(\mathbf{h}) \right\rangle \quad (1.17)$$

The summation in (1.16) is over all the partitions of p_k with a fixed sum, $p = p_1 + \ldots + p_m$.

It is easy to write down the polynomials σ_p. In the bivariate case we get

$$\sigma_2/2! = \phi^2(u_1^2 m_{20}/2! + u_2^2 m_{02}/2! + u_1 u_2 m_{11});$$

$$\sigma_4/4! = \phi^4(u_1^4 m_{40}/4! + u_2^4 m_{04}/4! + u_1^3 u_2 m_{31}/(3!1!) + u_1 u_2^3 m_{13}/(1!3!) +$$
$$+ u_1^2 u_2^2 m_{22}/(2!2!)) \quad (1.18)$$

Let us first clarify the meaning of the moments (1.17) by a simple example in space group $P\bar{1}$. Calculate for instance

$$m_{22} = \left\langle \xi^2(\mathbf{h}')\xi^2(\mathbf{h}'') \right\rangle. \quad (1.19)$$

From structure algebra[7, 8, 10, 11] we know that, in space group $P\bar{1}$

$$\xi(\mathbf{h}')\xi(\mathbf{h}'') = \xi(\mathbf{h}' + \mathbf{h}'') + \xi(\mathbf{h}' - \mathbf{h}''). \quad (1.20)$$

Squaring relation (1.20) and linearizing again, we get

$$\xi^2(\mathbf{h}')\xi^2(\mathbf{h}'') = 2\xi(0) + \xi(2\mathbf{h}' + 2\mathbf{h}'') + \xi(2\mathbf{h}' - 2\mathbf{h}'') + 2\xi(2\mathbf{h}') + 2\xi(2\mathbf{h}''). \quad (1.21)$$

Generally speaking any product of powers may be linearized into a sum of trigonometrical structure factors.

In the above example let

$$\mathbf{h}' = \mathbf{h}_1 + \mathbf{h}; \quad \mathbf{h}'' = \mathbf{h}_2 + \mathbf{h}; \quad (1.22)$$

where $\mathbf{h}_1$ and $\mathbf{h}_2$ are fixed, $\mathbf{h}$ being a variable vector. The average of any ξ having the variable vector $\mathbf{h}$ in the argument is zero so that we deduce from (1.21)

$$m_{22} = 2\xi(0) + \xi(2\mathbf{h}' - 2\mathbf{h}''). \quad (1.23)$$

This is a very general result. *Any moment $m_{p_1 \ldots p_m}$ may be linearized into a sum of trigonometrical structure factors.* Clearly for the evaluation of moments we must first linearize the product of structure factors ξ, then specify the relation between the $\mathbf{h}_k$, and finally carry out the averaging procedure.

Cumulants. We shall write K_j in a form similar to $\mathcal{M}_j$ with

$$K_j = \sum_p \tau_{p;j}/p!, \quad (1.24)$$

where

$$\tau_{p;j}/p! = \phi_j^p \sum_{pk} u_1^{p_1} \ldots u_m^{p_m} k_{p_1 \ldots p_m; j}/(p_1! \ldots p_m!). \qquad (1.25)$$

The $k_{p_1 \ldots p_m; j}$ are the cumulants corresponding to the moments $m_{p_1 \ldots p_m; j}$. Relations between cumulants and moments of *one* parameter, say k_p and m_p, have been extensively tabulated in the past[14]. At first sight it seems to be a formidable task to generalize such relations to the multivariate case $u_1, \ldots, u_m$. Actually the problem is easier to solve than it looks. It may be shown indeed[16] that the polynomials $\tau_{p;j}$ and $\sigma_{p;j}$ have the same relationship as the cumulants k_p and moments m_p in the one-variate case. In order to obtain the desired relations between $k_{p_1 \ldots p_m}$ and corresponding moments, one has only to identify the coefficients of $u_1^{p_1} \ldots u_m^{p_m}$ in the first and second member as shown by the following example. From

$$k_4/4! = m_4/4! - \tfrac{1}{2}(m_2/2!)^2, \qquad (1.26)$$

it follows that

$$\tau_4/4! = \sigma_4/4! - \tfrac{1}{2}(\sigma_2/2!)^2 \qquad (1.27)$$

By equating the coefficients of $u_1^2 u_2^2$ of the left and right member of relation (1.27) one gets

$$k_{22} = m_{22} - m_{20}m_{02} - 2m_{11}^2 \qquad (1.28)$$

By the same method one finds

$$k_{11} = m_{11}; \quad k_{31} = m_{31} - 3m_{20}m_{11}. \qquad (1.29)$$

(In relations (1.26), (1.28), (1.29) we have dropped the index j; the origin is taken at the mean, i.e. $m_{10} = m_{01} = 0$). Of course relations between cumulants $\kappa_{p_1 \ldots p_m}$ and moments $\mu_{p_1 \ldots p_m}$ are formally identical to those between cumulants $k_{p_1 \ldots p_m}$ and moments $m_{p_1 \ldots p_m}$.

STRUCTURE OF THE CUMULANT GENERATING
FUNCTION K

The cumulants $\kappa_{p_1 \ldots p_m}$ are obtained simply by multiplying $k_{p_1 \ldots p_m; j}$ by ϕ_j^p and by summing over $j(j = 1, \ldots, t)$ (1.33). Like the moments $m_{p_1 \ldots p_m; j}$ the cumulants $k_{p_1 \ldots p_m; j}$ are reducible to linear combinations of some $\xi_j(\mathbf{H})$. Here we suppose that the atoms are in general positions.

Let us define a " structure factor of order p " $E_p(\mathbf{H})$ by

$$E_p(\mathbf{H}) = \sum_{j=1}^{t} \phi_j^p \xi_j(\mathbf{H}). \qquad (1.30)$$

If $\mathbf{H} = 0$ we shall abbreviate

$$z_p = E_p(0) = \sum_{j=1}^{t} n_j \phi_j^p. \qquad (1.31)$$

The addition of the functions K_j (1.13) will give rise exactly to such " structure factors of order p." We reach the essential conclusion that *the $\kappa_{p_1 \ldots p_m}$ as well as the c.g.f. K (1.14) are linear in the structure factors of order p* (1.30). This also means that any moment of structure factors,

$$\mu_{p_1 \ldots p_m} = \langle E_1^{p_1}(\mathbf{h}_1) \ldots E_m^{p_m}(\mathbf{h}_m) \rangle, \tag{1.32}$$

may be related to the $E_p(\mathbf{H})$ structure factors.

To summarize, relations are obtained in two principal steps. The first one is to calculate

$$\kappa_{p_1 \ldots p_m} = \sum_{j=1}^{t} \phi_j^p k_{p_1 \ldots p_m;j} \tag{1.33}$$

by straight forward algebra in terms of structure factors of order $q \leqslant p$. The second step is to express $\kappa_{p_1 \ldots p_m}$ as a function of the observable moments $\mu_{p_1 \ldots p_m}$. In both steps the same formal cumulant-moment relations will be used. This will be described in the following examples.

PART II

THE BIVARIATE CASE

In the case of example (1.22) odd moments and cumulants vanish. The c.g.f. is, up to terms of the fourth order in u_k,

$$K = \frac{1}{2}(u_1^2 + u_2^2) + \kappa_{11}u_1u_2 + \frac{1}{4!}(\kappa_{40}u_1^4 + \kappa_{04}u_2^4) +$$

$$+ \frac{1}{3!}(\kappa_{13}u_1u_2^3 + \kappa_{31}u_1^3u_2) + \frac{1}{2!2!}\kappa_{22}u_1^2u_2^2 + \ldots \tag{2.1}$$

The abbreviations (2.2) will be used,

$$\mathbf{H} = \mathbf{h}_1 - \mathbf{h}_2; \quad M_{22} = \langle (E^2(\mathbf{h}') - 1)(E^2(\mathbf{h}'') - 1) \rangle. \tag{2.2}$$

One has, in each group,

$$\kappa_{20} = \mu_{20} = 1 \tag{2.3}$$

$$\kappa_{11} = \sum_{j=1}^{t} \phi_j^2 m_{11;j} = E_2(\mathbf{H}), \tag{2.4}$$

and also

$$\kappa_{11} = \mu_{11} = \langle E(\mathbf{h}')E(\mathbf{h}'') \rangle, \tag{2.5}$$

so that the Sayre equation[2] is obtained

$$E_2(\mathbf{H}) = \langle E(\mathbf{h}')E(\mathbf{h}'') \rangle. \tag{2.6}$$

In the same way we get from the study of κ_{40}

$$\kappa_{40} = \langle E^4(\mathbf{h}) - 3 \rangle = \sum_j \phi_j^4 m_{40;j} - 3\sum_j \phi_j^4 m_{20;j}^2, \tag{2.7}$$

where m_{40} and m_{20} must be computed for each space group.

The relation (which is probably most important) results from κ_{22},

$$\kappa_{22} = \mu_{22} - \mu_{20}\mu_{02} - 2\mu_{11}^2 = M_{22} - 2E_2^2(\mathbf{H}). \tag{2.8}$$

κ_{22} may be calculated again from (1.33) and (1.28). (2.8) constitutes a generalized Cochran[3] relation. We give the proof for space group $P\bar{1}$.

Space group $P\bar{1}$. After carrying out the linearizing procedure we find in $P\bar{1}$ the remarkable relations

$$k(2) = m(2); \quad k(4) = -m(4); \quad k(6) = 4m(6), \tag{2.9}$$

where $m(4)$ is any moment of order 4, $m(6)$ any moment of order 6 (for instance $k_{31} = -m_{31}$; $k_{123} = 4m_{123}$; $k_{222} = 4m_{222}$). Relation (2.9) is true for the one-, bi- and also trivariate case (2.19), discussed below. One finds then

$$\kappa_{22} = -\sum_{j=1}^{t} \phi_j^4 m_{22;j} = -E_4(2\mathbf{H}) - 2z_4. \tag{2.10}$$

By equating (2.8) and (2.10) one has

$$E_4(2\mathbf{H}) = 2E_2^2(\mathbf{H}) - 2z_4 - M_{22}. \tag{2.11}$$

This reduces to the Cochran relation (2.13) in the case of equal atoms, where

$$\phi_j = \phi = N^{-1/2}, \tag{2.12}$$

$$\phi^3 E(2\mathbf{H}) = 2\phi^2(E^2(\mathbf{H}) - 1) - M_{22}. \tag{2.13}$$

What is valid in space group $P\bar{1}$ is however not true in other space groups. The most general expression, obtained for κ_{22} (2.8) from (1.33) is, with the notations of the appendix (see also[7]),

$$\kappa_{22} = \Sigma^1_s(\gamma_s^2 p_s - 2\gamma_s)E_4(\mathbf{H}(I - C_s)). \tag{2.14}$$

We add the following relations, valid in $P\bar{1}$,

$$\kappa_{31} = -3E_4(\mathbf{H}) = \langle (E^3(\mathbf{h}')E(\mathbf{h}'')\rangle - 3E_2(\mathbf{H}), \tag{2.15}$$

$$\kappa_{42} = -6z_6 - 4E_6(2\mathbf{H}) = \langle E^4(\mathbf{h}')(E^2(\mathbf{h}'') - 1)\rangle - 6M_{22} + \\ + 24E_4(\mathbf{H})E_2(\mathbf{H}) \tag{2.16}$$

As an exercise the reader may prove the relation (2.18), due to Bullough and Cruickshank[17], by studying the bivariate case, but with (2.17) instead of (1.22),

$$\mathbf{h}' = \mathbf{h}_1 + 2\mathbf{h}; \quad \mathbf{h}'' = \mathbf{h}_2 + \mathbf{h} \tag{2.17}$$

$$\langle E(\mathbf{h}')E^2(\mathbf{h}'')\rangle = E_3(\mathbf{h}_1 - 2\mathbf{h}_2). \tag{2.18}$$

THE TRIVARIATE CASE

Consider three functions $E(\mathbf{h}')$, $E(\mathbf{h}'')$ and $E(\mathbf{h}''')$, with

$$\mathbf{h}' = \mathbf{h}_1 + \mathbf{h}; \quad \mathbf{h}'' = \mathbf{h}_2 + \mathbf{h}; \quad \mathbf{h}''' = \mathbf{h}_3 + \mathbf{h}; \tag{2.19}$$

$\mathbf{h}$ is a variable vector; $\mathbf{h}_1$, $\mathbf{h}_2$, $\mathbf{h}_3$ are fixed vectors. We abbreviate

$$\mathbf{H}_1 = \mathbf{h}_2 - \mathbf{h}_3; \quad \mathbf{H}_2 = \mathbf{h}_3 - \mathbf{h}_1; \quad \mathbf{H}_3 = \mathbf{h}_1 - \mathbf{h}_2;$$

$$M_{222} = \langle\, (E^2(\mathbf{h}') - 1)\,(E^2(\mathbf{h}'') - 1)\,(E^2(\mathbf{h}''') - 1)\, \rangle. \tag{2.20}$$

The c.g.f. is

$$K = \frac{1}{2}(u_1^2 + u_2^2 + u_3^2) + (\kappa_{110}u_1 u_2 + \mathfrak{I}) + \frac{1}{4!}(\kappa_{400}u_1^4 + \mathfrak{I}) +$$

$$+ \frac{1}{2!2!}\,(\kappa_{220}u_1^2 u_2^2 + \mathfrak{I}) + \frac{1}{3!1!}\,(\kappa_{310}u_1^3 u_2 + \mathfrak{I}) +$$

$$+ \frac{1}{2!1!1!}\,(\kappa_{211}u_1^2 u_2 u_3 + \mathfrak{I}) + \frac{1}{2!2!2!}\,\kappa_{222}u_1^2 u_2^2 u_3^2 + \ldots \tag{2.21}$$

The examination of κ_{110}, κ_{400}, κ_{220} gives rise to expressions already known from the preceding study. New features occur from κ_{211} and κ_{222}. We have the cumulant-moment relations,

$$\kappa_{211} = \mu_{211} - 2\mu_{110}\mu_{101} - \mu_{200}\mu_{011}, \tag{2.22}$$

$$\kappa_{222} = \mu_{222} - (\mu_{220}\mu_{002} + \mathfrak{I}) - 4(\mu_{211}\mu_{011} + \mathfrak{I}) -$$

$$- 2(\mu_{210}\mu_{012} + \mathfrak{I}) - 4\mu_{111}^2 + 2\mu_{200}\mu_{020}\mu_{002} +$$

$$+ 4(\mu_{200}\mu_{001}^2 + \mathfrak{I}) + 16\mu_{110}\mu_{101}\mu_{011}. \tag{2.23}$$

We only study space group $P\bar{1}$ where relations (2.9) hold. Moments of odd order as μ_{111} and μ_{210} vanish. We get from (2.22)

$$\mu_{211} = 2E_2(\mathbf{H}_3)E_2(\mathbf{H}_2) + E_2(\mathbf{H}_1) - 2E_4(\mathbf{H}_1) - E_4(\mathbf{H}_3 - \mathbf{H}_2). \tag{2.24}$$

With this result substituted in (2.23), we find

$$\kappa_{222} = 16z_6 + 8(E_6(2\mathbf{H}_1) + E_6(2\mathbf{H}_2) + E_6(2\mathbf{H}_3))$$

$$= M_{222} - 8E_2(\mathbf{H}_1)E_2(\mathbf{H}_2)E_2(\mathbf{H}_3) + 8\sum_{j=1}^{3} E_4(\mathbf{H}_j)E_2(\mathbf{H}_j)$$

$$+ 4(E_4(\mathbf{H}_1 - \mathbf{H}_2)E_2(\mathbf{H}_3) + E_4(\mathbf{H}_2 - \mathbf{H}_3)E_2(\mathbf{H}_1) + E_4(\mathbf{H}_3 - \mathbf{H}_1)E_2(\mathbf{H}_2)). \tag{2.25}$$

When all atoms are equal, (2.25) reduces to a relation given first by Hauptmann and Karle[5] and also by the author[8] by direct calculation. The interesting feature of (2.25) is the intervention of the triple product $E_2(\mathbf{H}_1)E_2(\mathbf{H}_2)E_2(\mathbf{H}_3)$, where $\mathbf{H}_1 + \mathbf{H}_2 + \mathbf{H}_3 = 0$. However the presence of product terms such as $E_4(\mathbf{H}_1 - \mathbf{H}_2)E_2(\mathbf{H}_3)$, of unknown signs, makes the practical value of relation (2.25) questionable, even if the signs of $E_6(\mathbf{H}_j)$ ($j = 1, 2, 3$) are known.

Another trivariate case. Let us consider briefly the case (2.26), where again $\mathbf{h}_1$, $\mathbf{h}_2$ and $\mathbf{h}_3$ are fixed, $\mathbf{h}$ and $\mathbf{k}$ variable vectors.

$$\mathbf{h}' = \mathbf{h}_1 + \mathbf{h}; \quad \mathbf{h}'' = \mathbf{h}_2 + \mathbf{h} + \mathbf{k}; \quad \mathbf{h}''' = \mathbf{h}_3 + \mathbf{k}. \tag{2.26}$$

We abbreviate

$$\mathbf{H} = \mathbf{h}_1 + \mathbf{h}_3 - \mathbf{h}_2. \tag{2.27}$$

Non-vanishing moments are in each space group

$$m_{200} = \xi(0); \quad m_{220} = \xi^2(0); \quad m_{111} = \xi(\mathbf{H}); \quad m_{222} = \xi^3(0) + \xi(2\mathbf{H}). \tag{2.28}$$

One finds easily,

$$\kappa_{111} = E_3(\mathbf{H}) = \langle \, E(\mathbf{h}')E(\mathbf{h}'')E(\mathbf{h}''') \, \rangle, \tag{2.29}$$

and in space group $P\bar{1}$

$$\kappa_{222} = - 4z_6 - 3E_6(2\mathbf{H}) = M_{222} - 4E_3^2(\mathbf{H}) \tag{2.30}$$

where M_{222} has formally the expression (2.20), but two averaging procedures with respect to the vectors $\mathbf{h}$ and $\mathbf{k}$ are involved.

THE UNIVARIATE CASE

The foregoing averaging procedure would only give rise to averages of powers of one structure factor, that is to trivial constants. More substantial results are obtained by writing

$$\mathcal{M} = \mathrm{op}\,(\exp uE) = \exp K \tag{2.31}$$

where " op " is an appropriate operation, compatible with cumulant techniques. Take the example of space group $P2_1/m$ where

$$\xi^2(hkl) = \xi(0) + \xi(2h, 2k, 2l) + (-1)^l(\xi(2h, 2k, 0) + \xi(0, 0, 2l)), \tag{2.32}$$

and define

$$m_p = \mathrm{op}\,\xi^p(hkl) = \langle \, (-1)^l \xi^p(hkl) \, \rangle_l;$$

$$\mu_p = \langle \, (-1)^l E^p(hkl) \, \rangle_l; \tag{2.33}$$

that is, the operation is a multiplication by $(-1)^l$ followed by an average over l. One has

$$m_2 = \xi(2h, 2k, 0); \quad m_4 = 8\xi(2h, 2k, 0). \tag{2.34}$$

By the usual cumulant method we get

$$\kappa_2 = E_2(2h, 2k, 0) = \langle \, (-1)^l E^2(hkl) \, \rangle_l \tag{2.35}$$

$$\kappa_4 = 8E_4(2h, 2k, 0) = \langle \, (-1)^l E^4(hkl) \, \rangle - 3(\langle \, (-1)^l E^2(hkl) \, \rangle)^2. \tag{2.36}$$

One may also construct the function (2.31) where " op " now means " averaging over h and k with l fixed." One finds then,

$$k_2 = m_2 = 4 + (-1)^l \xi(0, 0, 2l) \tag{2.37}$$

$$k_4 = -m_4 = -36 - 3\xi(0, 0, 4l) + 12(-1)^l\xi(0, 0, 2l), \quad (2.38)$$

and from (1.33)

$$\langle E^2(hkl) \rangle = 1 + (-1)^l E_2(0, 0, 2l) \quad (2.39)$$

$$\langle E^4(hkl) - 3E^2(hkl) \rangle = -9z_4 - 3E_4(0, 0, 4l) - 12(-1)^l E_4(0, 0, 2l) \quad (2.40)$$

Relations (2.35) and (2.39) may be easily checked by direct calculation of the averages.

APPROXIMATE EVALUATION OF HIGHER MOMENTS

In the foregoing sections we have established " exact " relations in the sense that the evaluation of a moment of order p always implies a parallel calculation of cumulants up to order p and vice versa.

Let us now stop the expansion of the c.g.f. K at some definite order p_1. What shall be the formal and approximate expression of moments of order p higher than p_1 when we restrict the solution to terms of order z_{p_1}? Consider the practical example of the bivariate case, the expansion of K including only terms up to the fourth order, and let us calculate the even moments up to order z_4.

$$\mu_{2p, 2q} = \langle E^{2p}(\mathbf{h}')E^{2q}(\mathbf{h}'') \rangle \quad (2.41)$$

with $p < 1, q < 1$. For this purpose $\mathcal{M}(u_1, u_2)$ is expanded up to order 4 in the form (2.42) which directly results from (2.1)

$$\mathcal{M}(u_1, u_2) = \exp K = \exp\left(\tfrac{1}{2}(u_1^2 + u_2^2)\right)$$

$$\left[1 + \kappa_{11}u_1u_2 + \frac{1}{4!}(\kappa_{40}u_1^4 + \kappa_{04}u_2^4) + \frac{1}{2!2!}M_{22}u_1^2u_2^2\right]. \quad (2.42)$$

Here we have abbreviated

$$M_{22} = \kappa_{22} + 2(\kappa_{11})^2. \quad (2.43)$$

M_{22} has the same meaning as in (2.2). At this point it is clear that the higher moments (2.41) will be expressed as functions of M_{22} (a term we already met in the Cochran relation (2.11)), and that these expressions will be only approximate.

Differentiating (2.42) $2p$ times with respect to u_1 and $2q$ times with respect to u_2, in agreement with the definition (1.6) of averages, we have

$$\mu_{2p, 2q} = S(2p)!\,(2q)!\,2^{-p-q}/(p!\,q!), \quad (2.44)$$

where

$$S = 1 + 2^2\left(\frac{1}{4!}p(p-1)\kappa_{40} + q(q-1)\kappa_{04} + \frac{1}{2!2!}pqM_{22}\right). \quad (2.45)$$

One has also

$$\langle E^{2p}(\mathbf{h}) \rangle = (2p)!/(2^p p!)\left(1 + \frac{2^2}{4!}p(p-1)\kappa_{40}\right) \qquad (2.46)$$

and a similar relation for $\langle E^{2q}(\mathbf{h}) \rangle$, so that finally

$$\langle (E^{2p}(\mathbf{h}')/\langle E^{2p}(\mathbf{h}) \rangle - 1)(E^{2q}(\mathbf{h}'')/\langle E^{2q}(\mathbf{h}) \rangle - 1) \rangle = pqM_{22}. \qquad (2.47)$$

Hauptmann and Karle[9], in their paper on " New Joint Probability Distributions," have recommended the use of such higher moment formulae, having an approximate degree of precision. In order to improve the result, they have integrated them with the help of an interpolation formula. It is quite obvious that an integration over less and less correct expressions (i.e. of higher moments) cannot give better results than the correct formula (i.e. the Cochran equation).

CONCLUSION

The examples we have described illustrate the point (known for a long time in statistics) that for the evaluation of moments there is no need to construct joint probability distribution functions. For that purpose moment and cumulant generating functions are very convenient mathematical tools. The clear result we have obtained is that the cumulant generating function is linear in " structure factors $E_p(\mathbf{H})$ (1.30) of order p." Experimental averages (moments) of structure factor products will always be related to the $E_p(\mathbf{H})$ by moment-cumulant relations.

What is the practical value of these relations ? Three cases may be distinguished.

1. If all the atoms are equal, $E_p(\mathbf{H})$ is proportional to an ordinary structure factor

$$E_p(\mathbf{H}) = \phi^{p-1}E(\mathbf{H}). \qquad (2.48)$$

2. If the atoms are not too different in diffracting power, the approximation (2.49), obtained by minimizing $(E_p(\mathbf{H}) - CE(\mathbf{H}))^2$ may be helpful

$$E_p(\mathbf{H}) \approx z_{p+1}E(\mathbf{H}). \qquad (2.49)$$

3. If there are heavy atoms, the sign of $E_p(\mathbf{H})$ will depend mainly on the part due to heavy atoms. Indeed these are favoured by the factor ϕ_j^p. (As an example the ratio of ϕ_j^p for Fe and O is 2·5 in $E(\mathbf{H})$, but about 40 in $E_4(\mathbf{H})$). In this case the principal use of $E_p(\mathbf{H})$ will be the location of heavy atoms.

We do not claim that statistics of structure factors with fixed coordinates and variable reciprocal vectors will definitely solve the phase problem. It is our opinion that all statistical methods should be thoroughly explored. We certainly hope that further progress will be made in coming years.

APPENDIX

$\xi^2(\mathbf{h})$ may be written[7] for a general reflection

$$\xi^2(\mathbf{h}) = \sum_s \gamma_s \xi(\mathbf{h}(\mathbf{I} - \mathbf{C}_s)) \tag{A.1}$$

Here the summation is over distinct $\xi(\mathbf{h}(\mathbf{I} - \mathbf{C}_s))$, γ_s is a numerical coefficient (1 or 2), $\mathbf{C}_s$ is the symmetry operator of the space group, $\mathbf{I}$ the identity operator, p_s the statistical weight of $\xi(\mathbf{h}(\mathbf{I} - \mathbf{C}_s))$. One has

$$m_{20} = m_{02} = \xi(0) \tag{A.2}$$

$$m_{11}^2 = \xi^2(\mathbf{H}) = \sum_s \gamma_s \xi(\mathbf{H}(\mathbf{I} - \mathbf{C}_s)), \tag{A.3}$$

$$m_{22} = \langle \xi^2(\mathbf{h}')\xi^2(\mathbf{h}'') \rangle = \sum_s \gamma_s^2 p_s \xi(\mathbf{H}(\mathbf{I} - \mathbf{C}_s)) \tag{A.4}$$

so that from (1.28) and (A.2) to (A.4) one easily obtains (2.14).

REFERENCES

1. BERTAUT, E. F. (1958). *Acta Cryst.* **11**, 405.
2. SAYRE, D. (1952). *Acta Cryst.* **5**, 60.
3. COCHRAN, W. (1954). *Acta Cryst.* **7**, 581.
4. COCHRAN, W. (1958). *Acta Cryst.* **11**, 579.
5. HAUPTMANN, H. and KARLE, J. (1957). *Acta Cryst.* **10**, 267.
6. HAUPTMANN, H. and KARLE, J. (1957). *Acta Cryst.* **10**, 515.
7. BERTAUT, E. F. (1959). *Acta Cryst.* **12**, 541.
8. BERTAUT, E. F. (1959). *Acta Cryst.* **12**, 570.
9. HAUPTMANN, H. and KARLE, J. (1958). *Acta Cryst.* **11**, 149.
10. BERTAUT, E. F. (1956). *Acta Cryst.* **9**, 769.
11. BERTAUT, E. F. and WASER, J. (1957). *Acta Cryst.* **10**, 606.
12. BERTAUT, E. F., BLUM, P. and MAGNANO, G. (1956). *Bull. Soc. Fr. Min. Crist.* **79**, 536.
13. KARLE, J. and HAUPTMANN, H. (1958). *Acta Cryst.* **11**, 757.
14. KENDALL, G. M. (1943). *The Advanced Theory of Statistics*, Chas. Griffin, London.
15. KLUG, A. (1958). *Acta Cryst.* **11**, 515.
16. BERTAUT, E. F. (1960). *Acta Cryst.* **13**, 546.
17. BULLOUGH, H. R. K. and CRUICKSHANK, D. W. J. (1955). *Acta Cryst.* **8**, 29.

Paper 21

ON DIRECT METHODS
OF PHASE DETERMINATION

by HERBERT HAUPTMAN

U.S. Naval Research Laboratory, Washington 25, D.C.

INTRODUCTION

This paper is concerned with formulas of a statistical nature which relate the phases of the structure factors to the magnitudes and phases of others. The methods for attacking this problem fall, generally speaking, into two categories, the probability approach and the algebraic approach. Although the algebraic methods are simpler in concept, the probability approach preceded the algebraic one historically, and even today has the advantage that it leads to more general formulas.

PART I
THE EARLY METHODS (1953-1956)

A. *The Probability Approach*

The early probability methods[1] were concerned with the problem of determining the probability distribution of a real structure factor on the basis that the atomic coordinates of the atoms in a crystal were uniformly distributed, subject however to the restriction that the magnitudes of a certain set of structure factors were known. From the probability distributions a procedure for phase determination, having a probable validity, could be inferred. Characteristic formulas obtainable in this way were:

$$\Sigma_1: \quad sE_{2H} \sim s(E_H^2 - 1),$$

$$\Sigma_2: \quad sE_H \sim s\sum_K E_K E_{H+K},$$

$$\Sigma_3: \quad sE_{2H} \sim s\sum_K E_{2K}(E_{H+K}^2 - 1); \qquad \left.\right\} \quad P\bar{1}$$

$$\Sigma_1: \quad sE_{2h02l} \sim s\sum_k (-1)^{h+k}(E_{hkl}^2 - 1),$$

$$\Sigma_1: \quad sE_{02k0} \sim s\sum_{h,l}(-1)^{h+k}(E_{hkl}^2 - 1); \qquad \left.\right\} \quad P2_1/a$$

214

where E is the normalized structure factor, s means " sign of," and $\sim$ means " probably is."

B. *The Algebraic Approach*

It was soon discovered[2, 3, 4, 5] that most of the probability relationships found previously had algebraic analogues which, for the case of N identical point atoms in the unit cell, possessed exact, rather than merely probable, validity. We list a few typical formulas, for the most part space group dependent, which can be found by these algebraic means:

$$
\left.
\begin{aligned}
E_H &= N^{1/2} \langle E_K E_{H+K} \rangle_K, \\
E_{2H} &= N \langle E_{2K} (E_{H+K}^2 - 1) \rangle_K;
\end{aligned}
\right\} \quad P\bar{1}
$$

$$
\left.
\begin{aligned}
E_{2h02l} &= N^{1/2} \langle (-1)^{h+k} (E_{hkl}^2 - 1) \rangle_k, \\
E_{02k0} &= N^{1/2} \langle (-1)^{h+k} (E_{hkl}^2 - 1) \rangle_{h,l};
\end{aligned}
\right\} \quad P2_1/a
$$

$$
E_{02k2l} = N^{1/2} \langle (-1)^{h+k} (E_{hkl}^2 - 1) \rangle_h; \qquad P2_1 2_1 2_1.
$$

PART II

THE LATER METHODS (1957-1960)

A. *The Algebraic Approach*

The algebraic methods of Part I, B were soon refined and generalized[6, 7, 8] to yield formulas valid for all the space groups and for the case that the crystal contains dissimilar atoms as well as only identical atoms. The main formulas, given here only for the special case of N identical point atoms per unit cell, are

$P1$: $\; |E_1 E_2 E_3| \cos(\phi_1 + \phi_2 + \phi_3)$

$$
= \frac{N^{3/2}}{2} \langle (|E_K|^2 - 1)(|E_{H_1+K}|^2 - 1)(|E_{H_1+H_2+K}|^2 - 1) \rangle_K +
$$

$$
+ \frac{1}{N^{1/2}} (|E_1|^2 + |E_2|^2 + |E_3|^2 - 2),
$$

$P\bar{1}$: $\; E_1 E_2 E_3$

$$
= \frac{N^{3/2}}{8} \langle (E_K^2 - 1)(E_{H_1+K}^2 - 1)(E_{H_1+H_2+K}^2 - 1) \rangle_K +
$$

$$
+ \frac{1}{N^{1/2}} (E_1^2 + E_2^2 + E_3^2 - 2) +
$$

$$
+ \frac{1}{2N^{1/2}} (E_{H_1} E_{H_2-H_3} + E_{H_2} E_{H_3-H_1} + E_{H_3} E_{H_1-H_2}) -
$$

$$
- \frac{1}{N} (E_{2H_1} + E_{2H_2} + E_{2H_3}),
$$

where $E_i = E_{H_i}$, ϕ_i is the phase of the structure factor E_i, and $H_1 + H_2 + H_3 = 0$. Hence $\phi_1 + \phi_2 + \phi_3$ is a structure invariant the value of which is uniquely determined by the structure (independent of the choice of origin). These formulas (and their analogues in the other space groups) are to be used in conjunction with procedures for fixing the origin and enantiomorph and with known relationships among the phases which are characteristic of the space group. It should be remarked that the validity of these formulas is subject to the non-existence of a special type of rational dependence among the atomic coordinates. It appears now that the rational dependence which occurs in actual crystals may often be sufficiently serious to cause some modification, in practice, of these formulas.

B. *The Probability Approach*

In contrast to the probability distributions obtained previously (Part I, A), the present distributions[9, 10] of several structure factors (both magnitudes and phases) are found by fixing the crystal structure and allowing the Miller indices to range uniformly, but not independently, over the integers. In this way the expected values of products of several structure factors are obtained, and these lead to generalizations of the algebraic formulas described in Part II, A.

PART III

APPLICATIONS

By this time several structures have been determined using the direct methods of phase determination[11-16]. Of these, the structures of p, p'-dimethoxybenzophenone[14] and the mineral spurrite[15, 16], both in the space group $P2_1/a$, are most interesting because of the presence of rational dependence. The rational dependence which occurs in these crystals is sufficiently severe, as shown by a statistical analysis of the observed magnitudes, that the formulas appropriate to the space group $P2_1/a$ (Part I, A) cannot be used. For the p, p'-dimethoxybenzophone the $P\bar{1}$ formulas (Part I, A), which are not affected by the type of rational dependence present, were sufficient to permit the determination of some 270 phases. The Fourier series using these 270 structure factors led immediately to the structure.

Owing to the limited number of data available for spurrite (only one-half the copper sphere) the $P\bar{1}$ formulas of Part I, A could not be used for this structure. Instead, a renormalization procedure[17], based on an analysis of certain subsets of the observed magnitudes in which the averages were anomalous, was first carried out. The $P2_1/a$ formulas (Part I, A) were then useful, provided that the normalized structure factors E were replaced by the renormalized structure factors. In this way a sufficient number of phases were determined to elucidate the structure.

REFERENCES

1. HAUPTMAN, H. and KARLE, J. (1954). *Solution of the Phase Problem.* 1. *The Centro-symmetric Crystal. A.C.A. Monograph No. 3.*
2. HUGHES, E. W. (1953). *Acta Cryst.* **6**, 871.
3. COCHRAN, W. (1954). *Acta Cryst.* **7**, 581.
4. BULLOUGH, R. K. and CRUICKSHANK, D. W. J. (1955). *Acta Cryst.* **8**, 29.
5. HAUPTMAN, H. and KARLE, J. (1955). *Acta Cryst.* **8**, 355.
6. HAUPTMAN, H. and KARLE, J. (1957). *Acta Cryst.* **10**, 267.
7. KARLE, J. and HAUPTMAN, H. (1957). *Acta Cryst.* **10**, 515.
8. VAUGHAN, P. A. (1958). *Acta Cryst.* **11**, 111.
9. HAUPTMAN, H. and KARLE, J. (1958). *Acta Cryst.* **11**, 149.
10. KARLE, J. and HAUPTMAN, H. (1958). *Acta Cryst.* **11**, 264.
11. KARLE, J., HAUPTMAN, H. and CHRIST, C. L. (1958). *Acta Cryst.* **11**, 757.
12. CHRIST, C. L., CLARK, JOAN R. and EVANS, H. T., Jr. (1958). *Acta Cryst.* **11**, 761.
13. CHRIST, C. L. and CLARK, JOAN R. (1956). *Acta Cryst.* **9**, 830.
14. KARLE, I. L., HAUPTMAN, H., KARLE, J. and WING, A. B. (1958). *Acta Cryst.* **11**, 257.
15. HAUPTMAN, H., KARLE, I. L. and KARLE, J. (1960). *Acta Cryst.* **13**, 451.
16. SMITH, J. V., KARLE, I. L., HAUPTMAN, H. and KARLE, J. (1960). *Acta Cryst.* **13**, 454.
17. HAUPTMAN, H. and KARLE, J. (1959). *Acta Cryst.* **12**, 846.

P

Paper 22

AN EDSAC II PROGRAM FOR SOLVING SAYRE'S EQUATION

by W. Cochran

Crystallographic Laboratory, Cavendish Laboratory,
Cambridge

Information about EDSAC II will be given in other papers presented at the Conference, and need not be repeated here. The method outlined here is an extension of earlier work with EDSAC I (Cochran and Douglas, 1954, 1957). It is based on the conviction that the more complicated sign-determining relations which have been put forward are of decreasing utility as the number of atoms in the unit cell of a crystal increases. These relations, in other words, are of high order, in the sense defined by Klug (1958). We have relied exclusively on the relation of the lowest order,

$$s(\mathbf{h}) \approx s(\mathbf{h}')s(\mathbf{h} + \mathbf{h}') \tag{1}$$

and on the related result

$$s(\mathbf{h}) \approx s[\sum_{\mathbf{h}'} U(\mathbf{h}')U(\mathbf{h} + \mathbf{h}')] \tag{2}$$

In the case of a structure containing equal atoms, this second relation becomes Sayre's equation,

$$U(\mathbf{h}) = \alpha\sum_{\mathbf{h}'} U(\mathbf{h}')U(\mathbf{h} + \mathbf{h}') \tag{3}$$

where α is a function of $|\mathbf{h}|$. When the condition of equal resolved atoms is not satisfied we may write

$$G(\mathbf{h}) = \alpha\sum_{\mathbf{h}'} U(\mathbf{h}')U(\mathbf{h} + \mathbf{h}') \tag{4}$$

where $G(\mathbf{h})$ is proportional to the unitary structure factor of the squared electron density distribution. Thus for the correct set of signs one may expect the quantity

$$T = (\sum_{\mathbf{h}} |U(\mathbf{h}) - G(\mathbf{h})|) \div (\sum_{\mathbf{h}} |U(\mathbf{h})|) \tag{5}$$

to be a minimum, and to have a value close to zero to the extent that the atoms are equal.

The machine is supplied with a table of values of $|U(\mathbf{h})|$. All the relations of type (1) are found, using a maximum of 38 structure factors at this stage. Let us define

$$Y(\mathbf{h}\mathbf{h}') = S(\mathbf{h})S(\mathbf{h}')S(\mathbf{h} + \mathbf{h}').$$

The machine constructs a matrix whose elements are either 0 or 1; this matrix gives the Y's in terms of the S's. For example, if the three largest unitary structure factors have indices related in the appropriate way, the first row of the matrix will be specified by a storage register containing the digits 111 followed by zeros. This matrix is now " inverted " to express the S's in terms of the Y's, as far as possible. Use is then made of the fact that most of the Y's, to an extent that can be predicted (using Woolfson's hyperbolic-tangent formula), are positive. Each set of signs for the Y's which is allowable is generated in turn, and a check is made to eliminate each corresponding set of signs for the S's which does not satisfy relation (2), in a slightly modified form. Those sets of signs for the S's which satisfy these conditions are stored. This completes the first stage of the operation, and experience has shown that anything from half a dozen to a hundred sets of signs may have been stored at the end of it. In a second stage, the machine proceeds to find the signs of smaller unitary structure factors, down to some specified limit, using relation (2). The value of $G(\mathbf{h})$ for all structure factors is then found, and finally T evaluated and printed out with each set of signs. The final test consists in evaluating electron density maps, beginning of course with the set of signs giving the lowest value of T.

In a test on a synthetic structure the correct set of signs gave $T = 0.04$, the increase over zero being attributable to the fact that the scaling factor α (Eqn. 4) is taken to be constant over small ranges of value of $|\mathbf{h}|$, rather than as a continuous function. The correct set of signs for a projection of nitroguanidine gave $T = 0.27$, compared with values of between 0.53 and 0.76 for the 26 other sets of signs retained by the machine at the end of stage one. A preliminary account of this work has been published (*Acta Cryst.* **11,** 392); since then the work has been interrupted but we hope to be able to present further results at the Conference. The program in an incomplete form has been used by Chatar Singh to determine the crystal structures of alloxantin and of alloxan. Extension of the method to utilize three-dimensional data would be possible, but each problem might then take hours of machine time.

Acknowledgments

Mr. E. J. McIver and Mr. P. Tollin have collaborated in different stages of this work. I am grateful to the Director of the University Mathematical Laboratory, Dr. M. V. Wilkes, for permission to use EDSAC II.

REFERENCES

COCHRAN, W. and DOUGLAS, A. S. (1954). *Proc. Roy Soc.* A **227,** 486; *ibid.* (1957) **243,** 281.
KLUG, A. (1958). *Acta Cryst.* **11,** 515.

Paper 23

A MULTIPLE-SOLUTION DIRECT-METHOD PROGRAMME FOR THE IBM 704 COMPUTER

by M. M. WOOLFSON

Physics Department, College of Science and Technology, Manchester 1, England

THE OBJECTIVE AND THE COMPUTER

The initial aim of this programme, subsequently modified, was to attempt to solve crystal structures, in two or three dimensions, directly with a computer which was fed only with the observable data and which finally produced a small number of plausible electron-density maps, there having been no intermediate intervention on the part of the operator. This goal was not realized. Although many of the decisions which must be made in a direct methods procedure have in fact been incorporated into the programme, there are a few points where the operator is allowed to exercise his own judgment and, indeed, where it would be foolish of him not to do so. These decisions are mostly those which concern the degree of complexity of search procedures which the operator is prepared to tolerate, which in turn depend on the time or even money available or perhaps the intensity of desire to have this particular problem solved. These factors are not readily assessed by a happy-go-lucky machine.

The attempt to use three-dimensional data was also abandoned. There are no difficulties of principle involved—it is just that even for a moderately complex structure, machine times of the order of 10 hours or so are required. For this order of problem it seems wiser to await the next generation of machines, soon to be delivered and of order 100 times faster than those we have now.

The machine available for the purposes outlined above was an IBM 704 with an 8192 word ferrite-core storage, 8192 word magnetic drum store and 10 tape units (only 4 are required by the programme). The programme was written in the FORTRAN machine language including the latest FORTRAN III facilities which allow the blending of conventional machine instructions and have some additional versatile input and output arrangements.

THE GENERAL STRATEGY

None of the individual techniques to be described here is new; the novelty is their coordination in a single composite programme. The description will therefore be somewhat skeletal and is intended to be supplemented by reference to the cited literature.

The information supplied to the machine consists of the space group number, the unit cell constants, wavelength of radiation, the numbers of each type of atom, tables of scattering factors and finally the observed intensities (or some related quantities) with corresponding reflection indices. Unitary structure factors are found from these data by a method somewhat similar to that described by Lipson and Cochran (1957).

A number of the largest U's are chosen and listed according to their parity groups. Signs are to be found for these U's; for descriptive purposes their signs can be indicated by subscripted letter symbols which represent plus or minus unity. For example, we may have

Parity group	Sign symbols
h even k even	$a_1, a_2, a_3 \ldots$
h even k odd	$b_1, b_2, b_3 \ldots$
h odd k even	$c_1, c_2, c_3 \ldots$
h odd k odd	$d_1, d_2, d_3 \ldots$

A number, n, of the structure invariants, the a's, are chosen. The value of n is based on the complexity of the structure whilst the actual a's selected are those which are most richly interrelated by sign relationships of the type

$$a_p a_q a_r \approx +1, \tag{1}$$

where $\approx$ means " probably equals."

Plausible sets of signs are found for these a's by a slight modification of the method of Cochran and Douglas (1954). This is a maximum-efficiency process for finding all sets of signs for the a's which will give less than some specified number, u, of failures of sign relationships of type (1).

Signs are now developed for the members of the other parity groups by the method of structure invariants (Woolfson, 1957). This involves the systematic exploitation of sets of pairs of sign relationships of the following type:

$$\left. \begin{array}{r} a_1 b_5 b_6 \approx +1 \\ - a_3 b_5 b_7 \approx +1 \end{array} \right\}$$

$$\left. \begin{array}{r} a_4 b_2 b_6 \approx +1 \\ a_5 b_2 b_7 \approx +1 \end{array} \right\}$$

$$\left. \begin{array}{r} - a_2 b_3 b_6 \approx +1 \\ a_4 b_3 b_7 \approx +1 \end{array} \right\} \tag{2}$$

If the signs of the a's are known as, say $a_1 = +1$, $a_2 = -1$, $a_3 = +1$, $a_4 = -1$ and $a_5 = +1$ then the conclusion which may be drawn from each pair of equations is $b_6 b_7 \approx -1$.

Within each parity group a pattern of signs is established; compatibility between the signs for groups b, c and d to conform to a unique choice of origin is accomplished by consideration of relationships of the type

$$\pm b_r c_s d_t \approx +1. \tag{3}$$

Not all the larger U's originally selected have been found at this stage—indeed some of them have never been involved at all. Further signs are deduced by application of the relationship

$$s(\mathbf{h}) \approx s\left\{ \sum_{\mathbf{h}'} s(\mathbf{h}')\, s(\mathbf{h} + \mathbf{h}') \right\} \quad \text{(Zachariasen, 1952)} \tag{4}$$

where the summation is carried out for the $\mathbf{h}$ for which the associated sign is required and over all $\mathbf{h}'$ for which products of s's are available.

The fraction, R, of sign relationships which hold is calculated at this stage and for each set of signs with R within some specified limits the Z-test is applied (Woolfson, 1958a, b). This uses an equation between structure factors

$$F_{\mathbf{h}} = A_{\mathbf{h}} \sum_{\mathbf{h}'} F_{\mathbf{h}'} F_{\mathbf{h} + \mathbf{h}'} + B_{\mathbf{h}} \sum_{\mathbf{h}'} \sum_{\mathbf{h}''} F_{\mathbf{h}'} F_{\mathbf{h}''} F_{\mathbf{h} + \mathbf{h}' + \mathbf{h}''} \tag{5}$$

which holds precisely for a structure containing only two atomic types and which, by a judicious choice of $A_{\mathbf{h}}$ and $B_{\mathbf{h}}$ may be made to hold reasonably well under a variety of other conditions. In the computer the summation is made for all $\mathbf{h}$ for which $\sin\theta \leqslant 0.5$ and with the F's of known sign incorporated on the right-hand side; the value of this summation may be denoted as $F_{\mathbf{h}}'$. The value of the test function is

$$Z = \frac{\sum_{\mathbf{h}} \left| \, |F_{\mathbf{h}}| - |F_{\mathbf{h}}'| \, \right|}{\sum_{\mathbf{h}} |F_{\mathbf{h}}|} \tag{6}$$

A correct set of signs would be expected to give a low value of Z.

Finally, for all sets of signs with Z within specified limits Fourier maps are calculated and printed on a grid, as true to scale as the output facilities of the machine readily allow. These are contoured and examined for expected features, the greatest credence being given to those solutions with higher values of R and lower values of Z.

If the correct solution is not revealed by the first run, it is possible to return to a number of points. The possibilities are to:

    (i) calculate additional Fourier maps with more liberal ranges of Z,

    (ii) calculate Z for additional sets of signs with lower values of R

or (iii) allow more than u failures of the " aaa " sign relationships in the initial stage.

While carrying out the retracing operations does increase the probability of snaring the correct set of signs, the operating time is also increased and usually somewhat disproportionately. Again, if the discriminating conditions must be relaxed, it usually means that the correct answer is less obviously correct and greater effort and diligence must be exercised in selecting the true solution from the many accompanying plausible but incorrect ones.

SOME PROGRAMME DETAILS

It was found convenient to write the programme in seven sections, to each of which there corresponds a deck of punched cards. These are fed into the machine individually, each after the previous part has completed its task. This sub-division of the programme is necessary because of the limited storage capacity of the computer but, happily, this also enables the programme to be run in short non-consecutive spells of time if machine time is only available in this way. A short description of the function of each part of the programme follows.

Part 1

The data, punched on cards, are read in. These consist of:

P the two-dimensional space group number (International Tables),

k a code number, described later,

e number of entries in scattering factor table,

t number of atomic types contained in the unit cell,

a, b, c, λ unit cell dimensions and wavelength of radiation,

α, β, γ unit cell angles,

ω_1, $\omega_2 \ldots \omega_t$ number of atoms of each atomic type,

$$
\left. \begin{array}{l} \left(\dfrac{\sin \theta}{\lambda}\right)_1 \quad (f_1)_1 \quad (f_2)_1 \ldots (f_t)_1 \\[2ex] \left(\dfrac{\sin \theta}{\lambda}\right)_e \quad (f_1)_e \quad (f_2)_e \ldots (f_t)_e \end{array} \right\}
$$

table of scattering factors for t types of atom and e values of $\sin \theta / \lambda$.

$$
\left. \begin{array}{l} A_1, h_1, k_1 \\ A_2, h_2, k_2 \\ \quad : \\ \quad : \end{array} \right\}
$$

If the code number k is unity then A must be the structure factor, F, or anything related to F by a function of $\sin \theta$ only. If $k = 2$ then A must be the intensity of the reflection or anything related to it by a function of $\sin \theta$ only.

The data are converted to unitary structure factors and stored with the input data on magnetic tape (tape 2 on the machine) for use by subsequent portions of the programme.

Running time: normally 2–4 minutes.

Part 2

Unitary structure factors are selected of such magnitude that no sign relationship will have a probability less than 0·8. The minimum value of U, U_{min}, is given by

$$0·8 = \tfrac{1}{2} + \tfrac{1}{2}\tanh\left(\frac{\epsilon_3}{\epsilon_3^3}U_{min}^3\right) \tag{7}$$

(Cochran and Woolfson, 1955).

The total number of such U's should be greater than twice the number of unknown structure parameters. If this is not so the value of U_{min} is reduced until there are sufficient U's to satisfy this condition. It is also possible that the value of U_{min} may be relaxed for individual parity groups if it is judged that there are too few members for them to be well related by relationships of type (2). All the sign relationships are found which involve the chosen U's and are tabulated according to the five possible types " aaa ", " abb ", " acc ", " add " or " bcd ". These are then added to the data on tape 2.

Running time: normally 3–5 minutes.

Part 3

The sign relationships are processed and re-arranged for use by subsequent portions of the programme. The best n structure invariants are chosen from the aspect of being best interrelated by sign relationships. In addition all the pairs of indices occurring on the right-hand sides of equations (4) are tabulated. This information is stored on tape 2.

Running time: normally 2–5 minutes.

Part 4

All plausible sets of signs for the n structure invariants are found by the Cochran and Douglas method. The value of u, the maximum number of failures of the " aaa " sign relationships, is calculated by the programme but there is provision for the operator to intervene and increase the value of u.

The plausible set of signs are stored on tape 2.

Running time: normally 3–10 minutes.

Part 5

A knowledge of signs is developed for the members of the other parity groups by means of relationships of type (2), made compatible by relationships (3) and extended by relationships (4). The values of R are also found and stored with the completed sets of signs on tape 2.

Running time: very variable but may be of order 30–60 minutes. There is provision for stops to be made in the middle of the programme at fairly short notice. A re-start can then be made either immediately or some time later. This facility is necessary because of the difficulty of predicting in advance the time required and also to ensure against loss of data or machine time in the event of a machine failure.

Part 6

Values of Z are calculated for each set of signs with R within a specified range. This range can be set by the programme as

$$0 \cdot 5 < R \leqslant 1 \cdot 0$$

which causes all sets of signs to be accepted or the limits can be read in on a punched card. The values of Z are added to the data on tape 2. Sets of signs with values of R outside the accepted range are preserved on tape 2 in the event that they are required on a re-run of this part.
Running time: remarks as for Part 5.

Part 7

Fourier maps are calculated and printed out for each set of signs within specified limits of Z values. This range may be set by the machine to include all values of Z or the limiting values may be read in on a punched card.

The maps are calculated at intervals of 1/50th cell edge and printed on a rectangular grid.

Running time: of order 1 second per reflection per map.

The programme is so arranged that after each part tape 2 contains all the information necessary for continuing with the programme. The maximum flexibility of operation is provided to allow for variable or intermittent machine availability and rescue facilities insure against machine failure at all times.

EXAMPLES OF OPERATION

At the time of presenting this account not very many applications of this programme have been made; the majority of such applications have been tests. It is pleasant to report that the programme is brilliantly successful in solving known structures.

The best example of the potentialities of the present programme are illustrated by the result achieved with a lash-up programme designed for the Ferranti Mercury computer, the solution of the structure of xylose (Woolfson, 1958*b*).

Acknowledgment

This work was carried out under the auspices of the Mathematics and Applications Group, Data Systems Division, I.B.M. Corporation, New York, U.S.A.

REFERENCES

COCHRAN, W. and DOUGLAS, A. S. (1954). *Proc. Roy. Soc.* A **227**, 486.
COCHRAN, W. and WOOLFSON, M. M. (1955). *Acta Cryst.* **8**, 1.
LIPSON, H. and COCHRAN, W. (1957). *The Determination of Crystal Structures.* Bell, London.
WOOLFSON, M. M. (1957). *Acta Cryst.* **10**, 116.
WOOLFSON, M. M. (1958a). *Acta Cryst.* **11**, 277.
WOOLFSON, M. M. (1958b). *Acta Cryst.* **11**, 393.
ZACHARIASEN, W. H. (1952). *Acta Cryst.* **5**, 65.

Paper 24

ASPECTS OF THE HEAVY-ATOM METHOD

by G. A. SIM

Chemistry Department, The University, Glasgow, W.2,
Scotland

INTRODUCTION

In the majority of cases where a crystal-structure analysis has established the molecular structure of a fairly complex organic chemical substance the solution of the phase problem has depended on the presence in the unit cell of a few atoms whose atomic numbers are considerably greater than those of the remaining atoms. The analyses of derivatives of penicillin (Crowfoot, Bunn, Rogers-Low and Turner-Jones, 1949), vitamin B_{12} (Hodgkin, Kamper, Lindsey, MacKay, Pickworth, Robertson, Brink, White, Prosen and Trueblood, 1957), phthalocyanine (Robertson, 1935, 1936; Robertson and Woodward, 1937, 1940) and limonin (Arnott, Davie, Robertson, Sim and Watson, 1960) may be quoted as fairly representative examples.

The practical importance of the heavy-atom method has, in recent years, stimulated theoretical treatment of the principles involved and some of the results obtained make up the contents of this paper.

THE CENTROSYMMETRICAL CASE

The structure-factor equation may be written as

$$F = F_H + F_L$$

where the subscripts H and L refer to the small number of atoms of high atomic number (e.g. iodine, bromine, sulphur, copper) and the larger number of atoms of low atomic number (usually carbon, oxygen and nitrogen), respectively.

A suitable heavy-atom derivative is one which satisfies the condition that F and F_H should have the same sign for a fairly large fraction of the reflections. The actual number of structure factors having the same sign as F_H can be calculated in any given case in terms of the number and kinds of atoms in the unit cell, a suitable parameter in terms of which the results may be expressed being defined by

$$r = (\Sigma f_H^2 / \Sigma f_L^2)^{\frac{1}{2}}.$$

The manner in which the fraction of structure factors with signs determined by the heavy-atom contributions varies as the parameter r varies is shown in Fig. 1 for the case of a molecule containing one heavy atom situated in a general position in a triclinic unit cell. In this case F and F_H have the same sign for 80% of the reflections when $r = 1$, while when $r = 2$ the proportion increases to 90%.

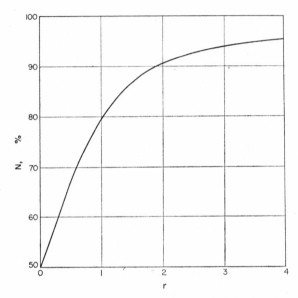

FIG. 1. The fraction of structure factors determined in sign by a heavy atom in the molecule.

In a typical application of the heavy-atom method, then, about 80–90% of the terms will be given the correct sign when the sign of F_H is used. If a Fourier synthesis is evaluated using signs indicated by F_H the terms which have been introduced with the wrong sign will cause errors in the electron-density distribution. Luzzati (1953) has given a theoretical treatment of the magnitude of the errors to be expected in such a Fourier synthesis. Woolfson (1956) has also discussed this question and has shown that in order to minimize these errors, and hence improve the resolution of the light atoms, a weight should be assigned to each term F according to the probability that the sign of F is the same as the sign of F_H. This probability is given by

$$P_+ = \tfrac{1}{2} + \tfrac{1}{2} \tanh \left(|F| \, |F_H| / \Sigma f_L^2 \right)$$

and the weight to be assigned to the term is defined by

$$W = 2P_+ - 1.$$

This weighting function is illustrated in Fig. 2.

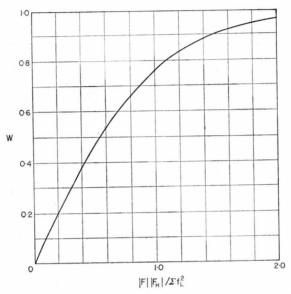

FIG. 2. The weighting function applicable to the centrosymmetrical case.

THE NON-CENTROSYMMETRICAL CASE

For the crystallographer interested in the elucidation of the molecular structure of complex organic molecules of biological importance the non-centrosymmetrical case of the heavy-atom method is of more importance than the centrosymmetrical case since naturally-occurring substances and their derivatives usually crystallize in non-centrosymmetric space groups. In this case, however, there is, unlike the centrosymmetrical case, no question of some of the phase angles being given correctly and some incorrectly by calculations based on the heavy atoms alone. There is instead a continuous distribution of errors, some large, some small, the detailed distribution being a function of $(\Sigma f_H^2 / \Sigma f_L^2)^{\frac{1}{2}}$.

The simplest case for theoretical treatment is that in which there is one heavy atom and a number of light atoms in a triclinic unit cell. If the true phase angle of a structure factor is α and that calculated on the basis of the heavy atom is α_H then the error is $\alpha - \alpha_H$ and this can vary between $\pm 180°$. The manner in which the fraction $N(\xi)$ of structure factors with phase-angle errors between $\pm\,\xi$ varies as r varies is illustrated in Fig. 3 for $\xi = 20°$, 60° and 100°. It can be seen, for example, that when $r = 1$, 38% of the errors lie in the range $\pm\,20°$ while when $r = 2$ the proportion confined to this range increases to 67%.

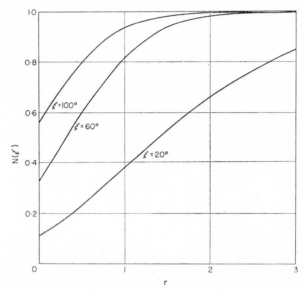

FIG. 3. $N\,(\xi)$ as a function of r. The curves shown are for $\xi = 20°$, 60° and 100°.

For other atomic arrangements somewhat different figures apply but in every case the greater the value of r the smaller is the average phase-angle error.

The use of phase angles α_H rather than the (unknown) true phase-angles α causes errors in the resulting electron-density distribution and so hinders the recognition of the sites of the light atoms. The greater the magnitude of the average phase-angle error the more difficult will it be to locate unambiguously light-atom peaks. This is illustrated in Fig. 4 by a hypothetical one-dimensional structure containing 9 atoms. The electron-density functions were calculated using phase angles based on only 4 of the atoms and three cases defined by $r = 1·5$, 1·0 and 0·5 were considered. The resolution of the atoms which make no contribution to the phase angles is seen to be worst when $r = 0·5$, a large number of spurious peaks being present in this case due to the errors in the phase angles. For $r = 1·5$, on the other hand, there is no real trouble in deciding which peaks represent true atomic sites.

Luzzati (1953) has shown that the resolution of the (unknown) light atoms is less favourable in the non-centrosymmetrical than in the centrosymmetrical case for a given value of $(\Sigma f_H^2/\Sigma f_L^2)^{\frac{1}{2}}$. The resolution of the light-atom peaks,

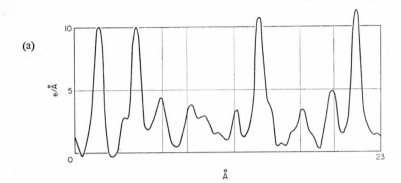

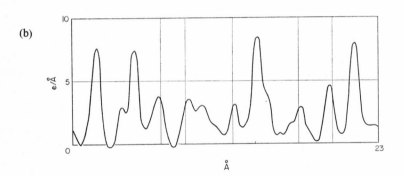

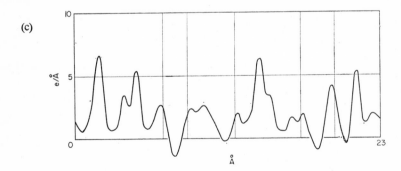

FIG. 4. Fourier synthesis with each term included at **full value**

(a) for $r = 1{\cdot}5$

(b) for $r = 1{\cdot}0$

(c) for $r = 0{\cdot}5$

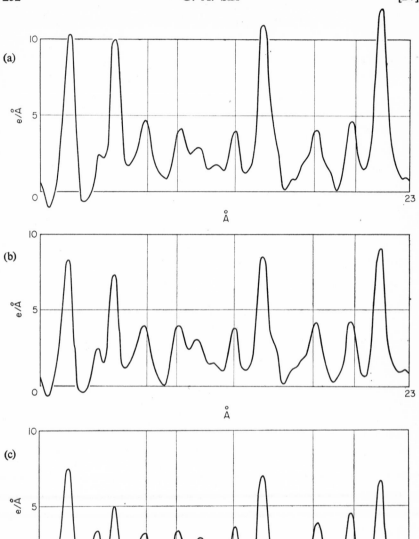

Fig. 5. Fourier synthesis with each term weighted according to the function
$$W = 2P(90°) - 1$$
(a) for $r = 1·5$
(b) for $r = 1·0$
(c) for $r = 0·5$

however, can be improved to some extent by a procedure analogous to Woolfson's treatment of the centrosymmetrical case, i.e. by assigning a weight to each term in the Fourier series according to the probable magnitude of the phase-angle error.

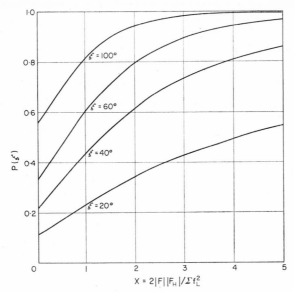

FIG. 6. The probability $P(\xi)$ that the phase-angle error lies between the limits $\pm \xi$ as a function of $X = 2 \mid F \mid F_H \mid/\Sigma f_L^2$.

For a structure factor with given values of $\mid F \mid$, $\mid F_H \mid$ and α_H the probability that the phase-angle error $(\alpha - \alpha_H)$ lies between the limits $\pm \xi$ is given by

$$P(\xi) = \int_{-\xi}^{+\xi} \exp(X \cos \xi) d\xi / 2\pi I_0(X),$$

where

$$X = 2 \mid F \mid \; \mid F_H \mid/\Sigma f_L^2$$

and I_0 is the zero-order modified Bessel function. $P(\xi)$ is shown as a function of X in Fig. 6, and it can be seen that the greater the value of X the more likely $(\alpha - \alpha_H)$ is to be small.

If the probable phase-angle error for a given term F is denoted by $\langle \alpha - \alpha_H \rangle$ then a suitable weighting function to improve light-atom resolution in the Fourier series calculated with the phase angles α_H should satisfy the conditions:

(1) as $\langle \alpha - \alpha_H \rangle \to 0$ $W \to 1$

(2) as $\langle \alpha - \alpha_H \rangle \to \dfrac{\pi}{2}$ $W \to 0$

Q

As the electron-density distribution is fairly insensitive to the precise set of weights adopted any weighting function which increases smoothly from 0 to 1 as $\langle \alpha - \alpha_H \rangle$ decreases from $\pi/2$ to 0 is probably satisfactory. In Fig. 5 the Fourier series illustrated in Fig. 4 have been recalculated with the terms weighted by such a function. In the case of $r = 1 \cdot 5$ there is only a slight improvement in resolution of the light-atom peaks, but this is only to be expected in view of the good resolution already obtained in the unweighted series. In the case of $r = 0 \cdot 5$, however, a marked improvement occurs.

When the parameter r has a value of about unity or less a Fourier series with terms weighted to discriminate against the more unreliable phase angles provides a distinctly better view of the crystal structure than does an unweighted series.

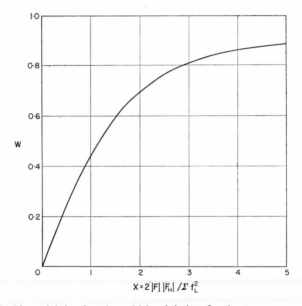

$$X = 2 |F| |F_H| / \Sigma f_L^2$$

Fig. 7. The weighting function which minimizes for the non-centrosymmetrical case the mean-square error in electron density due to the phase-angle errors $(\alpha - \alpha_H)$.

A convenient weighting function to use is that which ensures that the mean-square error in electron density due to the phase-angle errors is a minimum. This weighting function, shown in Fig. 7, is defined by

$$W = I_1(X)/I_0(X),$$

where I_0 and I_1 are respectively the zero-order and first-order modified Bessel functions of the first kind.

CONCLUSIONS

From the computational point of view the use of a weighting function when calculating an approximate electron-density distribution based on the heavy-atom phase angles α_H involves a number of advantages, particularly when dealing with the three-dimensional Fourier series which are necessary in the analysis of the large molecules encountered in natural-product chemistry.

Firstly, the representation of the structure which is obtained is the best that can be achieved from the approximate phase angles. Secondly, all the structure-amplitude data can be included from the beginning of the structure analysis. Thirdly, the weighting procedure can readily be programmed to follow structure-factor calculation and precede Fourier calculation on digital computers, permitting the derivation of the first approximate electron-density distribution from the heavy-atom coordinates in one operation, without the usual break between the structure-factor stage and the Fourier stage of the calculations to examine a list of possibly several thousand calculated and observed structure amplitudes with a view to deciding, in some more or less subjective manner, which are safe to be included in the Fourier calculation and which ought to be excluded. The latter procedure holds two dangers: either too few unreliable terms will be omitted or, on the other hand, an over-cautious omission of a number of terms may actually make the appearance of the distribution worse despite the phase-angle errors associated with the terms.

REFERENCES

ARNOTT, S., DAVIE, A. W., ROBERTSON, J. M., SIM, G. A. and WATSON, D. G. (1960). *Experientia* **16**, 49.

CROWFOOT, D., BUNN, C. W., ROGERS-LOW, B. W. and TURNER-JONES, A. (1949). *The Chemistry of Penicillin*, Princeton University Press, p.310.

HODGKIN, D. C., KAMPER, J., LINDSEY, J., MACKAY, M., PICKWORTH, J., ROBERTSON, J. H., BRINK, C., WHITE, J. G., PROSEN, R. J. and TRUEBLOOD, K. N. (1957). *Proc. Roy. Soc.* A **242**, 228.

LUZZATI, V. (1953). *Acta Cryst.* **6**, 142.

ROBERTSON, J. M. (1935). *J. Chem. Soc.*, p.615; (1936) *ibid.*, p.1195.

ROBERTSON, J. M. and WOODWARD, I. (1937). *J. Chem. Soc.*, p.219; (1940) *ibid.*, p.36.

WOOLFSON, M. M. (1956). *Acta Cryst.* **9**, 804.

Paper 25

THE PHASE PROBLEM AND ISOMORPHOUS REPLACEMENT METHODS IN PROTEIN STRUCTURES

by R. E. DICKERSON, J. C. KENDREW and B. E. STRANDBERG

M.R.C. Unit, Cavendish Laboratory, Cambridge

INTRODUCTION

Isomorphous replacement is not a new technique of crystal structure analysis. It has been used as long ago as 1937 by one of the sponsors of this conference, Professor Robertson, on the centric structure of phthalocyanine,[1] and has been used for other centric structures since. Bokhoven, Schoone and Bijvoet[2] proposed double isomorphous replacement for acentric structures in 1949, and Harker[3] in 1956 outlined in detail a graphical means of phase angle solution. Neither, however, put multiple isomorphous replacement to a practical test.

This paper is primarily concerned with the use of this technique with proteins, and by inference with other very large acentric molecules. It was Perutz[4] who in 1953 showed that two heavy metal atoms such as silver or mercury, when attached to as much as 68,000 molecular weight of protein, caused measurable intensity changes in the diffraction pattern. Since then the method has been used for centric projections of horse haemoglobin[5] and sperm whale myoglobin,[6] an acentric projection of haemoglobin,[7] the three-dimensional structure of myoglobin to a resolution of 6 Å,[8] and just this last autumn for the structure of haemoglobin to $5\frac{1}{2}$ Å[9] and myoglobin to $2\frac{1}{2}$ Å.[10] This latter project is the most ambitious completed to date, requiring five isomorphous compounds and a total of 48,000 reflections. It is of interest to examine several features of the phase determination which arise from the nature of proteins and from the sheer size of the problem. Most of the work to be described in this paper has been carried out on sperm whale myoglobin in the course of the 2 Å work.

The ideal isomorphous replacement analysis can be subdivided into the following steps:

    I. Preparation of suitable heavy atom bearing derivatives and testing for true isomorphism, completeness of substitution, existence and extent of secondary or multiple site substitution.

II. Collection of complete sets of data from parent compound and derivatives.

III. Characterization of heavy atoms.

    A. Initial location.

    B. Refinement of parameters (positions, temperature factors, extent of substitution, scale factors).

IV. Computation of phase angles using the above data.

  V. Use of suitable phase angles to calculate the best electron density map of the molecule.

The straightforward, systematic appearance of the above list is highly deceptive. In practice, feedback from one step to a previous one is continuous. This conference is concerned primarily with the phase problem, so we will consider principally steps III, IV and V, omitting steps I and II entirely.

The Method of Phase Angle Determination

The essence of the multiple isomorphous replacement method may be illustrated briefly by Harker's phase circle diagrams. Let the vector scattering amplitudes or structure factors of the parent compound, the heavy atom alone, and the derivative compound of parent plus heavy atom be represented by the vectors $\mathbf{F}$, $\mathbf{f_H}$ and $\mathbf{F_H}$ in the complex plane. Let their real and imaginary components be A, a_H, A_H, and B, b_H, B_H respectively.* The three $\mathbf{F}$ vectors should form a closed triangle in the complex plane since:

$$\mathbf{F_H} = A_H + iB_H = (A + a_H) + i(B + b_H) = (A + iB) + (a_H + ib_H) = \mathbf{F} + \mathbf{f_H}.$$

It is assumed that both the magnitude and phase of $\mathbf{f_H}$ are calculable from known heavy atom parameters, and that the magnitudes only of $\mathbf{F}$ and $\mathbf{F_H}$ are known from intensity data. If $-\mathbf{f_H}$ is plotted on the complex plane and if two circles are drawn, one from the origin with radius $|F|$ and one from the other end of the $-\mathbf{f_H}$ vector with radius $|F_H|$, then the two intersections of the circles mark the two acceptable values of the phase angle of $\mathbf{F}$ (points U and V, Fig. 1), only one of which can be correct. A second heavy atom compound will produce two intersections with the F circle, one new one and one coinciding with one of the first pair (points V and W, Fig. 1), which must therefore be the correct solution. Further heavy atom derivatives are in theory redundant but in practice increase the accuracy of determination of phase angles considerably. It is obvious that the success of this method depends to a great extent upon the accuracy with which $\mathbf{f_H}$ can

---

* All symbols in bold face type in this paper represent vectors. Magnitudes of vectors are represented either by magnitude brackets or occasionally by the vector symbols in normal type. Centric scattering amplitudes are represented as bold face vectors.

be calculated, that is, upon the accuracy with which the positions and other parameters of the heavy atoms are known.

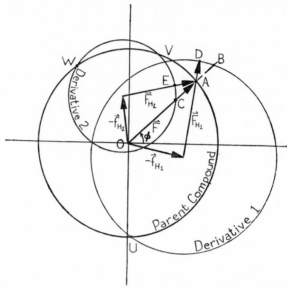

FIG. 1. Phase circle diagram of parent compound and two derivatives. Phase triangle closure complete for derivative 1 at points U and V; for derivative 2 at points V and W. For general phase angle ϕ, lack of closure errors for the two derivatives are shown as AD and AE respectively. Quantities x for mean scatter calculation are shown as OA, OB and OC for parent, derivative 1 and derivative 2 respectively.

LOCATION OF HEAVY ATOMS

For a centric structure or projection the location of heavy atoms is a relatively simple matter and can usually be achieved by the use of a difference Patterson synthesis with coefficients $(|F_H| - |F|)^2$. Errors will arise from " crossover " terms, reflections for which $\mathbf{F_H}$ and $\mathbf{F}$ have opposite signs and for which $(|F_H| + |F|)^2$ should be used. Most of these crossover terms can be detected from the magnitudes of the $\mathbf{F}$'s or even better from the change in $|F_H|$ for different degrees of partial heavy atom substitution if such data are available (Perutz et al.[4] §3; Kendrew et al.[6] §3).

Acentric structures present more of a problem. A difference Patterson as just described is, of course, invalid as a Patterson function, for $|F|$ and $|F_H|$ will have different phases and their sum or difference will, in general, not be equal to $|f_H|$. Buerger[11] has suggested a Patterson subtraction method or " ΔI synthesis " using $(F_H^2 - F^2)$ as coefficients. This yields the difference between the self-Pattersons of the derivative and parent, leaving only heavy-atom parent and heavy atom–heavy atom vector peaks. In proteins, however, the contribution of the heavy atom is so small that the *HH* (heavy–atom heavy atom) vectors are swamped by the ubiquitous *HP* (heavy atom-parent) cross vectors (Blow,[7] §4.2; Bragg and Perutz,[5] §6).

A further difficulty often arises in acentric space groups. The position of the origin in real space is not always dictated by symmetry; in space group $P2_1$ for example, location of the origin along the y axis is entirely at the discretion of the investigator. What are needed are not absolute coordinates of the heavy atom but the relative coordinates between two different heavy atoms. Kendrew overcame both difficulties with an elaborate Patterson subtraction method using data from four compounds simultaneously: parent; first heavy atom derivative; second heavy atom derivative; and double derivative of parent plus both heavy atoms. With the quantities $(F_{H_1H_2}^2 - F_{H_1}^2 - F_{H_2}^2 + F^2)$ as coefficients, all vectors are eliminated from the Patterson except the H_1H_2 vectors between different heavy atoms (Kendrew *et al.*[8] §4.c.i). Unfortunately the background in such a synthesis is high relative to the H_1H_2 peaks and is very sensitive to errors in scaling of the four sets of data.

In addition to the above Patterson methods, several correlation functions have been proposed which, although not true Patterson functions, yield peaks representing vectors between different heavy atoms. Perutz[12] proposed two such functions, one using as coefficients the quantities $[(F_{H_1}^2-F^2)(F_{H_2}^2-F^2)]$ and the other the quantities A_1A_2, where:

$$A_j = \frac{F_{H_j}^2 - F^2 - f_{H_j}^2}{2f_{H_j}}.$$

The quantity f_{H_j} is the structure factor of the heavy atom located *at the origin*. A_j is then the real component of **F** referred to heavy atom H_j as origin. Both of these functions, as he demonstrated, yield many background peaks plus a very strong dominant peak representing the heavy atom 1 — heavy atom 2 vector. Because the A_1A_2 synthesis tends to be dominated by terms of large structure factor, a modification was also used[8,10] employing $\cos \phi_1 . \cos \phi_2$ instead, where $\cos \phi_j = A_j/|F|$ and ϕ_j is the angle between the vectors f_{H_j} and **F**. The A_1A_2 and $\cos \phi_1 \cos \phi_2$ functions can be used only for single heavy atoms or centric constellations, while the other function can be used generally.

Another correlation function used by Blow for the acentric projection of haemoglobin uses the coefficients $(|F_H| - |F|)^2$. As he points out, although this " $(\Delta F)^2$ Patterson " is not a true Patterson function it does contain quite recognizable heavy atom–heavy atom vector peaks. The essence of the success of this method would seem to lie in the simplicity of the transform of the heavy atom distribution. The true heavy atom Patterson uses $f_H{}^2$ as coefficients, where f_H is the sampling at a reciprocal lattice point of the transform of the heavy atom distribution. The quantity actually used, $(|F_H| - |F|)^2$, must be equal to or less than $f_H{}^2$, and the $(\Delta F)^2$ distribution in reciprocal space may be regarded as a " damped " $f_H{}^2$ distribution. Near a nodal surface of the transform where f_H is small or zero, ΔF must be also. Where f_H is large, ΔF need not be; but if a reasonably random phase distribution can be assumed and if the heavy atom transform is sufficiently simple that each feature encompasses many reciprocal lattice points, then the general features of the original transform will be preserved. The Patterson of this transform will show the true vector distribution, although somewhat obscured by a higher background noise level.

Rossman[13] has extended this method to two heavy atom compounds, using $(|F_{H_1}| - |F_{H_2}|)^2$ as coefficients. The resulting correlation function has positive peaks representing H_1H_1 and H_2H_2 heavy atom–heavy atom vectors and negative peaks representing H_1H_2 cross vectors between different types of heavy atom. The vector peaks show not only the correct position but also the correct height and anisotropy as compared with the corresponding Fourier peaks and were sufficiently encouraging that a least squares refinement program was written based on this function which will be described later.

Earlier than either of these last two correlation methods, Sir Lawrence Bragg[14] had suggested methods of determining coordinates by observing the heavy atom transform directly and had tried these methods on sperm whale myoglobin. In space group $P2_1$, that of myoglobin, the magnitude of the structure factor of a single isotropic heavy atom depends only upon the x and z coordinates, while the phase angle depends only upon y:

$$\mathbf{f_H} = f_H \exp i\alpha_H \tag{1}$$

$$f_H = 2f \cdot t \cdot \cos 2\pi(hx + lz - \tfrac{1}{4}n) \tag{2}$$

$$\alpha_H = 2\pi(ky + \tfrac{1}{4}n) \tag{3}$$

where $n = 0$ for k even and $n = 1$ for k odd. As defined above, f_H is not purely a magnitude, but is a scalar which has the sign of the cosine in equation (2). The quantity f is the atomic scattering factor and t the temperature factor. Apart from temperature and scattering factor fall-off, f_H is the same for all reflections with the same h and l but different k. Since $\Delta F = ||F_H| - |F||$ is equal to or less than $|f_H|$, if ΔF (corrected for temperature and atomic scattering factor fall-off) is plotted as a function of h and l, reflections of various k will lie in a distribution, the envelope of which is $|2f_{000}(\genfrac{}{}{0pt}{}{\cos}{\sin})2\pi(hx + lz)|$, thus determining x and z. (k even and k odd terms are, of course, plotted separately.)

In order to determine the relative y coordinate between two heavy atoms, $\Delta y = |y_2 - y_1|$, Bragg made separate plots for each k value of cos ϕ_1 vs. cos ϕ_2 for reflections of various h and l values, where as in Perutz's correlation function ϕ_j is the angle between $\mathbf{f}_{Hj}$ and $\mathbf{F}$, except that the heavy atom is not now necessarily taken as the origin. The cosines may either be approximated as was done by Bragg, by:

$$\cos \phi_j \approx \frac{|F_{H_j}| - |F|}{f_{H_j}} \tag{4}$$

or calculated exactly from

$$\cos \phi_j = \frac{F_{H_j}^2 - F^2 - f_{H_j}^2}{2|F|f_{H_j}}. \tag{5}$$

The resulting plots were Lissajous-like figures. On the $k = 0$ plot the points fell on the straight line cos $\phi_1 = \cos \phi_2$. If for a particular k plot the points fell on the line cos $\phi_1 = - \cos \phi_2$, this would mean that $\phi_1 = \phi_2 \pm \pi$. Since from equation (3) it must follow that: $|\phi_1 - \phi_2| = |\alpha_{H_1} - \alpha_{H_2}| = 2\pi k \Delta y$, then for this k value $\Delta y = 1/2k$. In practice it was found necessary to interpolate between k values, but a value of Δy was found as accurately by this method as by the just-described Fourier series methods.

A method similar to Bragg's was tried by Dickerson on myoglobin, and may be of interest because it did *not* work. If all the magnitudes for two heavy atom compounds $|F|$, $|F_{H_1}|$, $|F_{H_2}|$, $|f_{H_1}|$ and $|f_{H_2}|$ are known or calculable, then the two quantities $|\phi_1|$ and $|\phi_2|$ may be found from equation (5). Their signs are indeterminate, but either their sum or difference will be equal to $2\pi k \Delta y$. For all reflections on a reciprocal space level with a common k value this quantity will be constant. It should have been possible on a digital computer to calculate $||\phi_1| + |\phi_2||$ and $||\phi_1| - |\phi_2||$ for each reflection in a given level, select the common angle from all the pairs of angles, and average this angle to obtain $2\pi k \Delta y$ for each k level. In practice, because $|F|$ and $|F_H|$ were usually much larger than $|f_H|$, reasonable errors* in the former quantities led to intolerable errors in the angles, making it impossible to select the proper angle from each pair. After some experimentation with weighting factors, the method was abandoned.

Two questions immediately arise from the failure of such a superficially promising method:

1. Why is it that Bragg's method does not suffer from the same difficulties?

---

*Mean experimental errors in scattering amplitudes, F, for myoglobin derivatives were 2·6 to 5·9% (2Å data). Mean errors from lack of isomorphism were around 10%.

2. If errors in $|F|$ and $|F_H|$ have such a drastic effect on the phase triangles, how can any phase determination based on them possibly be valid?

The second question will be discussed later in connection with phase determination. In answer to the first question it should be noted that Bragg's plots are also strongly affected by errors, giving very ragged Lissajous figures. It would be difficult if not impossible to deduce from one plot the phase difference between $\cos \phi_1$ and $\cos \phi_2$ which would be necessary for a value of $2\pi k \Delta y$. However, no attempt is made to extract information from any plot other than the one for which the phase difference is π and the distribution is a straight line. The visual mode of presentation assists in interpolating k values, and the use of $\cos \phi_j$ instead of ϕ_j avoids the question of the sign of ϕ_j. In sum, the Dickerson method in attempting to obtain a value of Δy from each k layer tries to do too much in the face of too great errors; the Bragg method settles for fewer determinations of Δy and accepts the fact of the errors, choosing a mode of presentation which minimizes their effect.

REFINEMENT OF HEAVY ATOM PARAMETERS

Once the heavy atoms have been located, their parameters must be refined as well as possible, these parameters being: (a) scale factor of heavy atom data relative to parent compound, (b) heavy atom coordinates, (c) temperature factor (isotropic or anisotropic), and (d) extent of substitution or effective atomic number.

Refinement using acentric data is difficult because one usually has no information about phases, and without this information it is difficult to find an experimental quantity with which to compare a calculated $\mathbf{f}_H$. With centric data there is only a sign ambiguity in the calculation of

$$|f_{H\text{obs}}| = \left| \, |F_H| \pm |F| \, \right|.$$

Analytical least squares methods are still impossible without tentative sign information but trial and error least squares refinement is both possible and practical.

In the method developed by Hart[15] for the centric $h0l$ projection of space group $P2_1$ the function chosen for minimization is:

$$E = \sum_n (\Delta F_{\text{calc}} - \Delta F_{\text{obs}})^2$$

$$= \sum_n \left(Z.\hat{f}_n.\exp\left[-B\frac{\sin^2\theta}{\lambda^2} \right] \cos 2\pi(hx + lz) \pm |F| \pm k|F_H| \right)^2. \quad (6)$$

The subscript n refers to a given $h0l$ reflection, $\hat{f}$ is a unitary scattering factor and Z is the effective atomic number. The heavy group is assumed to be a single isotropic atom, resulting in only five parameters to be refined: k, x, z, B and Z.

In the course of a cycle of refinement carried out on EDSAC II Hart varies each parameter alone in turn by $+2$, $+1$, -1 and -2 increments, the increments being specified at the beginning of the first cycle. Twenty-one different E values are found for the various combinations of parameters and the optimum shifts in the five parameters are computed by a method of steepest descents. When all parameters have been refined to within the intervals specified these intervals are quartered and refinement is continued without intermission. With only five parameters the rate of convergence is quite satisfactory, but there are obvious limitations to this method with several atoms both from the standpoint of increased time per cycle and slower convergence.

The correct values of the two unknown signs in equation (6) are assumed to be those which yield the smallest value of $|\Delta F_{calc} - \Delta F_{obs}|$. In the process of refinement a tentative sign determination is thus made for F and F_H. If several derivatives are used, a cross check on signs of F is possible, and the solution of the centric projection results more or less as a by-product of the refinement. In space group $P2_1$ Hart's method leaves unrefined the y coordinates, which affect only the acentric reflections. These can be refined in the course of phase determination using all heavy atom compounds at once, as will be described later.

Rossman[13] has approached the refinement problem in an entirely different manner. As has been mentioned, he calculated a correlation function using as coefficients the quantities $(|F_{H_2}| - |F_{H_1}|)^2$ and observed that positions, heights and shapes of the peaks were virtually identical with those to be expected from a true difference Patterson synthesis using $(\mathbf{f}_{H_2} - \mathbf{f}_{H_1})^2$ coefficients. With this reassurance he has developed an analytical least squares refinement program which minimizes the quantity:

$$E = \sum_n \epsilon_n^2 = \sum_n w[(|F_{H_2}| - k|F_{H_1}|)^2 - (\mathbf{f}_{H_2} - \mathbf{f}_{H_1})^2]^2. \qquad (7)$$

A weighting factor is used which treats preferentially those reflections for which ϵ_n should be zero, or for which $\mathbf{F}_{H_2}$ and $\mathbf{F}_{H_1}$ are most nearly co-linear.

This method, being three-dimensional, permits anisotropic temperature refinement. The rate of convergence to good minima is satisfactory and the final coordinates, temperature factors and scale factors agree well with Hart two-dimensional refinement. The effective atomic numbers tend to be around 20% greater than found by Hart on centric data, but too few comparisons have been made to enable any conclusions to be drawn other than to note that there is some indication from the final electron density maps that Rossman's values may be better than Hart's.

COMPUTATION OF PHASE ANGLES

A graphical phase solution is quite satisfactory for small structures and was even used for 6 Å myoglobin with 300 acentric reflections. But if the method is to be used for several thousand reflections, some way must be found to make the process automatic using a computer. Three questions arise:

1. What analytical function can one use to find the best point of inter-section of the phase circles?
2. How should experimental errors and differences in reliability of sets of data be handled?
3. Granting the imperfection of any real phase determination, how can one be sure of choosing the proper phase angle to yield the best possible electron density map, and should poorly determined reflections be omitted or given fractional weight?

One method of choosing the best phase angle would be to find the direction of the radial line along which the intesections with the phase circles lie most closely together. This criterion was incorporated into a phase program by Hilary Muirhead and tried with the 5·5 Å haemoglobin data. In this method, for a given angle the mean radial intersection distance is first found, the mean being taken treating all compounds alike (in Fig. 1 this mean intersection distance is $\frac{1}{3}(OC + OA + OB) = \bar{x}$). The mean scatter is then calculated $(\frac{1}{3}(|OC - \bar{x}| + |OA - \bar{x}| + |OB - \bar{x}|)$ in Fig. 1) and the best phase angle taken as that with the least mean scatter. The computation time on EDSAC II was about seven and one-half seconds per reflection.

Blow and Crick[16] have shown that it is legitimate to regard errors from all sources—experiment, lack of isomorphism, incomplete or imperfect refinement—as residing in the magnitude F_H and as representing a failure of the phase triangle to close exactly on the F_H side. Since the heavy atom scattering amplitude vector is fixed and known, if any arbitrary phase angle is selected for the parent compound then the third side of the phase triangle will be given by:

$$D_{(\phi)}^2 = F^2 + f_H^2 + 2|F||f_H|\cos(\phi - \alpha_H) \qquad (8)$$

where α_H is the phase of the heavy atom vector f_H, and $(\phi - \alpha_H)$ is therefore the angle between the vectors F and f_H (not between F and $-f_H$ as drawn on the phase circle diagram). The "lack of closure" error is then $||F_H| - |D_{H(\phi)}|| = \epsilon_{H(\phi)}$. In Fig. 1 these quantities are shown as AD and AE. If the distribution of errors may be considered as Gaussian then the probability that a given phase angle is correct based on one heavy atom compound alone is:

$$P_{H(\phi)} \propto \exp(-\epsilon_{H(\phi)}^2/2E_H^2). \tag{9}$$

The quantity E_H is the r.m.s. error in the heavy atom compound data, and may either be estimated, or calculated from a centric projection, if available, from the equation:

$$E_H^2 = \langle(\Delta F_{obs} - \Delta F_{calc})^2\rangle_{avg} = \langle(||F_H| - |F|| - |f_H|)^2\rangle_{avg}. \tag{10}$$

For several heavy atom compounds, j, the total probability of a given angle ϕ being correct is:

$$P_{(\phi)} \propto \exp(-\sum_j \epsilon_{j(\phi)}^2/2E_j^2). \tag{11}$$

The most probable phase angle ϕ_{max} is therefore that angle for which the following quantity is a minimum:

$$\mathscr{E}_{(\phi)} = \sum_j w_j^1(F_{H_j} - D_{H_j(\phi)})^2 \tag{12}$$

with the weighting factor $w_j^1 = 1/E_j^2$. This criterion was used by Roger Hart in a second trial phase program, with unit weighting factors. The computation time by this method per reflection on EDSAC II was about three seconds.

The most probable phase, as Blow and Crick have shown, is not necessarily the best one to use in a Fourier synthesis. The electron density calculated using $|F|$ and ϕ_{max}, although the *most probable* electron density, will not be the one statistically the *most error-free*. If one desires the synthesis with the least mean square error in electron density over the entire unit cell, then the proper vector coefficient in the Fourier synthesis is not $\mathbf{F}_{max}$ with components $(|F|, \phi_{max})$, but rather the vector to the center of gravity of the probability distribution. To show this let us consider the error in electron density arising from errors in one reflection and its Friedel conjugate. If the value of the coefficient used in the synthesis is $\mathbf{F}_s$ and if the true value is $\mathbf{F}_t$, then the mean square error over the entire unit cell from this reflection is

$$\langle\Delta\rho\rangle^2 = \frac{2}{V^2}(\mathbf{F}_s - \mathbf{F}_t)^2. \tag{13}*$$

All that is known about $\mathbf{F}_t$ is that it is a vector in the complex plane of magnitude $|F|$ and with a probability P_ϕ of having a phase angle ϕ. Alternatively, one can say that with this probability the vector $\mathbf{F}_t$ is given by $\mathbf{F}_t = |F|\mathbf{r}_\phi$, where $\mathbf{r}_\phi$ is a *unit* vector in the direction ϕ, so that

$$\mathbf{r}_\phi = \cos\phi + i\sin\phi.$$

Then equation (13) becomes:

$$\langle\Delta\rho\rangle^2 = \frac{2}{V^2}\int_{\mathbf{r}_\phi}(\mathbf{F}_s - |F|\mathbf{r}_\phi)^2 P_{(\phi)}d\mathbf{r}_\phi. \tag{14}$$

---

*The symbol $\langle\Delta\rho\rangle^2$ is here used as a convention representing the quantity $\langle(\Delta\rho)^2\rangle$, the mean of the square of the difference in ρ.

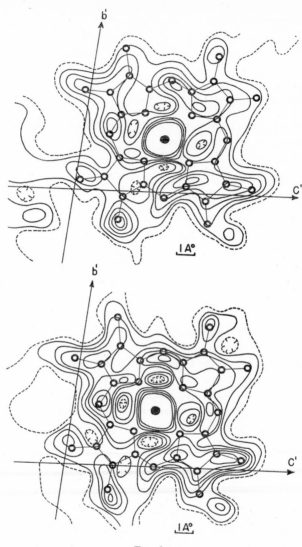

FIG. 2

FIG. 2. Sections through myoglobin electron density maps in the plane of the haem group. Circles represent positions of atoms in an ideal porphyrin ring. Inner contours of the iron atom are omitted.

(a) Most probable synthesis using coefficients ($|F|, \phi_{max}$).

(b) Least error synthesis using coefficients ($m|F|, \phi_{best}$) and sharpened so as to have the same average radial intensity fall-off as the previous synthesis. Note the slightly greater asymmetry in Fig. 2a.

Minimizing this quantity with respect to phase angle or directional vector $\mathbf{r}_\phi$, one obtains the following:

$$\frac{d\langle\Delta\rho\rangle^2}{d\mathbf{r}_\phi} = -\frac{4\,|\,F\,|}{V^2}\int_{\mathbf{r}_\phi}(\mathbf{F}_s - |\,F\,|\,\mathbf{r}_\phi)P_{(\phi)}d\mathbf{r}_\phi = 0 \tag{15}$$

$$\mathbf{F}_{s(\text{best})} = \int_{\mathbf{r}_\phi}P_{(\phi)}\,|\,F\,|\,\mathbf{r}_\phi d\mathbf{r}_\phi\Big/\int_{\mathbf{r}_\phi}P_{(\phi)}d\mathbf{r}_\phi = m\,|\,F\,|\,e^{i\phi_{\text{best}}}.$$

Equation (15) is just the expression for the centre of gravity of the probability distribution, with polar coordinates $(m\,|\,F\,|, \phi_{\text{best}})$.

The phase program finally used for the 2 Å myoglobin work is one, programmed by the author,[17] in which the above treatment of errors is taken into account. For a given reflection the total probability P_i is first computed in five degree intervals around the phase circle at angles β_i. The components (m, ϕ_{best}) of the centre of gravity of the probability distribution around a *unit* radius circle are calculated from:

$$m\cos\phi_{\text{best}} = \frac{\sum_i P_i\cos\beta_i}{\sum_i P_i}$$

$$\tag{16}$$

$$m\sin\phi_{\text{best}} = \frac{\sum_i P_i\sin\beta_i}{\sum_i P_i}.$$

The quantity m is called the " figure of merit " and is the mean value of the cosine of the error in phase angle for the reflection. This follows at once from equation (16) if the origin axis is taken along the direction of the centre of gravity, making β_i the error in phase angle. At the same time that m and ϕ_{best} are being calculated, a record is kept of the most probable phase angle ϕ_{max}. Quantities punched out on paper tape, aside from plane identification numbers, are $|\,F\,|$, ϕ_{max}, $m\,|\,F\,|$, ϕ_{best} and m. The phase output tape can be used directly as Fourier synthesis input for either a " most probable Fourier " or a " best Fourier " in the Blow and Crick sense. The computing and output time required with this program is about $3\frac{1}{2}$ to 4 seconds per reflection. The mean square error in electron density from all reflections is directly calculable from the figure of merit:

$$\langle\Delta\rho\rangle^2 = \frac{2}{V^2}\sum_0^\infty\sum_{-\infty}^\infty\sum_{-\infty}^\infty F_{hkl}^2(1 - m_{hkl}^2) \tag{17}$$

$$h \qquad k \qquad l$$

(Dickerson *et al.*,[17]; Blow and Crick[16]).

Comparisons between the three methods: minimum scatter, maximum probability and minimum error showed about what one would expect from an examination of the phase circle diagrams. For well-determined reflections all three, of course, give the same answer, usually to within five degrees. For poor reflections the first two methods were in general agreement, and there appeared to be no particular advantage, theoretical or practical, in the minimum scatter method. The choice lay between maximum probability and minimum error, and the arguments of Blow and Crick were convincing in favour of the latter method.

ALTERNATE REFINEMENT OF PHASE ANGLES AND HEAVY ATOM PARAMETERS

As was mentioned in connection with the Hart refinements, in the absence of preliminary phase angle information there is no way of refining parameters which influence only acentric reflections, such as relative y coordinates. But once rough phases have been found they can be used to obtain refined parameters, which can then be used to calculate better phases and the process continued until the desired degree of convergence is reached.

The most probable phase angle has been shown to be that one which minimizes the sum of errors $\mathscr{E}_{(\phi)}$ of equation (12). A similar error sum taken over all reflections for a given heavy atom derivative H_j provides a function whose minimization with respect to the heavy atom parameters will yield the optimum values of these parameters:

$$\mathscr{E}_{H_j} = \sum_n w_n (F_{H_{j,n}} - D_{H_{j,n}})^2. \tag{18}$$

All parameters of a given heavy atom derivative could in principle be refined simultaneously by least squares by solving the set of normal equations:

$$\sum_i (\sum_n w_n (\partial D_{H_j}/\partial \psi_i)(\partial D_{H_j}/\partial \psi_k)) \Delta \psi_k = \sum_n w_n (\partial D_{H_j}/\partial \psi_k)(F_{H_j} - D_{Hj}) \tag{19}$$

where subscripts i and k denumerate the individual parameters ψ_k, ψ_i of heavy atom j. In practice, with myoglobin it was felt that the Hart $h0l$ refinement values were trustworthy, and only y coordinates were refined, using the simplified expression valid for a single heavy atom:

$$\Delta y_j = \frac{\sum\limits_n w_n (\partial D_{H_j}/\partial y_j)(F_{H_j} - D_{H_j})}{\sum\limits_n w_n (\partial D_{H_j}/\partial y_j)^2}. \tag{20}$$

The extra time required in the phase determination program to calculate and sum the partial derivatives was entirely negligible, but since one complete 2 Å phase determination for 9600 reflections required twelve hours of computer time, refinement was carried out on randomly selected tenths of the data. Ten cycles of refinement on different samples of data were more than adequate.

At this point it may be asked why this refinement succeeds so well, and indeed why phase determination itself is possible if errors are so severe that the already mentioned method of calculating relative y's by solving phase triangles fails. The answer lies in the large number of heavy atom derivatives used simultaneously in calculating trial phase angles. In the relative y method derivatives were taken two at a time, and redundancy of data was insufficient to overcome the intrinsic errors in the data. A test was made on the 6 Å myoglobin data, determining phases using in succession all five, four, three and the minimum of two derivatives. Assuming the five-derivative phases to be, if not correct, at least the best set, a count was made of the percentage of phases in the other cases which were calculated to within plus or minus twenty degrees of the five-derivative phases. Using four derivatives, 93% of the phases were in agreement; using combinations of three derivatives gave only 70–83% agreements; while the two-derivative phases were much worse yet, only half being within $\pm$ 20° of the 5-derivative values. Thus the reliability of phase determination seems to be very rapidly enhanced by the use of more derivatives, up to about four to six heavy atom compounds.*

CALCULATION OF THE BEST ELECTRON DENSITY MAP

As a test of the Blow–Crick centroid method, several Fourier syntheses were calculated for a restricted part of the unit cell, using both $\mathbf{F}_{obs} = (\mid F \mid, \phi_{max})$ and $\mathbf{F}_{best} = (m \mid F \mid, \phi_{best})$ as coefficients and using several sharpening factors. As would be expected, the mean value of the figure of merit from the phase program decreased with increasing $\sin \theta$, reflecting the increased uncertainty in far-out reflections which contribute to fine details in the Fourier synthesis. At the 2 Å limit of the data the mean figure of merit was 0·45, as compared with nearly 0·90 for the innermost reflections. A Wilson-like plot of $\ln \overline{m}$ vs. $\sin^2\theta$ showed that the figure of merit behaved like an artificial temperature factor: $\exp(-B\sin^2\theta/\lambda^2)$, where $B = 14\cdot5$. Since this suppression of data occurred precisely in the region of reciprocal space from which new structural information would arise, it was considered worthwhile to calculate an F_{best} synthesis in which an artificial sharpening factor would exactly compensate for the mean figure of merit fall-off. This synthesis would then differ from the F_{obs} synthesis in that dependable reflections would be enhanced and undependable ones suppressed, with the

---

*M. Rossmann and D. M. Blow have recently conducted a series of experiments which seem to indicate that haemoglobin could have been solved with only two compounds, and that the large uncertainties in phase angle found here may affect the Fourier synthesis much less than would be expected.

R

overall intensity fall-off remaining unchanged. Syntheses were also calculated using F_{obs} and F_{best} coefficients with all radial fall-off removed and hence with essentially point atoms.

It was found that the damping effect of the figure of merit produced an undesirable loss of detail in the simple F_{best} synthesis as compared with the F_{obs} map. The F_{best} synthesis when sharpened to the level of F_{obs} appeared to be slightly better than it. Overall resolution of peaks was somewhat better, and from examination of areas of known structure such as polypeptide chain segments and haem groups this improvement was felt to be real and not an artifact of sharpening. The ultra-sharpened syntheses were definitely inferior and showed diffraction ripples about the iron atom of the haem group. Thus the F_{best} synthesis with radial fall-off due to the figure of merit removed was considered to be the most satisfactory and was finally used for the full electron density map. These conclusions were confirmed independently by the work of Perutz *et al.* on haemoglobin. A similar comparison of " most probable " and " least error " Fourier syntheses was made for $5\frac{1}{2}$ Å haemoglobin,[9] and again the synthesis using values of F_{best} from the centroid method was felt to be more satisfactory.

SUMMARY

Some of the problems inherent in the determination of phases by multiple isomorphous replacement for very large acentric structures have been discussed, and a concrete application made to the protein myoglobin. Various means of determining and refining heavy atom parameters have been considered, and the importance of obtaining the best possible values of these parameters emphasized.

The effect of the number of heavy atom derivatives used upon the accuracy of phase determination has been examined, and the conclusion reached that four to six derivatives seem to be a satisfactory number in practice.

The theoretical work of Blow and Crick on the proper treatment of errors has been put to a test, and has been found to yield slightly better results in terms of final electron density maps than a more conventional treatment. A convenient adaptation of the centre of gravity method for a digital computer has been described, which proved very satisfactory. Means have been described of calculating the errors in phase determination and also the mean errors in electron density in the final map, furnishing an estimate of the confidence which can be placed in the structural features found on the map.

Throughout the entire course of the work on myoglobin, care was taken to obtain the most accurate data possible, to refine heavy atom parameters to the limit of the data, and to treat the data in such a way as to obtain the best possible electron density map. In all fairness it should be admitted that there are cases in which such treatment may not be necessary. In particular, when quite a bit of structural information is known in advance, and when the final map is to be used only as the beginning point of a trial and error refinement with the known model fitted to features of the map, then the differences between an F_{obs} synthesis and an F_{best} synthesis may not be significant. However, particularly in protein work where one has little structural information against which to check observed features of the map, and when one may not in the initial stages be working to atomic resolution, then artifacts arising from improper treatment of errors which in other circumstances would be recognized and rejected may give rise to mistakes in interpretation of the results. In general, the more complex the molecule and the greater the credence to be placed in the electron density map without chemical confirmation, the greater is the importance of a proper treatment of errors.

REFERENCES

1. ROBERTSON, J. M. (1936). *J. Chem. Soc.* 1195.
   ROBERTSON, J. M. and WOODWARD, I. (1937). *J. Chem. Soc.* 219.
2. BOKHOVEN, C., SCHOONE, J. C. and BIJVOET, J. M. (1949). *Proc. Acad. Sci. Amst.* **52,** 120; (1951). *Acta Cryst.* **4,** 275.
3. HARKER, DAVID (1956). *Acta Cryst.* **9,** 1.
4. GREEN, D. W., INGRAM, V. M. and PERUTZ, M. F. (1954). *Proc. Roy. Soc.* A **225,** 287.
5. BRAGG, Sir LAWRENCE and PERUTZ, M. F. (1954). *Proc. Roy. Soc.* A **225,** 315.
6. BLUHM, M. M., BODO, G., DINTZIS, H. M. and KENDREW, J. C. (1958). *Proc. Roy. Soc.* A **246,** 369.
7. BLOW, D. M. (1958). *Proc. Roy. Soc.* A **247,** 302.
8. BODO, G., DINTZIS, H. M., KENDREW, J. C. and WYCKOFF, H. (1959). *Proc. Roy. Soc.* A **253,** 70.
9. PERUTZ, M. F., ROSSMANN, M. G., CULLIS, A. F., MUIRHEAD, H., WILL, G. and NORTH, A. C. T. (1960). *Nature* **185,** 416.
10. KENDREW, J. C., DICKERSON, R. E., STRANDBERG, B. E., HART, R. G., DAVIES, D. R., PHILLIPS, D. C. and SHORE, V. C. (1960). *Nature* **185,** 422.
11. BUERGER, M. J. (1942). *Proc. Nat. Acad. Sci., U.S.* **28,** 281.
12. PERUTZ, M. F. (1956). *Acta Cryst.* **9,** 867.
13. ROSSMANN, M. G. (1960). *Acta Cryst.* **13,** 221.
14. BRAGG, Sir LAWRWNCE (1958). *Acta Cryst.* **11,** 70.
15. HART, R. G., DICKERSON, R. E. and KENDREW, J. C. *Acta Cryst.* (to be published).
16. BLOW, D. M. and CRICK, F. H. C. (1959). *Acta Cryst.* **12,** 794.
17. DICKERSON, R. E., STRANDBERG, B. E. and KENDREW, J. C. *Acta Cryst.* (to be published).

Paper 26

APPLICATION OF
THE BUERGER MINIMUM FUNCTION
TO PROTEIN STRUCTURES

by MICHAEL G. ROSSMANN,

Medical Research Council Unit for Molecular Biology,
Cavendish Laboratory, Cambridge, England

ABSTRACT

The theory of the Buerger Minimum Function applied to a series of isomorphous protein heavy atom derivatives is developed for space group $P2$. Buerger's weighting scheme for matching images of different strengths is generalized to take into account the difference in the profile of images produced by heavy atoms of different isotropic, or even anisotropic, shape. The minimum conditions for the solution of the phase problem for a series of isomorphous protein compounds is investigated. Results of the application of the minimum function on the $5 \cdot 5\text{Å}$ horse haemoglobin data are compared with the electron density distribution calculated according to standard isomorphous replacement techniques. The minimum function is also used to find the iron containing haem groups in an analysis of anomalous dispersion data.

Introduction

Perutz et al. (1960) have recently used the isomorphous replacement technique to solve the tertiary structure of horse haemoglobin at $5 \cdot 5\text{Å}$ resolution. A number of derivatives of haemoglobin were prepared each with one or more independent heavy atom groups. The relative position of these groups, their shape and size were determined by an analysis of the small differences in the structure amplitudes of the different compounds (Perutz, 1956; Rossmann, 1960a). Each heavy atom group was regarded as being defined by ten parameters; three positional parameters, six shape parameters, and one which defines the amount of substitution. The ten parameters per atom were then used to calculate the heavy atom structure factor contribution for each reflection and combined with the corresponding observed structure factors in a phase diagram (Bijvoet, 1954; Harker, 1956). However, due to lack of isomorphism and experimental inaccuracies there is difficulty in deriving the exact phase from such a diagram. Blow and Crick (1959) developed a technique of expressing this uncertainty by suitably weighting the Fourier terms. Nevertheless it was felt desirable to find an alternative method independent of the large errors inherent in each individual phase diagram, and one which would give some indication in real space of the significance of the errors introduced due to lack of isomorphism.

The solution to most crystallographic problems may in general, be found both in vector and in reciprocal space. Hence the Buerger minimum function (Buerger, 1950 and 1951) appeared to be a good candidate for providing such an alternative method of finding the structure.

The determination of the common structure from a series of
difference Pattersons

The difference Patterson with $(F_H^2 - F^2)$ coefficients (Buerger 1942; Donnay and Buerger 1950), representing the difference in the Pattersons of the heavy atom containing protein (structure factors F_H) and the unsubstituted protein (structure factors F), will contain only vectors between the heavy atoms themselves (let these be called HH) and vectors between the heavy atoms and the protein (let us call these HP). Figure 1 shows the

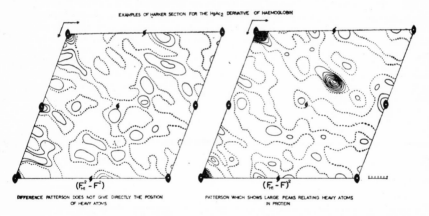

EXAMPLES OF HARKER SECTION FOR THE HgAc₂ DERIVATIVE OF HAEMOGLOBIN

$(F_H^2 - F^2)$

$(F_H - F)^2$

DIFFERENCE PATTERSON DOES NOT GIVE DIRECTLY THE POSITION OF HEAVY ATOMS

PATTERSON WHICH SHOWS LARGE PEAKS RELATING HEAVY ATOMS IN PROTEIN

FIG. 1. Comparison of the $(F^2{}_H - F^2)$ and $(\,|\,F_H\,|\,-\,|\,F\,|\,)^2$ Pattersons for the HgAc₂ haemoglobin derivative.

Harker section for the " HgAc₂" compound of horse haemoglobin compared to an $(\,|\,F_H\,|\,-\,|\,F\,|\,)^2$ synthesis. The latter can be shown to have strong peaks in the HH positions (Blow, 1958; Rossmann, 1960). It is apparent that the HP contribution virtually swamps the HH vectors in haemoglobin at 5·5 Å resolution, but the examples given in this paper will show that the minimum function can nevertheless deconvolute the HP vectors.

At 5·5 Å resolution the significant feature of a protein structure is likely to be the folded polypeptide chain running linearly through the molecule.

Let us, therefore, simplify the structure of a protein at this resolution not into point atoms, but into lines. Horse haemoglobin crystallizes in space group $C2$; let us simplify the argument by using space group $P2$. The discussion will be illustrated by the two-dimensional outline of a horse which is to represent the asymmetric unit of horse haemoglobin. The outline is to be regarded as having finite density, while everywhere else has zero density.

The complete structure of one unit cell in three isomorphous compounds is shown in Fig. 2. These three compounds are (a) the unsubstituted protein (structure F); (b) the derivative with heavy atoms in the front hoof (structure F_{H1}); (c) the derivative with heavy atoms in the hind hoofs (structure F_{H2}); Fig. 3 shows the two difference Pattersons with $(F^2_{H1} - F^2)$

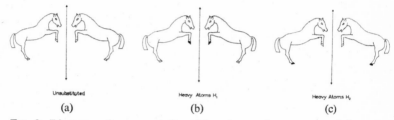

Unsubstituted	Heavy Atoms H₁	Heavy Atoms H₂
(a)	(b)	(c)

FIG. 2. Diagrammatic representation of three isomorphous compounds in space group $P2$. Full hoofs indicate " heavy atoms."

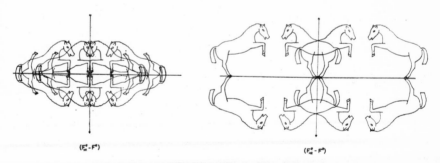

$(F^2_{H1} - F^2)$ $(F^2_{H2} - F^2)$

FIG. 3. Difference Pattersons $(F^2_{H1} - F^2)$ and $(F^2_{H2} - F^2)$.

and with $(F^2_{H2} - F^2)$ coefficients. There Pattersons represent all the vectors which can be drawn from the heavy atom positions to the remaining structure, and hence outline the shape of the horses in the cell with each heavy atom at the origin in turn, plus the centrosymmetrically related structure. The two Pattersons in Fig. 3 can be constructed from experimental data only. Our problem is to find the structure from these Pattersons, given the heavy atom-positions, shapes and weights. It will now be shown that the Buerger minimum function can be used for this purpose.

Let us take a copy of the $(F^2_{H1} - F^2)$ Patterson and translate it relative to the original Patterson through the vector distance between $H1$ and its symmetrically related equivalent atom. Then the images of the structure in these two atoms come in coincidence. This translation and superposition is shown in Fig. 4 which marks the coincident images in heavy outline. A new figure can be constructed which takes whatever density is the lower of the two superimposed maps. Hence only when images are in coincidence will the new density be other than zero. Figures 5a and 5b show the minimum function obtained by translating and superimposing the Pattersons of Fig. 3 in this fashion. The two maps of Fig. 5a and b can again be translated and

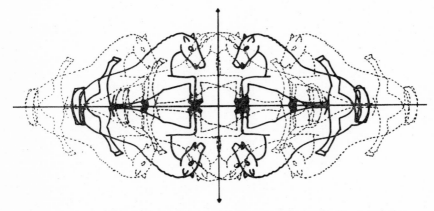

FIG. 4. Superpositions of the $(F^2_{H1} - F^2)$ Patterson on itself after translation through the vector distance between the symmetry related Hl atoms. Coincident images are shown in heavy outline.

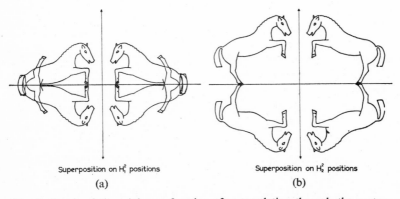

Superposition on H^2_1 positions

(a)

Superposition on H^2_2 positions

(b)

FIG. 5. Result of the minimum function after translating through the vector distance between two symmetry related heavy atoms (a) left for atom $H1$ (b) right for atom $H2$.

superimposed relative to each other through the difference in the y-coordinates (measured parallel to the two-fold axis) between the heavy atoms $H1$ and $H2$. If we now take the minimum between these two maps we may obtain either the true structure or its enantiomorph according to whether this last translation was " up " or " down " the two fold axis (Fig. 6). Unless the absolute configuration of the heavy atoms is known, it is impossible to know which of the two results shown in Fig. 6 represents the true absolute configuration of the original structure.

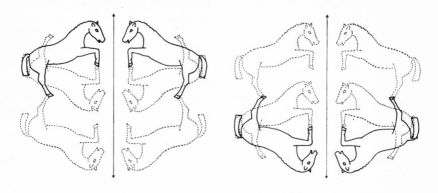

True structure   Enantiomorph of true structure

FIG. 6. Translation and superposition of diagrams in Fig. 5 through plus or minus the distance between $H1$ and $H2$ measured parallel to the twofold axis. Coincident images are shown in heavy outline.

If one or more other derivatives are available, then each may be taken to the stage represented in Fig. 5 and finally combined with the result depicted in Fig. 6. Each derivative will produce chance coincidences in different positions, causing erroneous high density. Since we are taking a minimum on each superposition these high densities will be removed unless they superimpose on another chance high density. Thus successive heavy atom derivatives must clarify the final image of the structure, unless lack of isomorphism causes distortions of the image in different compounds.

The image strength

So far the discussion has been based on the assumption that each image has the same height and profile. If heavy atoms $H1$ and $H2$ have different atomic numbers, say Z_{H1} and Z_{H2}, then the " strength " of their images will be very approximately PZ_{H1} and PZ_{H2}. Thus when matching these images their densities should be multiplied by $1/Z_{H1}$ and $1/Z_{H2}$ respectively (Buerger, 1959). The implicit assumption of this weighting system is that each image has the same shape and that their maximum heights are proportional to the number of electrons in the image producing heavy atom. However, the heavy atoms in haemoglobin had not only different shapes (i.e. different isotropic temperature factors), but were grossly anisotropic. For instance, one of the heavy atom groups employed for haemoglobin is dimercury acetate (DMA) which has two unresolved mercury atoms 3·5 Å apart.

The results shown in this paper are based on empirical isotropic weights proportional to the square root of the peak heights in the $(|F_H| - |F|)^2$ function. It is hoped soon to have some results based on the theoretical weighting scheme which will now be described.

Let us assume that the density of the nth heavy atom may be approximated by $\rho_n = A_n e^{-p_n r^2}$, where A_n is the maximum density, r is the distance from the atomic centre and p_n is a constant that determines its shape. We wish to choose a weighting factor w_n which will cause this atom to approximate as closely as possible to a " standard atom " given by $\rho = A e^{-p r^2}$. Hence, if E is the sum of the squares of the difference in densities between these two atoms,

$$E = \int_0^\infty (A e^{-p r^2} - w_n A_n e^{-p_n r^2})^2 dr$$

$$= \frac{A^2}{2}\sqrt{\frac{\pi}{2p}} - A A_n w_n \sqrt{\frac{\pi}{p+p_n}} + \frac{A_n^2 w_n^2}{2}\sqrt{\frac{\pi}{2p_n}}.$$

We wish to find the value of w_n for which E is a minimum, that is when

$$\frac{\partial E}{\partial w_n} = 0.$$

Thus

$$w_n = \frac{A}{A_n}\sqrt{\frac{2p_n}{p+p_n}}.$$

Now

$$Z_n = 2\int_0^\infty A_n e^{-p_n r^2} dr = A_n \sqrt{\frac{\pi}{p_n}},$$

$$\therefore w_n = \frac{Z}{Z_n}\sqrt{\frac{2p}{p+p_n}}. \tag{1}$$

Hence when all heavy atoms have the same isotropic shape

$$(p = p_1 = p_2 = \ldots = p_n),$$

we have the special case when Buerger's simple method of weighting is applicable, for now from (1) $w_n \propto 1/Z_n$.

This theory can be extended to cover images produced by anisotropic heavy atoms. We have to find the value of p_n which an isotropic atom would require to give the same profile as the anisotropic atom in a direction given by the line joining the point $(x_1x_2x_3)$ on the image to the centre of the heavy atom. Let $(x_1x_2x_3)$ be the coordinates of this point measured from the heavy atom along the direction of the crystal unit cell edges. We shall write $p_n(x_i)$ to signify that p_n changes according to the point on the image under consideration.

The density of the heavy atom may be represented by

$$\rho = A \exp\left[-\sum_{i=1}^{3} \sum_{j=1}^{3} \alpha_{ij} x_i x_j \right]$$

where α_{ij} are six constants determined by the atom's shape.

It can be shown that

$$p_n(x_i) = \frac{\sum\limits_{i=1}^{3} \sum\limits_{j=1}^{3} \alpha_{ij} x_i x_j}{\sum\limits_{i=1}^{3} \sum\limits_{j=1}^{3} \cos \theta_{ij} x_i x_j} . \tag{2}$$

Here θ_{ij} represents the angle between the i and j axes.

The procedure to be adopted in weighting an image is to change the origin to the heavy atom producing the image. Then the value of $p_n(x_i)$ is calculated from (2) and this in turn gives the weight $w_n(x_i)$ from (1). Finally the density at the point (x_i) is multiplied by $w_n(x_i)$ before comparison with another image. In order to apply this procedure it is necessary to know the constants α_{ij} but these can be calculated by making a least squares fit between the density given by

$$\rho = A \exp\left[-\sum_{i=1}^{3} \sum_{j=1}^{3} \alpha_{ij} x_i x_j \right]$$

and as determined from a three-dimensional Fourier summation representing the heavy atoms in the protein unit cell, that is

$$\rho = \frac{1}{V} \sum_{h_1}^{\text{cut off}} \sum_{h_2} \sum_{h_3} \left\{ \, |F(h_i)| \, \exp 2\pi_i \sum_{i=1}^{3} h_i x_i \right\}.$$

$F(h_i)$ can be calculated when the ten parameters per heavy atom have been found (Rossmann 1960a).

The minimum conditions required for solution

Let us consider the case when the heavy atoms $H1$ and $H2$ (Fig. 2) are in the same compound. The difference Patterson of this compound will then be the sum of both the Pattersons shown in Fig. 3. By superposition of this composite Patterson first after translation through the vector distance between the two $H1$ atoms and then after translation through the vector distance between the two $H2$ atoms the two diagrams shown in Fig. 5 can be recovered. Essentially the effect of dealing with the sum of the two Pattersons in Fig. 3, instead of each independently, is simply to introduce more " noise " due to a greater chance of image overlap. The true structure, or its enantiomorph, may then be found (see Fig. 6) as shown previously. While only one atom has been utilized the diagram remains centric. Thus the effective space group of each of the diagrams in Fig. 5 is $P2/m$ with the mirror plane perpendicular to the two fold axis and containing the heavy atoms. This would be the space group if only the single heavy atoms $H1$ or $H2$ were in the unit cell by themselves. The combination of the two diagrams in Fig. 5 makes use of the two heavy atoms $H1$ and $H2$ together. These, even by themselves, do not possess a centre of symmetry, and thus the structure, which cannot possess a centre of symmetry, can be solved.

The results may be summarized as follows: To solve the phase problem (i) It is necessary to have either three isomorphous compounds, or (ii) Only two isomorphous compounds are required provided the heavy atoms have a non-centric arrangement. Blow and Rossmann (1960) have investigated the second condition in relationship to the belief that at least three independent compounds (Harker 1956) are always required in order to solve the phase problem completely in reciprocal space.

The second condition implies that given only two isomorphous compounds, at least three roughly equal, independent, heavy atom sites are required for any protein crystallizing in $P1$, at least two sites must be found for any protein crystallizing in a monoclinic space group, while only one heavy atom is necessary for an orthorhombic space group.

The finite volume of each image

In all our considerations so far we have considered the horses to be lines of high density surrounded by no density. Under these conditions the minimum function is able to remove all " unwanted " images. If, however, we regard the horses as being lines of zero density surrounded by plateaux of high ground, then the Patterson will have zero density only in the image positions. Hence the minimum function would select not only the coincident images but all other images, as every image has zero density, while all other ground is higher. However, the maximum function would now lead us to select only the coincident images, for only in their position would the density be zero in both superimposed maps.

In practice the volume, v, of the required structure is neither negligibly small (the conditions required by the minimum function) nor almost as big as the unit cell, V, in which it is contained (the condition required by the maximum function). Usually $v \ll V$, in which case we are approaching the condition for the minimum function. It seems reasonable to suppose that when $v = \frac{1}{2} V$, that something like the sum function would be best suited to find the required image. Hence if we postulate that the new density, ρ, derived from the two superimposed weighted densities ρ_1, and ρ_2, is to be calculated by the function

$$\rho = \frac{\rho_1 \exp[(\rho_2 - \rho_1) \tan(\tfrac{1}{2} - v/V)\pi] + \rho_2 \exp[(\rho_1 - \rho_2) \tan(\tfrac{1}{2} - v/V)\pi]}{\exp[(\rho_2 - \rho_1) \tan(\tfrac{1}{2} - v/V)\pi] + \exp[(\rho_1 - \rho_2) \tan(\tfrac{1}{2} - v/V)\pi]},$$

then we are using the minimum function when $v = 0$, the sum function when $v = \tfrac{1}{2}V$ and the maximum function when $v = V$. For an α–protein at 6Å resolution v will be the volume of the polypeptide helices. This approach to the effect of finite volume of an image is tentative, but is enough to show that it is a very real problem.

Application to haemoglobin at 5.5 Å resolution

Horse haemoglobin crystallizes in space group $C2$ with cell dimensions $a = 109\cdot2$ Å, $b = 63\cdot2$ Å, $c = 54\cdot7$ Å, $\beta = 110\cdot7°$. There are two molecules in the unit cell, each of molecular weight 67,000. Thus half the molecule

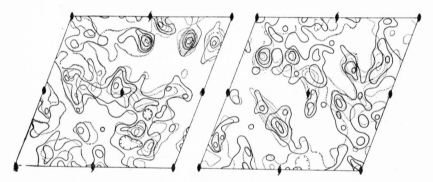

FIG. 8. Comparison of haem sections of superposition results of PCMB, $HgAc_2$ and oxy-haemoglobin (full lines) with the " standard " Fourier (dotted lines).

represents the asymmetric unit, and is related to the other half by means of a twofold axis. One asymmetric unit contains two distinct helical polypeptide chains, and with each is associated one iron containing haem group (Fig. 7). These results were obtained by means of standard isomorphous replacement techniques (Perutz et al., 1960) using a total of seven compounds and involving ten parameters per heavy atom. The superposition results obtained using the haemoglobin data have involved the use of an empirically deduced isotropic weighting scheme discussed in previous paragraphs. The initial Patterson synthesis was calculated at grid intervals of $1\cdot4 \times 1\cdot6 \times 1\cdot4$ Å along a, b, and c respectively. These were translated and superimposed by integral number of grid points, without interpolation, before selecting the lower density at consecutive grid points to form the new minimum function.

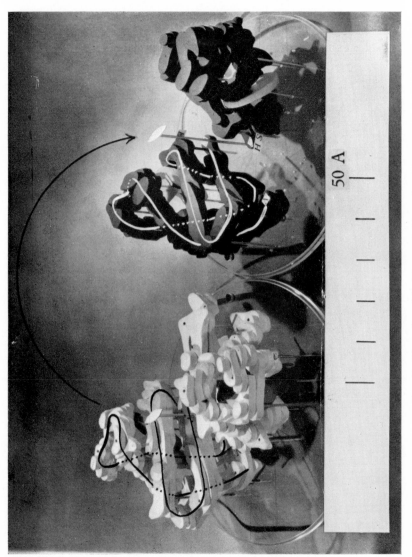

Fig. 7. View of model of haemoglobin molecule.

The initial Pattersons and successive minimum functions were automatically stored in packed form on EDSAC II magnetic tape. Results were punched out simultaneously if desired.

Sections of constant y, perpendicular to the b–axis which contain the haem groups will be used to compare the superposition results with the standard isomorphous replacement Fourier. Figure 8 shows the image of haemoglobin found by using the mercury derivatives PCMB, $HgAc_2$ (each with one mercury per asymmetric unit) and the unsubstituted oxy-haemoglobin. Figure 9 shows the same only the DMA has been used instead of the PCMB derivative. DMA has two mercuries 3·5 Å apart in much the same

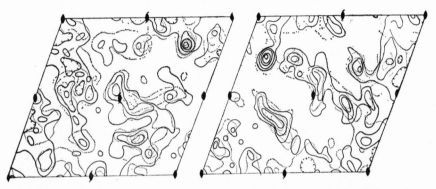

FIG. 9. Comparison of haem sections of superposition results of DMA, $HgAc_2$ and oxy-haemoglobin (full lines) with the " standard " Fourier (dotted lines).

position where PCMB has only one mercury atom. Thus, both Figs. 8 and 9 show the result of the superposition function applied to a minimum amount of data. Figure 10 gives what happens on combining Figs. 8 and 9; therefore, eliminating more chance coincidences of images.

Figures 11, 12 and 13 compare with Figs. 8 and 9, and 10 respectively. This time, however, instead of using two " single " compounds and the unsubstituted protein, one double compound and the unsubstituted protein was employed. Figure 11 gives the interpretation of the difference Patterson for the $4HgCl_2$ compound which has essentially one mercury at the $HgAc_2$ and one in the PCMB site. Figure 12 is the result for the (DMA + $HgAc_2$) compound. Figure 13 is a combination of the results shown in Figs. 11 and 12.

It was difficult to proceed any further with the superposition procedure owing to the difficulty of finding magnetic tape able to retain information over a long period of time. Nevertheless it is quite clear that even with these relatively few superpositions an approximation to the true structure has been obtained. Thus, instead of increasing the number of superpositions it was

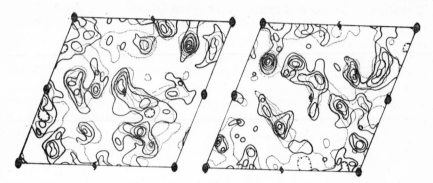

FIG. 10. Superposition of results in Figs. 8 and 9 on each other (full lines).

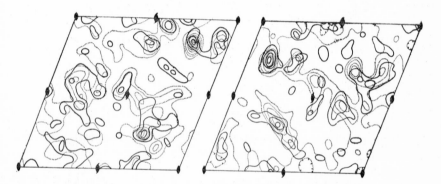

FIG. 11. Comparison of haem sections of superposition of $4HgCl_2$ and oxy-haemoglobin (full lines) with the " standard " Fourier (dotted lines).

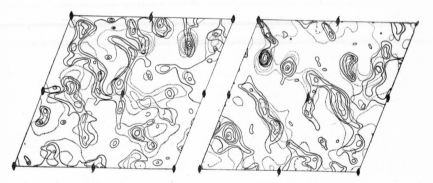

FIG. 12. Comparison of haem sections of superposition of $(DMA + HgAc_2)$ and oxy-haemoglobin (full lines) with the " standard " Fourier (dotted lines).

felt the next most worthwhile step would be to use an anisotropic weighting system and one which allows for the finite volume of each image. In the meantime the present results show (i) The use of the minimum number of compounds necessary for solution gives a reasonable approximation to the standard result. (ii) The use of an acentric set of heavy atoms in one double compound (Figs. 11–13) rather than in two different compounds (Figs. 8–11) is not quite as powerful. This is as predicted by theory. (iii) The addition of extra compounds has surprisingly little effect on the results.

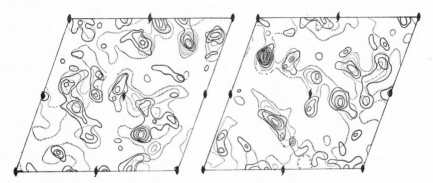

FIG. 13. Superposition of results in Figs 11 and 12 (full lines).

The accompanying table shows that the haem groups could not be selected unambiguously from the superposition results, but nevertheless were in general as high as the highest background peak, and frequently were the highest peaks in the map. The exact centres of the iron atoms in the different superpositions never differed by more than one grid point in any direction from the isomorphous replacement result.

Table showing the peak heights in arbitrary units of the two independent iron containing haem groups in comparison with the highest background

Method	Fe_1	Fe_2	Highest background
Standard isomorphous replacement technique (7 compounds)	40	34	26
PCMB, $HgAc_2$ and oxy (Fig. 8)	35	30	35
DMA, $HgAc_2$ and oxy (Fig. 9)	32	36	32
PCMB, DMA, $HgAc_2$ and oxy (Fig. 10)	33	33	34
$4HgCl_2$ and oxy (Fig. 11)	32	34	34
$(DMA + HgAc_2)$ and oxy (Fig. 12)	29	38	33
$4HgCl_2$, $(DMA + HgAc_2)$ and oxy (Fig. 13)	29	38	33

The use of the minimum function to seek iron atom positions from anomalous dispersion data

It can be shown (Rossmann, 1960b) that a Patterson with coefficients $\{ \, | \, F(hkl) \, | \, - \, | \, F(\overline{hkl}) \, | \, \}^2$ has positive peaks at the ends of vectors relating anomalous scatterers. Such Pattersons for the heavy atom compounds of haemoglobin showed clearly the positions of the mercury atoms, but the Fe–Hg vectors were lost in the background caused by the large observational errors in the coefficients of the Patterson. Hence the problem of determining the haem positions from the anomalous dispersion Patterson is one of

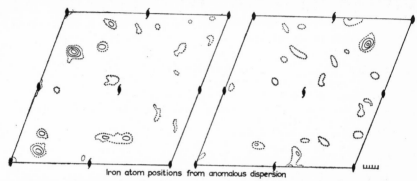

Iron atom positions from anomalous dispersion

FIG. 14. Sections showing the haems after the superposition of the $4HgCl_2$ and " Baker " compound anomalous dispersion Patterson to find a consistent set of Hg . . . Fe interactions.

selecting a set of consistent vector peaks corresponding to the distribution of iron and mercury atoms. It is to be hoped that all the other background peaks are sufficiently random that only one solution is possible. A super-position procedure, based on the $4HgCl_2$ and the " Baker " compound anomalous dispersion Pattersons, was adopted to search for the desired consistent set of vectors. The method is identical with the superposition method for isomorphous replacement, except that the weaker replacements in $4HgCl_2$ gave images which were too weak to be found in practice. The haem group sections derived in this way are shown in Fig. 14. The highest peaks, each of arbitrary height 34 units, were identical in position with the haem groups while the highest background peak in the whole synthesis did not exceed 32 units.

Normally it is assumed that the error due to the coincidences of images is far greater than that of experimental error, while for the last mentioned application of the minimum function experimental limitations are virtually the only cause of inaccuracy. Error introduced on this account can be positive or negative, while error due to coincidence of images can only be positive. Thus it may be that under these conditions an intermediate function such as the sum or product function would be more suitable.

Acknowledgments

I am indebted to Dr. M. F. Perutz for allowing me to use the horse haemoglobin data; to the invaluable help and assistance in all stages of the work by Miss Brenda Davies; to my wife for suggesting and designing the original horse used in the diagrams; and to Mrs. M. Allen for reproducing the diagrams with such skill and patience. I wish to thank Dr. D. M. Blow for a helpful discussion concerning the effect of the finite volume of an image on the minimum function as well as the University of Cambridge Mathematical Laboratory staff and engineers who spent many hours in fighting machine trouble on my behalf.

REFERENCES

BLOW, D. M. (1958). *Proc. Roy. Soc.* A **247**, 302.
BLOW, D. M. and CRICK, F. H. C. (1959). *Acta Cryst.* **12**, 794.
BLOW, D. M. and ROSSMANN, M. G. (1960). International Union of Crystallography Meeting, Cambridge, England.
BIJVOET, J. M. (1954). *Nature* **173**, 888.
BUERGER, M. J. (1942). *Nat. Acad. Sci., U.S.* **28**, 281.
BUERGER, M. J. (1950). *Nat. Acad. Sci., U.S.* **36**, 738.
BUERGER, M. J. (1951). *Acta Cryst.* **4**, 531.
BUERGER, M. J. (1959). *Vector Space*, John Wiley, New York, pp. 240–242.
DONNAY, G., BUERGER, M. J. (1950). *Acta Cryst.* **3**, 379.
HARKER, D. (1956). *Acta Cryst.* **9**, 1.
PERUTZ, M. F. (1956). *Acta Cryst.* **9**, 867.
PERUTZ, M. F., ROSSMANN, M. G., CULLIS, A. F., MUIRHEAD, H., WILL, G. and NORTH, A. C. T. (1960). *Nature* **185**, 416.
ROSSMANN, M. G. (1960a). *Acta Cryst.* **13**, 221.
ROSSMANN, M. G. (1960b). *Acta Cryst.* (in press).

S

Paper 27

THE USE OF A MONTE CARLO METHOD
IN X-RAY STRUCTURE ANALYSIS

by V. VAND and A. NIGGLI*

Crystal Research Laboratory and The Groth Institute
College of Chemistry and Physics, The Pennsylvania State University
University Park, Pa., U.S.A.

ABSTRACT

The use of Monte Carlo method as a computing technique has been made possible by the availability of fast digital computers and subprograms for random number generation. However, the direct application to crystal structures, consisting of emitting a large number of random structures and comparing their structure factors with those of an unknown structure to be solved, seems to be still inapplicable in practice owing to the low probability of a sufficiently close hit. A more promising method consists of emitting random structures, refining them partially, and then comparing them with the unknown structure. If the comparison is made on a small set of structure factors, in order to increase the speed, the least squares method becomes inapplicable and the optimal shift method can be used for refinement.

Introduction

The finding of initial crystal structures suitable for further refinement has usually been done by: the heavy atom method; the anomalous scattering method; isomorphous replacement methods; interpretation of various Patterson, Harker, superposition and allied functions; sign permutations and sign determination by statistical methods and the use of inequalities; by model fitting; and by " intuitive " trial and error.

It is of interest to see whether the new Monte Carlo methods, so often successful in other applications, could be used for the initial stages of obtaining initial models of crystal structures. Using new high-speed computers, it is possible to obtain atomic coordinates or consecutive sets of random numbers from a random-number generator program, and calculate from them a preferably restricted set of the most important structure factors. These are then compared with a given observed set; and if sufficiently good

---

* Permanent Address: Institut für Kristallographie und Petrographie, Eidg. Techn. Hochschule, Sonneggstr. 5, Zürich 6, Switzerland.

agreement has been obtained, the structure found is pointed out, together with the sets of structure factors and a measure of disagreement. This is then used as a starting point for a refinement.

A direct Monte Carlo method

A fast random number generator program is presently available, based on division of certain numbers. Such generators are only pseudo-random with very large cycles before they repeat themselves, but this does not interfere with their practical use. Using table look-ups for cosines, comparison programs for restricted sets of structure factors can be written with execution times shorter than one second on a computer such as the IBM 704, which requires $24 \, \mu sec$ per addition.

At each trial, the program can be arranged so that only one random atom can be added and one random atom removed; this results in another random structure, but involves only two-atom trigonometric calculation for a structure containing any number of equal atoms. The speed thus does not depend on the number of atoms, but on the number of reflections only.

In order to estimate the probability of success of such a method, it is necessary to know how close a hit is good enough for starting successful refinement of a structure, and how such a successful hit can be recognized.

A rough idea of the required closeness of a hit may be obtained from the well-known condition for convergence of the least squares method. In order to refine, the initial positions must lie within the true Fourier peaks of the atoms. However, the extent of the Fourier peaks depends on the termination of the series cut-off and on the weighting by a (natural or artificial) temperature factor, so that the fewer the terms taken, the broader are the Fourier peaks and the larger is the radius of convergence. However, there is a practical limit to this procedure in the eventual peak overlap. Taking all of this into consideration, a target volume of about 1 Å³ for each atom might be of the right order of magnitude.

Another estimate can be arrived at as follows: taking, say, only structure factors larger than average ($E > 1$) and reflections up to $\sin \theta = 0.5$ CuKα radiation, one can obtain a dispersion σ of atomic coordinates for which all the structure factors have weight $W > 0.5$ and therefore can be included in a Fourier series. According to a formula for weighting a Fourier series given by Vand and Pepinsky[1] the estimate of $\sigma = 0.312$ Å fulfils these conditions. To this σ corresponds an average radial error in three dimensions of $1.5958 \, \sigma = 0.5$ Å. The target sphere must have twice this volume, so that 50% of accepted hits will fall within the average radial error sphere This again gives a volume of 1 Å³ for the target sphere.

Let us consider the probability of successful hits with the random number generator of such N spheres, N being the number of equal atoms in the structure of space group $P1$. The non-centrosymmetrical case will be considered. Hydrogens in organic structures can be neglected. If the target volume around each atom is v and the volume of the unit cell is V, the first hit has the probability of success Nv/V, as all the atoms are interchangeable. The target volume must not be hit twice, and so the next hit probability is $(N-1)v/V$, etc. This gives the following formula for the probability p of success:

$$p = (v/V)^N . N!$$

In many structures the individual atoms occupy about 25 Å³ each, so that the unit cell volume is about $25N$ Å³. Substituting for v the value of 1 Å³, we obtain for the practical values of the probability

$$p = (25N)^{-N} . N!$$

In space group $P1$ there is freedom of choice of the origin, which can be taken so as to include one extra atom of known position. Then N is replaced in the above formula by $N-1$. In space group $P\bar{1}$, N is the number of atoms per asymmetric unit and p is to be divided by 8, corresponding to 8 centers of symmetry. The inverse values of probabilities, which correspond to the number of trials necessary, then run to 4×10^6 for 5-atom non-centrosymmetrical structures, and 1.6×10^{10} for 7-atom structures. Even with fast computers testing 10 random structures per second, the time and computer cost would be prohibitive even for small structures; this would involve millions of hours. The situation for centrosymmetric structures is only slightly better. It follows that a direct Monte Carlo method is impracticable for initial structure analysis in three dimensions, even if computers several orders of magnitude faster than the present ones were available. Even if such structures were eventually obtained, their recognition would present difficulties.

For a structure having $\sigma = 0.312$ Å, the disagreement factor R, which is a function of the angle θ, will reach its half maximum value at $\sin \theta = 0.22$; i.e. if any higher-angle reflections were considered, the structures, although acceptable, would present unusually high R-factors—often probably higher than for some other structures which would never converge to the correct structure.

Indirect Monte Carlo method, involving refinement before testing

There is, however, another possibility open. That is to use the Monte Carlo method to obtain random structures, to *refine* every randomly-emitted structure first, and *then* test for the goodness of fit. This is entirely feasible, since fast refinement programs can be written which sacrifice some accuracy for speed, but which are suitable for the initial stages of refinement. In this way, refinement moves every random structure in a general direction to the nearest atoms to decrease the residuals; and if the result is near to the correct structure, the refinement can be regarded as a modulation of the original probability field in some systematic way. The resulting structures can again be regarded as random, but with modulated probability of distribution of the resulting atomic positions. In general, one can imagine as a first approximation to the refinement process, that each atom is surrounded by a polyhedral region of space with faces bisecting distances between atoms, from which refinement is eventually successful. Since these polyhedral regions are N in number and are space-filling, each must have average volume V/N. The condition that a random structure eventually refine to the correct structure is that each target region around each atom is hit just once. The previous probability formula again holds with $v = V/N$, and we obtain, for a non-centrosymmetrical structure of equal atoms,

$$p = N^{-N}.N!$$

Using Stirling's formula, we can also write with good approximation for larger values of N

$$p = \overline{2\pi N}. \exp (- N).$$

The formula has to be now modified by the following considerations: in space group $P1$ there is free choice of the origin. If, therefore, one atom is chosen at the origin, its position is known and the above considerations apply to the remaining $N - 1$ atoms. The value N is therefore to be replaced by $N - 1$.

In space group $P\bar{1}$, in three dimensions, there are eight choices of origin. Every test of a structure is thus equivalent of testing 8 structures, with all the origins taken in turn. The value of the probability therefore is to be multiplied by 8 and N stands for the number of atoms per asymmetric unit. In two dimensions there are 4 origins.

The reciprocal probabilities now have the values given in Table 1. They are equal to the expected number of trials for obtaining the required structure after refinement of each trial structure.

One might question the correctness of this derivation, because some of the emitted atoms of the trial structures might occasionally fail to refine to their nearest atoms, and instead move out of their allotted regions towards other more distant neighbors, in this case, although it is considered that the emitted structure correctly hit the target, the refinement would end in a wrong structure. However, on the average these cases will be exactly compensated by structures emitted into wrong areas which diffuse into the correct areas; thus the formula should hold even in case of some escape of solutions.

We see that the situation is now much better. The time necessary for individual calculation is now longer; but for a structure with 8 atoms per asymmetric unit only about 50 trial structures must be refined, in order that there be a reasonable chance of success of finding the correct structure. It is possible that in practice a less strict criterion for a successful hit may be satisfactory, i.e. it may be possible to refine a structure *via* a Fourier series which has let us say, 10% of the atoms in wrong places, provided that the rest of the atoms are in the right positions. *Least squares* methods must have all of the atoms in correct places. Thus the probability-of-success figures given below may require alteration.

TABLE 1

VALUES OF RECIPROCAL PROBABILITIES, OR THE EXPECTED
NUMBER OF TRIALS, FOR REFINED RANDOM STRUCTURES

N	$1/p$ Space group $P1$	$1/p$ Space group $P\bar{1}$
2	1·0	—
3	2·0	—
4	4·5	1·2
5	9·7	3·2
6	26·0	8·1
7	64·8	20·6
8	165·0	52·6
9	420·0	135·0
10	1080·0	350·0

If this method is to be applied in practice, decisions must be made as to which refinement method to use, when to stop refinement, and what structures are to be accepted for further study.

The method should be as fast as possible, in order that very large numbers of trial structures can be examined. The speed of the methods depends on the number of structure factors which must be taken. Thus methods must be examined which require a small set of structure factors. The least squares method fails when the number m of equations is smaller than the number n of the unknowns; therefore it is not suitable for initial stages of refinement. Search for a better method led us to the optimal shift method, which converges well when $m < n$, and therefore is considerably faster than the least squares method at the initial stages of refinement. Details are provided in the paper by Niggli, Vand and Pepinsky at this Conference (Paper [16]).

In order to use this method, structure factors must be selected according to their weight. In general, the most economical procedure is to choose a working set of structure factors, and then when a trial structure has been obtained, to select from this set a subset of structure factors having the largest weight. Theory indicates as the most economical size of the subset the square root of the size of the main set.

The size of the main set should be related to the number of unknowns; it can be taken as about $6N$, where N is the number of atoms per asymmetric unit.

In order to judge when to stop the refinement, the usual measure of disagreement, $R = \Sigma \mid F_0 - F_c \mid / \Sigma \mid F_0 \mid$, can be used. However, this measure varies with $\sin \theta$, and does not convey good measure of the dispersion σ unless taken over small ranges of $\sin \theta$.

To the first approximation (for small R),

$$R = 4\pi\sigma.\sin \theta/\lambda,$$

which suggests that a better measure of disagreement for our purposes is a function such as

$$R' = \Sigma \mid \Delta F/f \sin \theta \mid / \Sigma \mid F_0 \mid;$$

then one can approximate σ as $\lambda R'/4\pi$. The refinement should be stopped when the disagreement measure stops decreasing. This should occur quite soon when there is little relation between the correct structure and the trial structure, but after many more cycles when there is agreement.

What structures are to be accepted for further study? This can also be answered from the magnitude of the disagreement factor, since this reflects the value of the final dispersion in coordinates. In practice it may be difficult to decide on the actual value of a limit. We have therefore adopted the following automatic procedure. A provisional value of R_{max} is arbitrarily chosen, and all structures with $R < R_{max}$ are accepted; the others are rejected. However, every time a structure is accepted, R_{max} is raised by a constant value ΔR_{pass}. Every time a structure is rejected, R_{max} is lowered by ΔR_{fail}. In this way, the program stabilizes itself at such level of R_{max} that on the average only the ratio of $\Delta R_{fail}/\Delta R_{pass}$ is accepted. Typical values to choose are $R_{max} = 0.35$, $\Delta R_{fail} = 0.001$, $\Delta R_{pass} = 0.02$. Then 5% of the test structures will be accepted. The ratio then can be decided from such practical considerations as the length of available running time and facilities for examination of the resulting accepted structures, rather than from theory.

The Monte Carlo method thus performs in crystal space, what usually is accomplished in reciprocal space by the application of inequalities: the trial structures consist of discrete point atoms, and the electron density function is non-negative. All the phase or sign combinations to be tested are therefore compatible with these criteria. Further conditions, such as minimal distances between the atoms, could easily be introduced, but they seem to increase the computing time unduly.

Acknowledgments

We are grateful for support of this research under Contract No. N6onr–26916 with the Office of Naval Research, AF 49(638)–416 with the Directorate of Solid State Sciences of the Air Force Office of Scientific Research (ARDC), and AT(30–1)–1516 with the U.S. Atomic Energy Commission; and Grant No. A–228 from the National Institutes of Health. IBM 704 calculations have been accomplished at the New York University Computing Center, with support of the Atomic Energy Commission.

REFERENCES

1. Vand, V. and Pepinsky, R. (1957) *Acta Cryst.* 10, 563.

Paper 28

NEW DEVELOPMENTS IN THE
ANOMALOUS DISPERSION METHOD FOR
STRUCTURE ANALYSIS

by Yoshiharu Okaya and Ray Pepinsky

Crystal Research Laboratory, Department of Physics
The Pennsylvania State University, University Park, Pa., U.S.A.

Introduction

Anomalous dispersion has been excellently utilized in determining the absolute configurations of inorganic and organic compounds. The method first employed[1-12] required that the crystal structure be first solved by classical or statistical techniques; and then certain pairs of $|F_{hkl}|^2$ and $|F_{\overline{hkl}}|^2$ were examined to permit a choice between right- and left-handed configurations. In 1955 a new method was developed[13-15] which involves use of not merely $|F_{hkl}|^2$ at the outset of the analysis, but the differences between $|F_{hkl}|^2$ and $|F_{\overline{hkl}}|^2$. The most significant point of the new method is that it provides an essential direct route to the structures as well as the absolute configurations of non-centrosymmetric crystals. The phase problem, which is usually very difficult in non-centrosymmetric structures, can thus effectively be by-passed.

The method is based on evaluation of a new function, $P_s(u, v, w)$. The derivation, interpretation and application of the P_s function are described here. Another method has also been derived,[16] using anomalous scattering, to overcome the phase problem for non-centrosymmetric crystals. This depends on the solution of quadratic equations formed by pairs of reflections $|F_{hkl}|^2$ and $|F_{\overline{hkl}}|^2$. This second method is less practical,[17] and will be mentioned only briefly here.

In the following analyses and discussions, u is written for $au + bv + cw$, H for the triplet h, k, l, x for (x, y, z). Thus the reciprocal lattice vector $B_{hkl} = ha^* + kb^* + lc^*$ becomes B_H; F_{hkl} becomes F_H; $P_s(u, v, w)$ becomes $P_s(u)$; $x = ax + by + cz$, etc.

Friedel's law, and the effect of anomalous dispersion

When no anomalous dispersion occurs during X-ray scattering, the atomic scattering factors f for all atoms j are *real*. Since the crystal cell structure factor is

$$F_H = \sum_{j=1}^{n} f_j e^{2\pi i H \cdot x_j}, \tag{1}$$

and the intensity I_H of scattering from the plane H is

$$I_H = K.F_H.F_H^*, \tag{2}$$

it immediately follows from the real character of f_j ($f_j = f_j^*$) that

$$F_H.F_H^* = F_{\bar{H}}.F_{\bar{H}}^*. \tag{3}$$

Here $\bar{H} = -H$, and the asterisk * denotes the complex conjugate.

This is demonstrated by the expansion of $F_H.F_H^*$ and $F_{\bar{H}}.F_{\bar{H}}^*$, under the condition that $f_j = f_j^*$:

$$F_H^* = \sum_j f_j^* e^{-2\pi i H \cdot x_j} = \sum_j f_j e^{2\pi i \bar{H} \cdot x} = F_H,$$

and

$$F_{\bar{H}}^* = \sum_j f_j^* e^{-2\pi i \bar{H} \cdot x} = \sum f_j e^{2\pi i H \cdot x} = F_H.$$

Hence

$$F_H.F_H^* = F_{\bar{H}}.F_{\bar{H}}^*, \text{ so that } I_H = I_{\bar{H}}. \tag{4}$$

This is the expression for Friedel's law, which states in words that when no anomalous dispersion exists, X-rays are scattered with equal intensities from planes H and $\bar{H}$; and thus if a crystal is non-centrosymmetric, this fact is not revealed in scattered X-ray intensities. Another statement of Friedel's law, which is actually incorrect, is that in the absence of anomalous dispersion, "X-ray scattering appears to add a center of symmetry to the crystal." (As was first demonstrated by Wilson, the statistical distribution of X-ray intensities *versus* scattering angle is different for centrosymmetric and non-centrosymmetric crystals.[18] Hence the alternative statement of Friedel's law is not acceptable.)

Now consider the case when several atoms of different types occupy ordered positions in a crystal, and some of them scatter anomalously. The atomic scattering factors for these anomalous scatterers are *complex*:

$$f_j = (f_0)_j + \Delta f_j' + i f_j''{}^{(19)} = f_j' + i f_j'', \tag{5}$$

and of course

$$f_j^* \neq f_j. \tag{6}$$

Under this condition, and if the crystal has no center of symmetry,

$$F_H = \sum_j f_j e^{2\pi i H \cdot x_j},$$

$$F_H^* = \sum_j f_j^* e^{2\pi i H \cdot x_j},$$

$$F_{\bar{H}} = \sum_j f_j e^{2\pi i \bar{H} \cdot x_j} = \sum_j f_j e^{-2\pi i H \cdot x_j}, \tag{7}$$

and

$$F_{\bar{H}}^* = \sum_j f_j^* e^{-2\pi i \bar{H} \cdot x_j} = \sum_j f_j^* e^{2\pi i H \cdot x_j}.$$

Since F_H no longer equals $F_{\bar{H}}^*$, and $F_{\bar{H}}$ differs from F_H^*,

$$I_H \neq I_{\bar{H}}; \tag{8}$$

and so Friedel's law does not hold.

It should be noted that if a crystal is composed of one kind of anomalous scatterer only, so that

$$F_H = f \sum_j e^{2\pi i H \cdot x_j},$$

$$F_{\bar{H}} = f \sum_j e^{2\pi i \bar{H} \cdot x_j},$$

$$F_H^* = f^* \sum_j e^{2\pi i \bar{H} \cdot x_j},$$

and

$$F_{\bar{H}}^* = f^* \sum_j e^{2\pi i H \cdot x_j}.$$

Here

$$F_H \cdot F_H^* = f \cdot f^* \sum_j \sum_k e^{2\pi i H \cdot (x_j - x_k)},$$

and

$$F_{\bar{H}} \cdot F_{\bar{H}}^* = f \cdot f^* \sum_j \sum_k e^{2\pi i H \cdot (x_k - x_j)}.$$

Since the order of summation in the double sums is immaterial, we again have $F_H \cdot F_H^* = F_{\bar{H}} \cdot F_{\bar{H}}^*$, and hence Friedel's law applies.

Derivation of the convolution

The electron density function for a crystal can be expressed as the Fourier series

$$\rho(x) = \sum_H F_H e^{-2\pi i H \cdot x}; \tag{9}$$

and the convolution of $\rho(x)$ and $\rho(-x)$, which is the Patterson function, is

$$P(u) = \sum_H |F_H|^2 e^{-2\pi H \cdot u}. \tag{10a}$$

It is well known that for the case of normal scatterers only, $P(u)$ is centrosymmetric, and can be written as

$$[P(u)]_n = 2\Sigma'_H |F_H|^2 \cos 2\pi H.u, \tag{10b}$$

where Σ' indicates summation over half of the reciprocal lattice only. The convolution can be described as $\rho(x)$ *viewed through* $\rho(-x)$. If the density function is comprised of nearly spherical atoms $a_1, a_2, \ldots, a_j, \ldots, a_k, \ldots, a_n$ with form factors $f_1, f_2, \ldots, f_n$, and the atom centers are at $x_1, x_2, \ldots, x_n$, then $P(u)$ will be formed of maxima with centers at points $u = x_j - x_k$, where j and k range over all the indices $1, 2, \ldots n$; and the heights and shapes of these maxima will correspond to the convolutions of f_j and f_k: i.e. the maxima will correspond to the transforms of pairs $f_j.f_k$. Overlapping of these maxima in $P(u)$ may occur, of course, so that the individual maxima corresponding to interactions of pairs of atoms may not be discernible.

When anomalous dispersion occurs,

$$|F_H|^2 = [\Sigma_j (f'_j + if''_j)e^{2\pi iH.x_j}].[\Sigma_k (f'_k - if''_k)e^{-2\pi iH.x_k}]$$

$$= \Sigma_j \Sigma_k (f'_j f'_k + f''_j f''_k)e^{2\pi iH.(x_j - x_k)}$$

$$- i\Sigma_j \Sigma_k (f'_j f''_k - f'_k f''_j)e^{2\pi iH.(x_j - x_k)}, \tag{11a}$$

$$= \Sigma_j \Sigma_k (f'_j f'_k + f''_j f''_k) \cos 2\pi H(x_j - x_k)$$

$$+ \Sigma_j \Sigma_k (f'_j f''_k - f''_j f'_k) \sin 2\pi H.(x_j - x_k). \tag{11b}$$

From (11) we can obtain

$$|F_H|^2 + |F_{\bar{H}}|^2 = 2\Sigma_j \Sigma_k (f'_j f'_k + f''_j f''_k) \cos 2\pi H.(x_j - x_k), \tag{12}$$

and $\quad |F_H|^2 - |F_{\bar{H}}|^2 = 2\Sigma_j \Sigma_k (f'_j f''_k - f''_j f'_k) \sin 2\pi H.(x_j - x_k). \tag{13}$

Inserting these expressions in (10), we have

$$P(u) = P_c(u) - iP_s(u). \tag{14}$$

Letting Σ' indicate summation over half of reciprocal space only, we write

$$P_c(u) = \Sigma_H |F_H|^2 \cos 2\pi H.(x_j - x_k), \tag{15}$$

$$= \Sigma'_H (|F_H|^2 + |F_{\bar{H}}|^2) \cos 2\pi H.(x_j - x_k), \tag{16}$$

and $\quad P_s(u) = \Sigma'_H (|F_H|^2 - |F_{\bar{H}}|^2) \sin 2\pi H.(x_j - x_k) \tag{17}$

$$= \Sigma'_H \Delta |F_H|^2 \sin 2\pi H.(x_j - x_k) \tag{18}$$

$$= \Sigma_H |F_H|^2 \sin 2\pi H.(x_j - x_k). \tag{19}$$

In (17), $\quad \Delta |F_H|^2 = |F_H|^2 - |F_{\bar{H}}|^2. \tag{20}$

If anomalous scatterers are absent, it is obvious from (12) and (13) that $|F_H|^2 + |F_{\bar{H}}|^2 = 2\sum_{jk} f'_j f'_k$ and $\Delta|F_H|^2 = 0$. In the absence of anomalous scattering, the convolution (10) has peaks corresponding to the transform of $f_j \cdot f_k$ at $u = x_j - x_k$. Analogously, $P_c(u)$ has peaks corresponding to the transform of $f'_j \cdot f'_k + f''_j \cdot f''_k$ at $u = x_j - x_k$ and $-u = x_k - x_j$; hence $P_c(u)$ is *centrosymmetric*, as is $P(u)$ without anomalous dispersion. Also analogously, $P_s(u)$ has peaks corresponding to the transform of $f'_j \cdot f''_j - f''_j \cdot f'_k$ at $u = x_j - x_k$, and peaks corresponding to the transform of $-(f'_j \cdot f''_k - f''_j \cdot f'_k)$ at $-u = x_k - x_j$; hence $P_s(u)$ is *antisymmetric*.

Significance of the convolution for the anomalous dispersion case, I: the P_c function

In the case of anomalous dispersion, $P(u) = P_c(u) - iP_s(u)$ is the convolution of the now *complex* electron density function $\rho(x)$ with the complex conjugate $\rho^*(x)$.

$P_c(u)$ is *not* equivalent to the ordinary Patterson function for normal scattering, since it is now necessary to take average of $|F_H|^2$ and $|F_{\bar{H}}|^2$, which quantities are unequal when dispersion exists, in computing $P_c(u)$. It will on occasion be useful to examine both $P(u)$ with no dispersion and $P_c(u)$ when dispersion is present, and specifically to evaluate $P(u) - P_c(u)$. It is readily shown that peaks in $P(u) - P_c(u)$ correspond to the transform of $-\Delta f'_j \cdot \Delta f'_k - f''_j \cdot f''_k - (f_0)_j \cdot \Delta f'_k - (f_0)_k \cdot \Delta f'_j$. If the jth atom scatters anomalously but the kth does not, the peak height corresponding to the interaction between j and k will be $(f_0)_k \cdot \Delta f'_j$. Peaks in $P - P_c$ for interactions between like species of anomalous scatterers will be of height corresponding to the transform of $-[(\Delta f'_j)^2 + (f''_j)^2 + 2(f_0)_j \Delta f'_j]$. No peaks will appear in $P - P_c$ for interactions between normal scatterers.

If there are only M similar anomalous scatterers per cell, and $N - M$ normal scatterers, $M(N - M)$ peaks appear of height corresponding to the transform of $-f_k \cdot \Delta f'_m$, where f_k is the form-factor for one of the normal scatterers and $\Delta f'_m$ is the real component of the change in scattering factor for the excited atom m, as given in (5); and there are $M(M - 1)$ peaks of height corresponding to the transform of $-[(\Delta f'_m)^2 + (f''_m)^2 + 2(f_0)_m \cdot \Delta f'_m]$.

Values of $\Delta f'_j$ and f''_j are given in a later section of this paper, for various atoms and exciting radiations. They do not exceed 10% of the value of $(f_0)_j$. Although it is theoretically possible to identify vectors in the difference of the convolutions $[P_c(u)] - [P(u)]_n$ interactions between anomalous scatterers (changing the incident wavelength to obtain these two functions), in practice this will be difficult. Another indication of this difficulty is provided by the fact that differences between $|F_H|^2_{an}$ and $|F_{\bar{H}}|^2_{an}$ are small, and thus the Fourier coefficients $(|F_H|^2_{an} + |F_{\bar{H}}|^2_{an})/2$ for $P_c(u)$ will not differ very much from the coefficients $|F_H|^2_n$ for the convolution for normal scattering only.

Significance of the convolution, II: the P_s function

The antisymmetric function $P_s(u)$, however, is of very great importance, and has led directly to the elucidation of several structures which were extremely recalcitrant when attacked by classical methods. P_s exists of course only for non-centrosymmetric crystals, and its excursions indicate the degree of non-centricity. (This was first pointed out in our References 14 and 15, but has been restated by investigators who failed to read those papers. P_c and $P - P_c$ of course both exist for centric crystals).

$P_s(u)$ has peaks only corresponding to interactions between anomalous and normal scatterers, and between unlike anomalous scatterers if these exist in the structure. Chemical preparation and/or choice of exciting radiation are of importance in controlling the number of anomalous scatters in the cell. In certain cases it is readily possible to study the same crystal with two different wavelengths, in order to excite first one type of anomalous scatterer and then another. This will be discussed below. In general, it is a simple matter to guarantee only one type of excited atom per cell; it is this common case which will receive our major attention.

Positive peaks appear in $P_s(u)$ at positions corresponding to vectors *from excited atoms to normal scatterers*. When more than one type of anomalous scatterer appears, these peaks are of heights corresponding to the transform of $f'_j f''_k - f''_j f'_k$. *Negative* peaks appear at positions corresponding to vectors *from non-excited to excited atoms*; they are of the same magnitude but opposite in sign to the former peaks in $P_s(u)$.

In the generally attainable case involving only one type of excited atom per cell, and M of these, there are M clusters of positive peaks, of heights corresponding to $f''_m f_j$, where the f_j's are the form factors for normal scatterers; and there are likewise M clusters of negative peaks, of height corresponding to $- f'_m f_j$. A cluster about any one excited atom thus provides the *sense* of vectors from the excited atom to all the normal atoms: i.e. the absolute configuration is provided.

If only one anomalous scatterer exists per cell (e.g. in space group $P1$), P_s immediately provides the entire non-centrosymmetric distribution around the excited atom, and also the absolute configuration. In cases where this ideal situation does not appear, P_s must be de-convoluted. Since the number of peaks in P_s is very limited compared to the number in a normal Patterson (P) or in P_c, this de-convolution is readily and directly achievable.

Concerning the excursions of $P_s(u)$

Whereas peaks in the function $P_c(u) - [P(u)]_n$ are very small, those in $P_s(u)$ can be large and are easily observable when " good " X-ray data are available. " Good " can mean photographic data, obtained by the multiple film method or by photometering, and accurate to perhaps $\pm 5\%$ in intensities, with effects of spot size carefully evaluated. Crystals must be carefully oriented so that both H and $\bar{H}$ reflections can be accurately brought into positions of maximum scattering and integrated intensities can be observed. Better data can, of course, be obtained by scanning counter measurements, when these are properly carried out. Accuracies of $\pm 1\%$ in intensities are then possible.

Effects of absorption will be high, and must be minimized by crystal size and shape, and when possible by computed corrections. Extinction effects should also be minimized, or corrections made for them.

It is to be noted that $\Delta |F_H|^2$ values are needed, and that it is generally possible to obtain quite accurate $\Delta |F_H|^2 / |F_H|^2$ values. The difficulties lie chiefly in obtaining all $\Delta |F_H|^2$ values on the same scale.

The magnitude of $\Delta |F_H|^2$ values are given by Equation (13). If we consider the usual case, of one type of anomalous scatterer per cell,

$$\Delta |F_H|^2 = 2f''_m \sum_j \sum_m f'_j \sin 2\pi H(x_j - x_m), \tag{13}$$

where j refers to normal scatterers and m to the anomalous scatterer. The magnitude of $\Delta |F_H|^2$ thus depends on the magnitude of f''_m, the degree of non-centricity of the distribution of normal scatterers about atoms m, and the magnitudes of f'_j.

These factors are discussed in later sections.

Symmetry of $P_s(u)$

A detailed discussion of the symmetry of P_s functions for various non-centrosymmetric point groups has been provided by Y. Takeuchi,[20] of the Mineralogical Institute, University of Tokyo. This discussion involves the concept of the black and white space groups.[21]

The symmetry of P_s can be derived by combining an antisymmetry operation with the symmetry operation of the non-centrosymmetric point group, and distributing the resulted anticentrosymmetric point group over the Bravais lattice of the crystal. In Table 1, which is essentially Takeuchi's representation, the anticentrosymmetric groups are listed for all non-centrosymmetric point groups. The notation is similar to that used by Cochran[22] in his discussion of the symmetry of generalized projections. In addition to the usual operations 1, 2, 3, 4, 6 and m, the following anti-symmetry operations are introduced: 1–, 2–, 3–, 4–, 6– and m–. The symbol 1– indicates an anticentrosymmetry operation, m– an antimirror, and, for example, 4– indicates a rotation through an angle of 90° followed by a change of sign. By changing the antisymmetry operation into the corresponding symmetry operation, the symmetry of the $P_c(u)$ function is obtained for each point group.

We are grateful to Prof. Takeuchi for transmitting to us a copy of his unpublished manuscript, from which the above discussion is obtained.

Table 1

SYMMETRY OF THE $P_s(u)$ FUNCTION, AFTER TAKEUCHI[20],
BUT WITH SOME CHANGES IN NOTATION

POINT GROUPS	$P_s(u)$
$C_1 - 1$	1^-
$C_2 - 2$	$2/m^-$
$C_s - m$	$2^-/m$
$C_{2v} - mm2$	$m\,m\,m^-$
$D_2 - 222$	$m^-\,m^-\,m^-$
$S_4 - \bar{4}$	$4^-/m^-$
$C_4 - 4$	$4/m^-$
$D_{2d}\ \ \dfrac{-\bar{4}2m}{-\bar{4}m2}$	$4^-/m^-\,m^-\,m\ \cdot$ \ $4^-/m^-\,m\,m^-$
$C_{4v} - 4mm$	$4/m^-\,m\,m$
$D_4 - 422$	$4/m^-\,m^-\,m^-$
$C_3 - 3$	$\bar{3}^-$
$C_{3v}\ \ \dfrac{-3m1}{-31m}$	$\bar{3}^-\,m\,2^-$ \ $\bar{3}^-\,2^-\,m$
$D_3\ \ \dfrac{-312}{-321}$	$\bar{3}^-\,m^-\,2$ \ $\bar{3}^-\,2\,m^-$
$C_6 - 6$	$6/m^-$
$C_{3h} - \bar{6}$	$6^-/m$
$C_{6v} - 6mm$	$6/m^-\,mm$
$D_6 - 622$	$6/m^-\,m^-\,m^-$
$D_{3h}\ \ \dfrac{-\bar{6}m2}{-\bar{6}2m}$	$6^-/mmm^-$ \ $6^-/mm^-\,m$
$T - 23$	$m^-\,\bar{3}^-$
$O - 432$	$m^-\,\bar{3}^-\,m^-$
$T_d - \bar{4}3m$	$m^-\,\bar{3}^-\,m$

De-convolution of the $P_s(u)$ function

The $P_s(u)$ function is a highly de-convoluted interatomic vector (Patterson) function. Whereas the usual Patterson has $2N(N-1)$ positive peaks (where N is the number of atoms per cell), plus a large peak at the origin, $P_s(u)$ has $M(N-M)$ positive peaks and an equal number of negative peaks. (Hydrogen atoms are neglected in this discussion.) If the number of atoms per cell is 56, and 4 of these are anomalous scatterers of one type only, the Patterson function contains, beside a large peak at the origin, 6160 positive peaks. The $P_s(u)$ function contains 208 positive peaks, and an equal number of negative. De-convolution is readily attained through the use of a simple type of image-seeking sum function (cf. Buerger[23]). When the origin of the $P_s(u)$ function is shifted to the positions x_{an}^m of the M anomalous scatterers and the resulted shifted maps P_s^m are summed, the positive area of the sum function $S(u)$ is the structure. The summation can be made using the following formula[15, 24]:

$$S(u) = \sum_m^M p_s^m(u)$$

$$= \sum_m^M [\sum_H |F_H|^2 \sin 2\pi H.(u - x_{an}^m)]$$

$$= \sum_H [|F_H|^2 (\sin 2\pi H.u) \sum_m^M \cos 2\pi H.x_{an}^m]$$

$$- \sum_H [|F_H|^2 (\cos 2\pi H.u) \sum_m^M \sin 2\pi H.x_{an}^m]$$

$$= \sum_H |F_H|^2 (\sin 2\pi H.u).A_{an}$$

$$- \sum_H |F_H|^2 (\cos 2\pi H.u).B_{an}. \tag{21}$$

A_{an} and B_{an} are the contribution of the anomalous scatterers to the real and imaginary parts of the structure factors, respectively. It should be noticed here that the sum function can be calculated directly from the experimental data, provided the positions of the anomalous scatterers are known. These can easily be obtained by means of any one of several classical methods.

It seems worth while to illustrate the procedure of de-convolution using a simple artificial structure in space group $P2_1$, as shown in Figs. 1(a)–1(e).[15, 24]

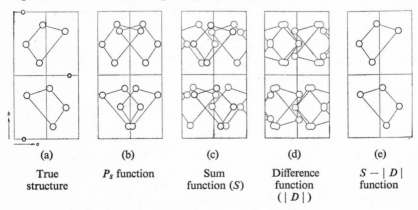

(a)	(b)	(c)	(d)	(e)
True structure	P_s function	Sum function (S)	Difference function $(|D|)$	$S - |D|$ function

FIG. 1.   De-convolution of the P_s function.

T

Figure 1(a) corresponds to the true structure. The positive part of the $P_s(u)$ function of the structure is shown in Fig. 1(b). The above-mentioned method of computing a sum function was applied graphically to $P_s(u)$; the map of Fig. 1(c) shows the structure plus extra peaks in half weight. The sum function can be improved by subtracting the absolute value of a difference function D, as in Fig. 1(d). The function $S - |D|$ as shown in Fig. 1(e) provides the structure minus the anomalous scatterers, without any superfluous peaks. For crystals where two anomalous scatterers are centrosymmetrically located at $\pm x_{an}$, the procedure can be carried out numerically, using a modification[24] of an analytical representation of Buerger's image-seeking method as derived by Taylor.[25] For the case of normal scattering, the minimum function $M(u)$ can be expressed as the difference between a sum function $S(u)$ and the absolute value of a minimum function $D(u)$:

$$M(u) = S(u) - |D(u)|, \tag{22}$$

where
$$S(u) = 2\Sigma_H |F_H|^2 (\sin 2\pi H . u)(\cos 2\pi H . x_{an}) \tag{23}$$

and
$$D(u) = 2\Sigma_H |F_H|^2 (\cos 2\pi H . u)(\sin 2\pi H . x_{an}). \tag{24}$$

Here $S(u)$ corresponds to the sum function of Equation (21). If the crystal contains more than one centrosymmetrically-related pair of anomalous scatterers, the above procedure can be carried out for each pair; and the minimum functions so obtained are then to be added.

These computations are completely straightforward, provided that the positions of the anomalous scatterers are known. In Figs. 2(a) to 2(e), the the computations, accomplished directly on X–RAC, are illustrated. It must be emphasized that no phase information is called on in solving the structure.

The sum-function method has been successfully applied to the de-convolution of the three-dimensional P_s function of cobaltous L-aspartate trihydrate.[26] This is illustrated in Figs. 3(a), (b) and (c). In Fig. 3(a), a part of the $P_s(u)$ function is shown. The function was then converted to the sum function, a composite diagram of which is shown in Fig. 3(b). Figure 3(c) is a composite diagram of the final three-dimensional electron-density function, which is the structure. It might be interesting to report that the atomic coordinates derived from the sum function differ from the final values by less than two-hundredths of the cell edges.

A variant of our methods of deconvolution is obtained *via* the β_{an} synthesis, reported by Ramachandran and Raman.[27, 28] Their experience, from analyses of several modified Patterson syntheses, is that the following function is convenient:

$$\beta_{an} = \Sigma_H [\Delta |F_H|^2 - 2(F'_H.F''^*_H + F'^*_H.F''_H)] / |F''_H| e^{-i(2\pi H.x - a''_H)} \tag{25}$$

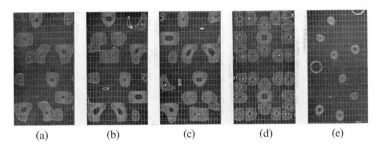

(a)   (b)   (c)   (d)   (e)

FIG. 2. De-convolution of the $P_s(u)$ function, artificial structure ($S = $ sum function, $D = $ difference function): (a) S; (b) $S + D$; (c) $S - D$; (d) $|D|$; (e) True structure.

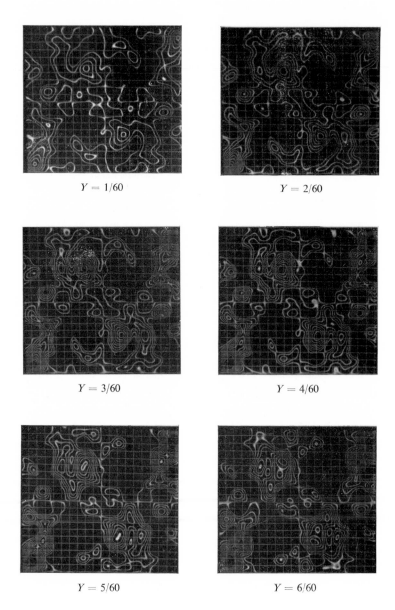

$Y = 1/60$

$Y = 2/60$

$Y = 3/60$

$Y = 4/60$

$Y = 5/60$

$Y = 6/60$

FIG. 3(a). Cobaltous aspartate trihydrate: Negative regions of the three-dimensional $P_s(u)$ synthesis, origin corner.

here F'_H and F''_H are the contributions of the real and imaginary parts of the atomic scattering factors of the anomalous scatterers to the cell structure factors, respectively, and α''_H is the phase angle of F''_H.

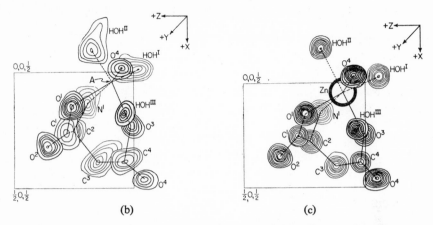

(b)   (c)

FIG. 3(b).   Cobaltous aspartate trihydrate: A composite diagram of the three-dimensional sum function synthesis of the $P_s(u)$ function, showing one asymmetric unit. The structure can be obtained by putting a cobaltous ion at " A."

FIG. 3(c).   Zinc aspartate trihydrate: A composite diagram of the three-dimensional electron density synthesis, showing one asymmetric unit.

The β_{an} synthesis of Ramachandran and Raman can be simplified in the usual case where all the anomalous scatterers are of the same kind. Then the second term within the brackets of Equation (25) is zero, and

$$\beta'_{an} = \sum_H (F^*_H / |F''_H|) \cdot e^{-i(2\pi H . x - \alpha''_H)} \tag{26}$$

As in all of our derivations of $P_s(u)$, the β'_{an} synthesis can be calculated from experimental data, without the need to put these on an absolute scale. The synthesis provides the positions of the normal scatterers on positive peaks in a background of unwanted completely negative peaks. The advantage lies in the possibility of direct computation and elimination of superfluous positive peaks. For certain space groups in which anomalous scatterers are centrosymmetrically arranged (e.g. $P2_1$), β_{an} gives the structure duplicated by its inverse with negative weight; in other cases, unwanted negative peaks are dispersed into a general background. The absolute configuration is retained in all cases.

The basic synthesis on which the various modified syntheses of Ramachandran and Raman rest is of course the $P_s(u)$ function. These investigators have actively refused to recognize the identity, although reprints of our papers were in their hands well in advance of their work.

Although de-convolution of the P_s function is particularly simple for crystals containing only one kind of anomalous scatterer distributed among normal scatterers, it should be borne in mind that the formulae presented here are quite general, and can be applied to crystals containing several kinds of anomalous scatterers. In this respect no limitation is imposed on practical applications of our dispersion method.

Use of generalized projections

As in the case of the classical Patterson function, projections of the P_s function can also be computed using properly selected $|F_H|^2$ values. Many non-centrosymmetric crystals possess projections which are centrosymmetric, for which projections of P_s are zero. Useful information is obtained by using generalized projections in such cases. For crystals with certain symmetry elements, it is only necessary to determine whether the position of a normal scatterer is higher or lower than that of the anomalous scatterer. Generalized projections such as

$$\int_0^1 P_s(u, v, w) \cdot \sin 2\pi Lw . dw \qquad (27)$$

are typically useful. When $L = 1$, positive peaks represent normal scatterers whose z coordinates are higher than those of anomalous scatterers (between z_m and $z_m + \frac{1}{2}$); the meaning of negative peaks is then obvious.

Generalized projections were successfully applied in obtaining the absolute configurations of hexagonal

$$\text{D-[Co(en)}_3]\text{Cl.NaCl}_3.3\text{H}_2\text{O (en = ethylenediamine)}[15, 8]$$

and tetragonal KH_2AsO_4.[29] The former structure was examined in order to establish the absolute configuration of the complex ion $\text{D-[Co(en)}_3]^{+3}$; and the latter analysis was carried out to establish the relation between the absolute configuration and the piezoelectric and ferroelectric behavior.

The structure of KD_2AsO_4 is shown in Fig. 4(a), and the generalized projection

$$\int_0^1 P_s(u, v, w) \sin 2\pi Lwdw$$

in Fig. 4(b). It is seen that the edge of the AsO_4 tetrahedron which is almost parallel to the P_1 axis is higher than As with respect to the positive c axis. The c axis is correctly chosen in the positive direction of the piezoelectric effect.

Another beautiful example of the use of a generalized projection appears in the determination of the absolute configuration of ferroelectric (glycine)$_3$. H_2SO_4 under an electric field. A full three-dimensional structure analysis of this crystal[30] and a subsequent study of the mechanism of the ferroelectric activity revealed that upon the reversal of an electric field, the structure takes its mirror image with respect to a plane at $y = \frac{1}{4}$. However, the relation between the direction of electric polarization and the two states of the structure had to be determined *via* an absolute configuration determination.

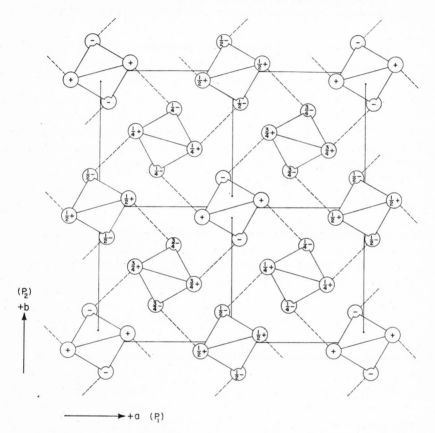

FIG. 4(a). KD_2AsO_4: Projection of the structure along the *c* axis. Only the AsO_4 tetrahedra are shown.

In $(glycine)_3 \cdot H_2SO_4$, sulfur is the heaviest atom and the only one which can be expected to be excited measurably by convenient X-ray wavelengths. For $CuK\alpha$ radiation, f_s'' has a value of 0·5 electron. Since f_s'' is so small, very accurate values of $|F_H|^2$ were required. These were achieved by taking advantage of the effect of reversal of the polarizing electric field. This reversal alters the direction of the *b* axis, while maintaining the same geometric configuration for the X-ray beam, crystal and X-ray detector (a proportional counter). F_{hkl} is changed to $F_{h\bar{k}l}$ by the field; and due to the crystal symmetry,

$F_{\bar{h}\bar{k}l}$ is equivalent to $F_{\overline{hkl}}$. Thus observations of $|F_H|^2$ were attained which were highly accurate.

Positive and negative regions of the generalized projection

$$\int_0^1 P_s(u, v, w) . \sin 2\pi 2v . dv$$

are shown in Figs. 5(a) and (b). Comparison with the structure established the absolute configuration directly. Further measurements showed that the entire structure could be obtained by this technique.

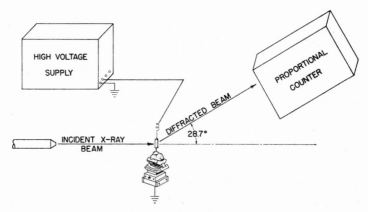

Fig. 6. Experimental arrangement for application of the reversing electric field, for anomalous dispersion observation of the structures and absolute configurations of ferroelectric crystals. The electric field must, of course, exceed the coercive field of the ferroelectric.

The experimental arrangement for this technique is shown in Fig. 6. Some scintillation-counter observations are shown in Fig. 7, for the case of KH_2AsO_4 with incident $MoK\alpha$ radiation and scattering from the (511), $(5\bar{1}\bar{1})$ and related planes. It is the most effective method, not merely for obtaining the absolute configuration of a ferroelectric containing an anomalous scatterer, but for establishing the structure from the outset. This is the case because the field-reversal method for changing $|F_H|^2$ to $|F_{\bar{H}}|^2$ avoids major difficulties of absorption and extinction corrections, and in all cases we have studied completely avoids crystal-orientation disturbances. The method is recommended for all ferroelectric structure studies where anomalous scattering is possible.

The use of periodic electric field reversal, using square waves over a range of frequencies from d.c. to 100 kc, combined with the stroboscopic pulsed X-ray method of Pepinsky[31] appears to be an even superior method for ferroelectric structure studies.

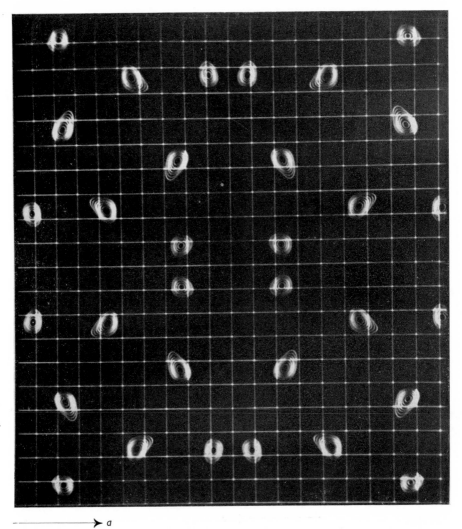

FIG. 4(b). KD_2AsO_4: $P_s'(u, v) = \int_0^1 P_s(u, v, w) \sin 2\pi w \, dw$. Positive contours only. Mo–Kα data.

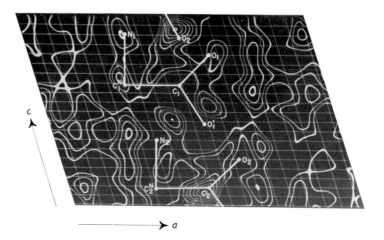

FIG. 5(a).   (Glycine)$_3$.H$_2$SO$_4$: $P_s'(u, w) = \int_0^1 P_s(u, v, w) \sin 2\pi v dv$.   Positive contours only.   Cu–Kα data.

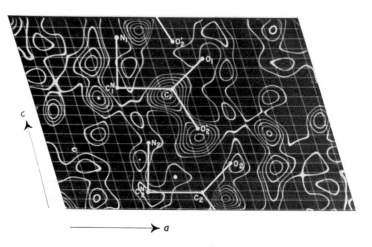

FIG. 5(b).   (Glycine)$_3$.H$_2$SO$_4$: $P_s'(u, w) = \int_0^1 P_s(u, v, w) \sin 2\pi v dv$.   Negative contours only.   Cu–Kα data.

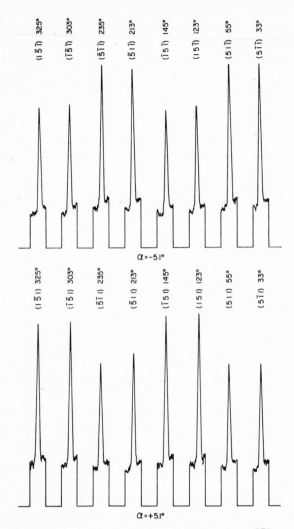

FIG. 7. Effect of electric field reversal on KH_2AsO_4 (511), ($5\bar{1}\bar{1}$) and related planes. Electric field is along tetragonal axis, and exceeds coercive field. Arsenic atom is excited by Mo$K\alpha$.

Cases where some atoms around an anomalous scatterer are centrosymmetrically deployed

One further comment should be made about the $P_s(u)$ method. When the distribution of normal scatterers about an anomalous scatterer is such that some normal scatterers are centrosymmetrically deployed with respect to the excited atom, the centrosymmetrically-related atoms will not appear for space group $P1$. In another space group *all* normal scatterers will be observed, whether or not some are centrosymmetric or not; because they will be viewed from all symmetry-related anomalous scatterers.

This situation is illustrated in the case of any structure containing D- or L-$[Co(en)_3]^{+3}$, where (en) is ethylenediamine, $NH_2—CH_2—CH_2—NH_2$. In

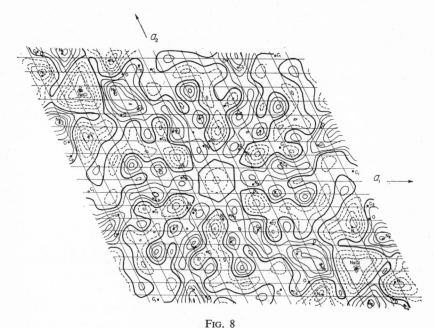

FIG. 8

2 D-$[Co(en)_3]Cl_3 \cdot NaCl \cdot 6H_2O$

Generalized projection of $\int_0^1 P_s(u, v, w) \sin 2\pi . 2w . dw$

Contour lines at arbitrary intervals; Zero level heavy, negative contours broken.

this complex ion the nitrogens are deployed at the corners of an octahedron with the cobalt atom at the center; and the chelated ethylenediamines then form right-handed or left-handed screws, depending on the corners of the octahedra occupied by two nitrogens from each ethylenediamine. The nitrogens are thus centrosymmetrically disposed with respect to the cobalt to which they chelate; the —CH_2— groups are non-centrically arranged, of course. Thus the —CH_2— groups appear with respect to the nearest Co, but the NH_2— groups do not.

The NH_2— groups are *not* centrosymmetrically arranged with respect to *another* D-$[Co(en)_3]$ ion, however. Thus they can be found in $P_s(u)$.

This situation is illustrated in the generalized projection shown as Fig. 8.

The quadratic equation method[16, 17]

When anomalous scatterers are present in a crystal, the structure factors can be decomposed into two parts: one to which normal scatterers alone contribute, and one to which the excited atoms only contribute.

$$F_H = F_H^{\text{n.s.}} + F_H^{\text{a.s.}} \tag{28}$$

We can write

$$F_H = A_H + iB_H, \tag{29}$$

and then

$$F_H = A_H^{\text{n.s.}} + iB_H^{\text{n.s.}} + A_H^{\text{a.s.}} + iB_H^{\text{a.s.}}. \tag{30}$$

For the normally-scattering components,

$$A_H^{\text{n.s.}} = A_{\bar{H}}^{\text{n.s.}} \tag{31}$$

and

$$B_H^{\text{n.s.}} = - B_{\bar{H}}^{\text{n.s.}}. \tag{32}$$

But the relations (31) and (32) do not hold for $A_H^{\text{a.s.}}$ and $B_H^{\text{a.s.}}$.

We write

$$F_H^2 = (A_H^{\text{n.s.}} + A_H^{\text{a.s.}})^2 + (B_H^{\text{n.s.}} + B_H^{\text{a.s.}})^2 \tag{33}$$

and

$$F_{\bar{H}}^2 = (A_{\bar{H}}^{\text{n.s.}} + A_{\bar{H}}^{\text{a.s.}})^2 + (B_{\bar{H}}^{\text{n.s.}} + B_{\bar{H}}^{\text{a.s.}})^2 \tag{34}$$

If the positions of the anomalous scatterers are known from a Patterson analysis, the phase problem is reduced to solution for $A_H^{\text{n.s.}}$ and $B_H^{\text{n.s.}}$.

Equations (33) and (34) are simultaneous quadratic equations in two unknowns; and hence there are two roots for each pair of such equations. Several procedures theoretically permit an approach to choice between the roots. These include use of heavy atom methods, change of the incident wavelength to alter or eliminate anomalous scattering and therewith achieve one or two more simultaneous equations, use of isomorphous replacement, use of $P_s(u)$, and use of a modification of Sayre's method for non-centric crystals.

The quadratic equation method has several disadvantages, compared to the $P_s(u)$ method. (1) The data must be placed on an absolute scale, whereas no such effort is necessary for the evaluation of the P_s function. (2) Since anomalous scatterers are usually heavier atoms, their coordinates and, in particular, individual temperature factors must be established with high accuracy. (3) The choice between the two roots is not always easily made, because atoms may lie in positions which result in disadvantageous values of the quantities required in Equations (33) and (34). The method is interesting in view of the fact that the phase problem for non-centrosymmetric structures is reduced to a level equal to that for centrosymmetric crystals.

Choice of X-ray wavelength and anomalous scatterers

In order that the preceding theory can be applied, the wavelength of X-rays used in the diffraction experiment must be chosen properly with respect to some particular atom or atoms in the structure.

Hönl[19] has treated the theory of anomalous dispersion. Variations of $\Delta f'_j$ and $\Delta f''_j$ are shown in Fig. 9, as functions of the ratio of the exciting X-ray frequency to the frequency of the absorption edge. It is f''_m which will concern us here. It may be necessary to consider $f'_j = (f_0)_j + \Delta f'_j$ on some occasions if we are very close to an absorption edge: but the effect of this on $P_s(u)$ is entirely negligible, so we disregard $\Delta f'_j$ here. The influence of f''_j on $P_s(u)$ is indicated in Equation (13′), with $j = m$, and it is obvious that we should select experimental conditions under which f''_j is as large as possible.

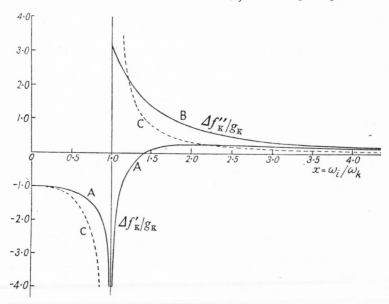

FIG. 9. Corrections to the scattering factor on account of dispersion for a K electron whose contribution to the atomic absorption coefficient varies as the inverse cube of the frequency of the radiation. Curve A shows $\Delta f'_k/g_k$ and curve B $\Delta f''_k/g_k$. Curve C is the corresponding curve for a simple harmonic oscillator.
Figure and legend taken from R. W. JAMES, *Optical Principles of the Diffraction of X-Rays*, Fig. 52, p. 150. G. Bell & Sons, London, 1954.

It has been somewhat surprising to discover that the f'' contribution for sulfur and even for silicon, excited by Cu$K\alpha$, is sufficient to permit establishment of the absolute configurations of $(glycine)_3 . H_2SO_4$ and α-naphthyl-phenylmethylsilane, respectively.

Values for f''_m can be calculated from Hönl's[19] curves, presented in Fig. 9

as reproduced from James' treatise.[32] Very useful values of $\Delta f'_m$ and $\Delta f''_m$ have been provided by Dauben and Templeton,[33] and Templeton has recently derived an extensive table of these terms for Cr$K\alpha$, Cu$K\alpha$ and Mo$K\alpha$. A suitable choice of anomalous scatterer, wavelength and method of intensity measurement can be made from these tables.

Pepinsky[15] has discussed chemical methods for inclusion of useful anomalous scatterers in compounds, and a more extensive treatment of the subject is available in unpublished form from him.

X-ray tubes with various target materials are available, in sealed-off construction, from several manufacturers. When more esoteric targets are required, a demountable tube with a rapidly-interchangeable target is advisable. The designs of these are well known. We have a very convenient construction in our own laboratory, in which an O-ring seal is used to permit rapid target removal and replacement.

In Table 2, a list of useful radiations and corresponding anomalous scatterers is presented. Values of $\Delta f'_m$ and $\Delta f''_m$ are given in a manner which should be useful for investigators in this field.

Direct photon counters should be used—with proper techniques, of course —when these are available. With good technique, counter measurements reveal $\Delta |F_H|^2$ values not achievable at all with films. Film methods can be used when f''_m exceeds 3 K electrons. K electrons are concentrated so closely to the nucleus that $(f''_m)_k$ as a function of $(\sin \theta)/\lambda$ is essentially flat to high θ values; and hence K dispersion is particularly useful for higher-index reflections. L dispersion from heavy atoms also leads to a fairly flat $(f''_m)_L$ value, *versus* θ; here a fairly large value of virtual oscillator strength appears necessary. The $(f''_m)_L$ values which Dauben and Templeton have provided are reproduced in Reference 15, in conjunction with chemical advice; for heavy atoms, $(f''_m)_L$ values over 20 electrons are achievable. In crystals containing such scatterers, properly excited, the dispersion effects will be overwhelming, and $P_s(u)$ will be very easily interpreted.

Anomalous dispersion, which depends upon excitation of inner-shell electrons to higher quantum levels, is of course always accompanied by fluorescence. This is not at all serious for counter measurements, but may affect film techniques. Properly chosen absorbing foils can reduce the effects of fluorescence. In the case of counter measurements, fluorescent radiation can be eliminated entirely through use of a monochromator mounted integrally on the counter arm. Pulse height discrimination will be helpful, but should be unnecessary.

Use of two or more non-equivalent scatterers in one crystal

The $P_s(u)$ function, when de-convoluted, provides a view of the distribution of normal scatterers, and their absolute configuration, around each anomalous

Table 2

CONVENIENT RADIATIONS AND CORRESPONDING ANOMALOUS SCATTERERS

Column groups: **Incident radiations** (Target materials, Atomic number, Emission series, Wavelengths α_1, α_2) — **Elements with K absorption edge close to (but shorter than) the incident wavelengths** (Atom, Atomic number, K abs. edge, λ/λ_k, $\Delta f'_k$, $\Delta f''_k$) — **Elements with $\Delta f'' = 2\cdot0$ by the K excitation** — **Elements with $\Delta f'' = 1\cdot0$ by the K excitation** — **Range of atoms with $\Delta f'' = 2\cdot0$ and up by the L excitation**.

Target materials	Atomic number	Emission series	α_1	α_2	Atom	Atomic number	K abs. edge	λ/λ_k	$\Delta f'_k$	$\Delta f''_k$	Elements with $\Delta f'' = 2\cdot0$ by the K excitation	Elements with $\Delta f'' = 1\cdot0$ by the K excitation	Range of atoms with $\Delta f'' = 2\cdot0$ and up by the L excitation
Cr	24	K	2·290	2·293	Ti	22	2·502	0·916	−1·9	3·0	A 18*	P 15*	As(33)–Ba(56)*
Mn	25	K	2·102	2·105	V	23	2·268	0·928	−2·3	3·3	K 19	P 15	Se(34)–Ce(58)
Fe	26	K	1·936	1·940	Cr	24	2·070	0·936	−2·5	3·3	Ca 20	S 16	Br(35)–Ce(58)
Co	27	K	1·789	1·793	Mn	25	1·896	0·944	−3·8	3·5	Ca 20	S 16	Br(35)–Pr(59)
Ni	28	K	1·658	1·661	Fe	26	1·742	0·952	−2·8	3·5	Sc 21	S 16	Rb(37)–Dy(60)
Hf	72	L	1·569	1·580	Co	27	1·607	0·976	−3·6	3·5	Sc 21	Cl 17	
Cu	29	K	1·540	1·544	Co	27	1·607	0·959	−3·0	3·4	Ti 22*	Cl 17*	Sr(38)–Dy(60)*
W	74	L	1·476	1·487	Ni	28	1·487	0·993	−5·0	3·5	V 23	A 18	
Zn	30	K	1·435	1·439	Ni	28	1·487	0·966	−3·2	3·2	V 23	A 18	
Ir	77	L	1·351	1·363	Cu	29	1·380	0·979	−3·7	3·3	V 23	K 19	
Ga	31	K	1·340	1·344	Cu	29	1·380	0·972	−3·4	3·4	Cr 24	K 19	
Au	79	L	1·276	1·287	Zn	30	1·284	0·995	−5·1	3·5	Co 27	Ca 20	
Th	90	L	0·956	0·968	As	33	1·045	0·915	−1·9	3·0	Co 27	Ti 22	
					Se	34	0·980	0·975	−3·4	3·3	Ni 28	V 28	
U	92	L	0·911	0·922	Br	35	0·920	0·990	−4·5	3·4	Zn 30	Mn 25	
Zr	40	K	0·786	0·791	Rb	37	0·816	0·964	−3·0	3·2	Ga 31	Mn 25	
Nb	41	K	0·746	0·750	Sr	38	0·770	0·971	−3·2	3·2	Ge 32*	Fe 26*	Sb(51)–Rn(86)*
Mo	42	K	0·709	0·713	Sr	38	0·770	0·923	−2·0	3·0	As 33	Fe 26	
					Zr	40	0·688	0·926	−2·2	3·0			
Ru	44	K	0·643	0·647	Nb	41	0·653	0·986	−4·0	3·3	Br 35	Cu 29	
Ag	47	K	0·559	0·564	Ru	44	0·561	0·996	−5·3	3·6			

* Values from the table of Templeton. Other values in the last three columns are interpolated or extrapolated from the values with an asterisk.

scatterer. By a suitable choice of two unequal excitable atoms, in non-equivalent positions in the structure, and by the wise choice of corresponding wavelengths, first one and then the other, or both, atoms can be excited. In this case one observes the structure first from one anomalous scatterer position and then the other, or as a superposition of these two views.

This is a most powerful technique, and is often applicable. In the case of the vitamin B_{12} analysis, for example, a study of the selenocyanide with correct radiations would have revealed the distribution of C, N, O and P atoms first around the chelated cobalt, and then around the selenium atom. If these data had been collected and analysed, the analysis would have been vastly simplified.

Indexing of reflections to establish absolute configurations

For establishment of absolute configurations, it is essential to hold strictly to a right-handed coordinate system throughout the experiments; any departure from this is dangerous. Following are a few recommendations, especially for the orthogonal system, where the signs of indices are usually neglected:

- (a) set up a strict relationship between the real axes and the reciprocal axes, including the correct directions of the axes;
- (b) the usual concept of rotation of the reflecting sphere should be used with great care;
- (c) if the photographic method is employed with a Weissenberg camera, the relation between the direction of casette motion and the rotation of the crystal should be established carefully;
- (d) the final result must be represented in the same coordinate system as that used in defining the axes.

Peerdeman and Bijvoet have made some useful comments on those methods.[10]

Equality relations among reflections

For non-centrosymmetric crystals in point groups other than triclinic, certain equivalence conditions occur between reflections. These are useful in minimizing experimental difficulties, and from them the accuracy of intensity measurements may be checked. It is also possible to obtain an adequate absorption correction factor for crystals with irregular shape by considering the relations; e.g. for a crystal in 222, the absorption correction for hkl and $\bar{h}kl$ ($= \overline{h\bar{k}\bar{l}}$) can be made experimentally on the basis of the required equivalence of $hk0$ and $\bar{h}k0$ (valid only for $l = 0$). The equivalence conditions depend upon point-group and not space-group symmetry. The relations for all non-centrosymmetric point groups are given in Table 3.

TABLE 3

THE EQUALITY RELATIONS AMONG REFLECTIONS §

(Header: $hkl \;\not\equiv\; \bar{h}\bar{k}\bar{l}$)

POINT GROUPS	hkl	$\bar{h}\bar{k}\bar{l}$
C_1-1	hkl	$\bar{h}\bar{k}\bar{l}$
C_2-2 *	$hkl = \bar{h}k\bar{l}$	$\bar{h}\bar{k}\bar{l} = h\bar{k}l$
C_s-m *	$hkl = h\bar{k}l$	$\bar{h}\bar{k}\bar{l} = \bar{h}k\bar{l}$
$C_{2v}-mm2$ **	$hkl = \bar{h}kl = h\bar{k}l = \bar{h}\bar{k}l$	$\bar{h}\bar{k}\bar{l} = h\bar{k}\bar{l} = \bar{h}k\bar{l} = hk\bar{l}$
D_2-222	$hkl = \bar{h}k\bar{l} = h\bar{k}\bar{l} = \bar{h}\bar{k}l$	$\bar{h}\bar{k}\bar{l} = h\bar{k}l = \bar{h}kl = hk\bar{l}$
$S_4-\bar{4}$	$hkl = \bar{k}h\bar{l} = \bar{h}\bar{k}l = k\bar{h}\bar{l}$	$\bar{h}\bar{k}\bar{l} = k\bar{h}l = hk\bar{l} = \bar{k}hl$
C_4-4	$hkl = \bar{k}hl = \bar{h}\bar{k}l = k\bar{h}l$	$\bar{h}\bar{k}\bar{l} = k\bar{h}\bar{l} = hk\bar{l} = \bar{k}h\bar{l}$
D_{2d} † — $\bar{4}2m$	$hkl = khl \qquad +\bar{4}$	$\bar{h}\bar{k}\bar{l} = \bar{k}\bar{h}\bar{l} \qquad +\bar{4}$
D_{2d} — $\bar{4}m2$	$hkl = kh\bar{l} \qquad +\bar{4}$	$\bar{h}\bar{k}\bar{l} = \bar{k}\bar{h}l \qquad +\bar{4}$
$C_{4v}-4mm$	$hkl = \bar{h}kl \qquad +4$	$\bar{h}\bar{k}\bar{l} = h\bar{k}\bar{l} \qquad +4$
D_4-422	$hkl = \bar{k}\bar{h}\bar{l} \qquad +4$	$\bar{h}\bar{k}\bar{l} = khl \qquad +4$
C_3-3 — PRIMITIVE SPACE GROUPS	$hkl = ihl = kil$	$\bar{h}\bar{k}\bar{l} = \bar{i}\bar{h}\bar{l} = \bar{k}\bar{i}\bar{l}$
C_3-3 — RHOMBOHEDRAL SPACE GROUP	$hkl = klh = lhk$ (CYCLIC PERMUTATION)	$\bar{h}\bar{k}\bar{l} = \bar{k}\bar{l}\bar{h} = \bar{l}\bar{h}\bar{k}$ (CYCLIC PERMUTATION)
C_{3v} †† — P.S. $-3m1$	$hkl = \bar{k}\bar{h}l \qquad +3$	$\bar{h}\bar{k}\bar{l} = kh\bar{l} \qquad +3$
C_{3v} — P.S. $-31m$	$hkl = khl \qquad +3$	$\bar{h}\bar{k}\bar{l} = \bar{k}\bar{h}\bar{l} \qquad +3$
C_{3v} — R.S. $-3m$	$hkl = khl$ + (CYCLIC PERMUTATION)	$\bar{h}\bar{k}\bar{l} = \bar{k}\bar{h}\bar{l}$ + (CYCLIC PERMUTATION)
D_3 †† — P.S. -312	$hkl = \bar{k}\bar{h}\bar{l} \qquad +3$	$\bar{h}\bar{k}\bar{l} = khl \qquad +3$
D_3 — P.S. -321	$hkl = kh\bar{l} \qquad +3$	$\bar{h}\bar{k}\bar{l} = \bar{k}\bar{h}l \qquad +3$
D_3 — R.S. -32	$hkl = \bar{k}\bar{h}\bar{l}$ + (CYCLIC PERMUTATION)	$\bar{h}\bar{k}\bar{l} = khl$ + (CYCLIC PERMUTATION)
C_6-6	$hkl = ihl = kil = \bar{h}\bar{k}l = \bar{i}\bar{h}l = \bar{k}\bar{i}l$	$\bar{h}\bar{k}\bar{l} = \bar{i}\bar{h}\bar{l} = \bar{k}\bar{i}\bar{l} = hk\bar{l} = ih\bar{l} = ki\bar{l}$
$C_{3h}-\bar{6}$	$hkl = ihl = kil = hk\bar{l} = ih\bar{l} = ki\bar{l}$	$\bar{h}\bar{k}\bar{l} = \bar{i}\bar{h}\bar{l} = \bar{k}\bar{i}\bar{l} = \bar{h}\bar{k}l = \bar{i}\bar{h}l = \bar{k}\bar{i}l$
D_6-622	$hkl = kh\bar{l} \qquad +6$	$\bar{h}\bar{k}\bar{l} = \bar{k}\bar{h}l \qquad +6$
$C_{6v}-6mm$	$hkl = khl \qquad +6$	$\bar{h}\bar{k}\bar{l} = \bar{k}\bar{h}\bar{l} \qquad +6$
D_{3h} — $\bar{6}m2$	$hkl = \bar{k}\bar{h}l \qquad +\bar{6}$	$\bar{h}\bar{k}\bar{l} = kh\bar{l} \qquad +\bar{6}$
D_{3h} — $\bar{6}2m$	$hkl = khl \qquad +\bar{6}$	$\bar{h}\bar{k}\bar{l} = \bar{k}\bar{h}\bar{l} \qquad +\bar{6}$
$T-23$	(SAME AS 222 + CYCLIC PERMUTATION)	
$O-432$	(SAME AS 422 + CYCLIC PERMUTATION)	
$T_d-\bar{4}3m$	(SAME AS $\bar{4}2m$ + CYCLIC PERMUTATION)	

* The second setting is used for monoclinic crystals; the b axis is unique.

** The unique axis is along c.

† For the tetragonal system, the diagonal transformation does not affect the relations except in D_{2d}.

†† P.S. and R.S. denote primitive and rhombohedral space groups, respectively. If the rhombohedral space groups are described in the hexagonal setting, use the relations for 3m1 or 321.

§ Point groups to which crystals containing optically-active molecules and/or ions can belong.

These are determined by the Laue symmetry of each point group, less the conditions imposed by Friedel's rule. Special care must be taken with respect to the settings used in the tetragonal, trigonal and hexagonal systems. In Fig. 7, a typical example of equivalence relations is shown by using a set of reflections equivalent to (511) or ($\overline{5}1\overline{1}$) of KH_2AsO_4, in $F\overline{4}d2$; As is excited by MoKα, here.

The relations may also be used to remove ambiguities in point group determination. The present authors first pointed out that non-equivalence conditions between *hkl* and $\overline{hkl}$ in anomalous dispersion could be used to distinguish between centrosymmetric and non-centrosymmetric crystals.[14, 15] A careful inspection of the relations may also be used to solve ambiguities in point group determination (e.g. between C_2–2 and C_s–*m*).

It seems worthwhile to mention here that for a non-centrosymmetric crystal containing anomalous scatterers, a class with symmetry lower than the actual symmetry of the crystal might be chosen erroneously through observation of the departure from Laue symmetry. For example, an ortho-rhombic crystal in point group 222 could be thought to be monoclinic because of the lack of mirror symmetry across the principle axes on upper-layer Weissenberg photographs.

The anomalous neutron diffraction technique

Peterson and Smith[35] have recently carried out an experiment on the coherent neutron scattering of α-CdS, and obtained the real and imaginary parts of the scattering amplitude of cadmium as a function of neutron wavelengths.

The technique will be quite useful when a number of isotopes with reson-ances close to the thermal energies of neutrons can be found: especially when a crystal contains light atoms only (e.g. Li, B and Cl) and the wave-lengths of the commonly-used X-ray radiations are too far from the absorption edges of these light atoms.

Absolute configuration and its significance to physics and chemistry:
organic crystals

Although the number of absolute configurations determined to date is rather small, it seems worthwhile at this moment to make a list of the studies and discuss the significance of absolute configurations for physical and chemical problems.

The first example of absolute configuration determination was made about thirty years ago by Nishikawa and Matsukawa[1] and also by Coster, Knol and Prins[2]; they determined the absolute configuration of ZnS (zincblende) by exciting Zn by Au–$L\alpha_1$. The use of the dispersion techniques was then long neglected, and only in 1951 were the techniques again used. Bijvoet and his co-workers determined the absolute configuration of the L-(+)-tartrate ion by exciting Rb in NaRb tartrate and RbH tartrate. These determinations are based on the classical method; here a structure must be solved in the usual way, and a few pairs of reflections $|F_H|^2$ and $|F_{\bar{H}}|^2$ are examined to determine the *hand* of the structure. The L-configuration of natural amino acids was first established, using unnatural D-(−)-isoleucine hydrohalides, by Trommel and Bijvoet,[6] and subsequently the absolute configuration of L-aspartic acid in its cobaltous salt was determined by the newly-developed $P_s(u)$ function (Doyne, Pepinsky and Watanabe).[37] Other examples of absolute configuration determination of organic molecules include: ephedrine,[38] natural strychnine,[9] d-methadone,[39] L-lysine[40] and codeine.[41]

One of us (R. P.) first remarked[15] that if the absolute configuration of a part of a structure is known, then the absolute configuration of the total structure is established by the usual structure analysis without carrying out a dispersion experiment. This is useful in studying the total absolute configurations of large organic molecules; the absolute configuration of a part of an enzyme system chelated to an anomalous scatterer is often useful in obtaining the total configuration of the system.

It is strongly recommended that the newly-developed dispersion techniques be applied to the structure determinations of proteins. The encouraging factors are the recent development of the preparation of crystalline proteins containing heavy atoms (which can easily become anomalous scatterers) and direct and rapid photon-counting methods. The protein structure problem will no doubt take on an entirely different complexion, once this approach is made.

Furthermore, the use of $P_s(u)$ provides the only assured route known to us for the determination of a *portion* of a structure, without a determination of the entire. This excepts establishment of certain features of a simple structure from examination of the region around the origin peak (after sharpening). In large biological systems, such as enzymes, which contain anomalous scatterers such as divalent metal ions, the configuration of lighter atoms about these anomalous scatterers can be obtained directly from a Sum (S) or Minimum (M) function.

Extensive studies of the absolute configurations of various organic molecules must be carried out. The absolute configurations of the molecules before and after a stereospecific reaction answer, without ambiguity, the question of retention or inversion of the configuration. The results can elucidate mechanisms of many key chemical reactions in organic chemistry. This is one of the main directions of our own work at present.

Inorganic, complex ion, and piezo-, pyro- and ferroelectric crystal studies

Among optically-active inorganic crystals, or inorganic crystals with optically-active constituents, the following determinations may be mentioned. D-$[Co(en)_3]^{3+}$,[8] the 9-manganomolybdate ion,[42] ullmanite $(NiSbS)$,[43] $NaClO_3$,[44] and $NaBrO_3$.[12] The absolute configuration of α-quatrz[11] has been established in order to correlate optical rotation to the arrangement of tetrahedral SiO_4 groups in the crystal. The neutron determination of the absolute configuration of α-CdS has already been mentioned.[35]

In order to obtain unequivocal relations between crystal structures and polar phenomena such as piezoelectric, pyroelectric effects and others, it is essential to establish the absolute configurations of crystals showing such physical behavior, with respect to the polarity of the properties. The absolute configurations of crystals belonging to the KH_2PO_4 family[29] were determined, and the piezoelectric effect of the crystals is correlated to the structures. The relation between the morphology and the structure has been studied for semiconductors such as InSb.[45]

For ferroelectric crystals, unambiguous relations must be established between the directions of shifts of atoms and the electrical polarization. The determination of the absolute configurations of polarized ferroelectrics[29] was also undertaken on $BaTiO_3$, $(glycine)_3 \cdot H_2SO_4$ and the low-temperature phase of KH_2AsO_4; and many others are under examination in our laboratory.

Final comments

It must be understood that these new developments of dispersion techniques places the solution of non-centrosymmetric crystals on a completely new basis; the solution is now in the data, and all that is required are proper measurements. The solution of non-centrosymmetric structures containing excited atoms is now essentially direct, whereas the same remark cannot be made for centrosymmetric structures. This is a strange twist in crystallography.

Accurate measurements of diffracted data are now readily possible, and with vastly reduced personal effort, through the availability of automatic single-crystal photon-counting instruments.

Chemical ingenuity to insure incorporation of suitable scatterers in structures, plus wise choice of X-ray wavelengths, is still required. Considering the possible gains from exercise of such wisdom, collaboration between chemists and physicists should be much more extensive than heretofore.

Acknowledgments

The development of the $P_s(u)$ function technique has been aided from the outset by financial support from the National Institutes of Health (Grant

U

No. A–228), and by Contract No. N6onr–26916 with the Office of Naval Research. Instrumental developments and absolute configuration studies of physical properties have been supported by: the Office of Ordnance Research, U.S. Army (Contract No. DA–36–061–ORD–601, for construction of our automatic single-crystal photon-counting goniometer SCADAC); by the Directorate of Solid State Sciences of the Air Force Office of Scientific Research, ARDC (Contract No. AF 18(603)–35); and by the U.S. Atomic Energy Commission (Contract No. AT(30–1)–1516). Work on optically-active complex ion structures, and their use in absolute configuration studies *via* salt formation with optically-active organic ions, was supported by the Directorate of Chemical Sciences, Air Force Office of Scientific Research, ARDC (Contract No. AF 18(600)–1516). We are, of course, very pleased to be able to acknowledge all of this support.

REFERENCES

1. NISHIKAWA, S. and MATSUKAWA, K. (1928). *Proc. Imp. Acad. Japan* **4**, 96.
2. COSTER, D., KNOL, K. S. and PRINS, J. (1930). *Z. Physik.* **63**, 345.
3. BIJVOET, J. M. (1949). *Koninkl. Ned. Akad. Wetenschap.* **52**, 313.
4. PEERDEMAN, A. F., VAN BOMMEL, A. J. and BIJVOET, J. M. (1951). *Proc. Roy. Soc. Amsterdam* **B54**, 16.
5. BIJVOET, J. M. (1954). *Nature* **173**, 888.
6. TROMMEL, J. and BIJVOET, J. M. (1954). *Acta Cryst.* **7**, 703.
7. BIJVOET, J. M. (1955). *Endeavour* **14**, 71.
8. SAITO, Y., NAKATSU, K., SHIRO, M. and KUROYA, H. (1955). *Acta Cryst.* **8**, 729.
9. PEERDEMAN, A. F. (1956). *Acta Cryst.* **9**, 824.
10. PEERDEMAN, A. F. and BIJVOET, J. M. (1956). *Acta Cryst.* **9**, 1012.
11. DE VRIES, A. (1958). *Nature* **181**, 1193.
12. BIJVOET, J. M. (1960). Abstract, 19.7 Fifth Congress, International Union of Crystallography, Cambridge, England. August, 1960.
13. OKAYA, Y., SAITO, Y. and PEPINSKY, R. (1955). *Phys. Rev.* **98**, 1857.
14. PEPINSKY, R. and OKAYA, Y. (1956). *Proc. Nat. Acad. Sci. U.S.* **42**, 286.
15. PEPINSKY, R. (1956). *Record Chem. Progress* (Kresge Hooker, Sci. Lib.) **17**, 145.
16. OKAYA, Y. and PEPINSKY, R. (1956). *Phys. Rev.* **103**, 1645.
17. PEPINSKY, R. and OKAYA, Y. (1957). *Phys. Rev.* **108**, 1231.
18. WILSON, A. J. C. (1949). *Acta Cryst.* **2**, 318.
19. HÖNL, H. (1933). *Z. Physik.* **84**, 1.
20. TAKEUCHI, Y. (1960). Private communication to R. Pepinsky, March 1, 1960.
21. MACKAY, A. L. (1957). *Acta Cryst.* **10**, 542.
22. COCHRAN, W. (1953). *Acta Cryst.* **5**, 620.
23. BUERGER, M. J. (1959). *Vector Space.* Wiley, New York.
24. TAKEUCHI, Y., OKAYA, Y. and PEPINSKY, R. (1956). Abstract B–4, Am. Cryst. Assoc. Meeting, French Lick, Indiana, June 1956.
25. TAYLOR, W. J. (1953). *J. Appl. Phys.* **24**, 662.
26. DOYNE, T., PEPINSKY, R. and WATANABE, T. (1957). *Acta Cryst.* **10**, 438.
27. RAMACHANDRAN, G. N. and RAMAN, S. (1959). *Acta Cryst.* **12**, 957.
28. RAMAN, S. (1959). *Acta Cryst.* **12**, 964.
29. PEPINSKY, R., OKAYA, Y. and UNTERLEITNER, F. Abstract 12.3, Fifth Congress, International Union of Crystallography, Cambridge, England. August, 1960. Also *Phys. Rev.* (to be published).
30. HOSHINO, S., OKAYA, Y. and PEPINSKY, R. (1959). *Phys. Rev.* **115**, 323.

31. PEPINSKY, R. (1945) *Phys. Rev.* **67**, 308; (1946) **69**, 546; (1948) **74**, 126. Cf. also DRENCK, K. and PEPINSKY, R. (1951) *Rev. Sci. Instr.* **22**, 539.
32. JAMES, R. W. (1950). *Optical Principles of the Diffraction of X-Rays.* G. Bell, London, p. 608.
33. DAUBEN, C. H. and TEMPLETON, D. H. (1955). *Acta Cryst.* **8**, 841.
34. TEMPLETON, D. H. (1960). *Dispersion Corrections for Atomic Scattering Factors.* University of California, Lawrence Radiation Laboratory, Berkeley, Report UCRL–9146, March 1960.
35. PETERSON, S. W. and SMITH, H. G. (1960). Abstract 15.3, Fifth Congress, International Union of Crystallography, Cambridge, England, August 1960.
36. VAN BOMMELL, A. J. (1953). *Proc. Roy. Soc. Amsterdam* **B56**, 268.
37. DOYNE, T., PEPINSKY, R. and WATANABE, T. (1957). *Acta Cryst.* **10**, 438.
38. RAMACHANDRAN, G. N. and RAMAN, S. (1956). *Curr. Sci. India* **25**, 348.
39. HANSON, A. W. and AHMED, F. R. (1958). *Acta Cryst.* **11**, 724.
40. RAMAN, S. (1959). *Z. Krist.* **111**, 301.
41. KARTHA, G., AHMED, F. R. and BARNES, W. H. (1960). Abstract 6.18, Fifth Congress, International Union of Crystallography, Cambridge, England, August 1960.
42. METZGER, P. H., CONNER, G., RYBA, E. R. and SHOEMAKER, D. P. (1959). Abstract, A.C.A. meeting, July, 1959.
43. TAKEUCHI, Y. (1957). *Mineral. J.* **2**, 90.
44. RAMACHANDRAN, G. N. and CHANDRASEKARAN, K. S. (1957). *Acta Cryst.* **10**, 671.
45. WAREKOIS, E. P. and METZGER, P. H. (1900). *J. Appl. Phys.* **30**, 960.

DISCUSSION

Some account of the discussions at the Conference is collected here. Sometimes the discussion following a single paper is given; at other times the discussion of several consecutive papers is collected together. It has in some cases seemed desirable to edit the discussion. The Editor (J. C. S.) wishes to apologize to any contributors whose views may thereby have been slightly distorted.

Papers 1-6a

(Read by D. ROGERS, H. JAGGI, A. NIGGLI, G. A. JEFFREY, D. W. J. CRUICKSHANK and H. J. MILLEDGE)

S. C. ABRAHAMS commented on the disturbing fact that the larger and more rapid computers tend to become obsolete more quickly. However, he suggested that the smaller, and out-dated machines may continue to be useful for simple operations. A number of other speakers (including G. A. JEFFREY, J. L. KATZ and J. LADELL) agreed, and pointed out their value for teaching purposes, and as taking the place of the desk calculator.

F. H. HERBSTEIN stressed the desirability of crystallographers having immediate access to a small machine for the earlier stages of a structure analysis, and some easy means of access to a large machine for the later stages—and this latter without excessive expense. D. P. SHOEMAKER mentioned a project being undertaken by the A.C.A. Computing Committee to provide a list of programs (primarily for machines available in the United States), with as much information on each program as can be accommodated in a small space. The list already contains over 200 programs, and should be issued shortly. The usefulness of any such list remains to be seen.

F. R. AHMED described programs he had developed for IBM 650, and stressed the desirability of designing generalized programs, applicable to any space group. J. LADELL mentioned programs for the Royal Precision McBee LGP 30 and the Bendix G 15 machines.

M. G. ROSSMANN explained how interatomic distances and angles could be derived, by vector methods, from fractional coordinates, without the necessity for orthogonalization; but several other speakers felt that such orthogonalization was generally useful.

300

P. PAULING suggested a new use for a general-purpose electronic digital computer. " There have been many people interested in the automatic collection of single crystal diffraction data and several solutions to the problems involved have been proposed and tried. Any automatic instrument involves some sort of logical operations and those instruments built or designed so far involve mechanical and simple types of electronic logic. I think the time has now arrived when the cost of the simplest specialized home-made logical apparatus of the complexity required by this problem is higher than the cost of mass-produced completely general electronic logic in the form of a small digital computer. There are at least two machines available in the United States (and one of them is marketed in the United Kingdom) for less than $30,000 and the cost of such machines is falling fairly rapidly while the cost of specialized equipment is rising.

So used a computer allows very complicated logical operations to control apparatus which give a number of additional advantages: the physical apparatus can be the simplest possible, the processes involved in the collection of data can be as complicated as desired or required, the collection procedure can be changed easily and rapidly without modification of the physical equipment, elaborate checking procedures are possible, and so forth."

Papers 7-9

(Read by J. S. ROLLETT, M. WELLS and O. S. MILLS)

M. M. WOOLFSON described a MERCURY program for applying absorption corrections. It assumes that the crystal is a parallelepiped, and with this simplification works out correction-factors at the rate of about one per second.

There was some discussion of the usefulness of encouraging crystallographers to develop small, individual programs; and the general opinion was that even " amateur " programmers should be thus encouraged.

J. C. SPEAKMAN explained how valuable and effective had been the DEUCE programs, developed by Rollett, in expediting the structural analyses done at Glasgow during the past eighteen months. O. KENNARD expressed similar appreciation of the Mills–Rollett programs for MERCURY.

DEUCE programs written and tested by members of the Chemistry Department, Glasgow University

(1) *General Fourier Section* (J. G. SIME)

Space groups of monoclinic, or higher, symmetry. Values of z corresponding to a specified xy-grid are calculated in the plane, $k_1x+k_2y+k_3z+k_4 = 0$, and rounded off to the nearest 1/3600th. The series is then summed at these points. Time: about 40 msec per reflection-point.

(2) *Data Reduction* (J. G. SIME)

Applies Lorentz-polarization and Tunell factors to intensity data from equi-inclination, Weissenberg photographs. Triclinic data can be dealt with. Output: $|F|$, another program being available for converting these to F^2. Time: about 3 min per 100 reflections.

(3) *Interatomic Distance Routine* (J. G. SIME)

Accepts triclinic data, for up to 128 atoms with 12 related molecules. The maximum and minimum distances required are specified, and all distances between these limits are punched. Orthogonal coordinates can be output optionally. Time: for 76 atoms, 9 related molecules, distances up to 4·0 Å, 25 min.

A related program calculates the two distances and the bond-angle between any three specified atoms. Time: 2 sec per angle.

(4) *Bond-Angles* (J. C. SPEAKMAN)

Inputs three interatomic distances per card; outputs bond-angle in degrees to 3 dec. places. Time: 1 sec per angle.

(5) *Mean Molecular Plane* (D. G. WATSON)

Determines the best plane by the method of Schomaker *et al.* (1959). Accepts monoclinic coordinates; atoms can be weighted in any desired way.

(6) T and ω *Tensors* (J. G. SIME)

An alpha-code program in 5 parts, following the method of Cruickshank (1956).

Paper 10

(Read by W. N. LIPSCOMB)

J. M. ROBERTSON asked what criteria limit the resolution obtainable by superposition methods, and LIPSCOMB replied: " One relative parameter in estimating the complexity of structure which may be solved by consecutive superposition techniques may be the number of Patterson peaks per cubic Ångstrom. This number is 2·8 peaks/Å³ for cellobiose. With the use of careful resolution of superimposed peaks by empirical or analytical methods which make use of the known shapes of these peaks, it seems possible to increase the complexity of equal-atom structures which might be solved by this method very considerably. Each structure has its own personality, however, and the cellobiose structure was characterized by many almost six-membered rings, all non-planar, and probably had more than its share of nearly homometric structures." LIPSCOMB went on to stress the importance of a correct choice of small peaks for superposition, and added: " The three peaks of the first three three-dimensional superpositions were chosen with the view that they were a bond distance apart and at a tetrahedral angle, and hence contained some chemical information. Indeed, a very important aspect of these procedures is that any chemical information that one has is usually very useful even at the start and certainly at the end of the consecutive superpositions."

J. LADELL asked whether statistical methods were required for the removal of the origin-peak, and LIPSCOMB replied: " Statistical methods are essential in order to recognize which interactions are single, double, or more complicated. We do remove the origin peak, however, mostly for reasons of numerical convenience, even though its removal does not seem essential in most applications. What is essential is that a consecutive set of three-dimensional superpositions be carried out on Patterson peaks the centers of which represent *accurately* the true interatomic distances. Small errors (0·2 Å?) in the locations of these centers can cause the true structure to disappear almost completely into the general background after several consecutive superpositions."

K. DORNBERGER-SCHIFF asked whether the modification of the Patterson function might lead to secondary (diffraction) maxima which might lead to errors in peak positions in the superposition function; and LIPSCOMB replied: " Both the subsidiary minima and maxima are reduced in our sharpening procedures. Their complete elimination would broaden the main maximum so much as to spoil the resolution. The minor ripple around a nicely resolved single maximum is not great enough to be of any importance. However, in the example of cellobiose, one of the Harker peaks chosen for superposition was really only a small shoulder on a much larger peak, and it is precisely here that the minima around the comparatively uninformative large peak can displace the location of the small single or double interaction which must be accurately located if the several consecutive superpositions are to yield the structure. Hence it is important to reduce both the subsidiary maxima and minima associated with termination of the data."

H. J. MILLEDGE suggested that low-temperature data might be better because they would need less sharpening than those obtained at room temperature; and H. N. SHRIVASTAVA questioned the advisability of over-much sharpening.

R. PEPINSKY mentioned an analytical expression for the minimum function; this was given by M. G. ROSSMANN as follows:
$$\text{`` } \rho_{\text{new}} = (\rho_1 + \rho_2) - \mid (\rho_1 - \rho_2) \mid$$

where ρ_1 and ρ_2 are the superimposed densities. Thus $\rho_{new} =$ Sum Function $-$ | Diff. Function |. While both the Sum Function and the Difference Function may be computed by suitable Fourier summations, it is impossible to determine the *modulus* of the Difference Function simultaneously with the calculation of the Sum Function. Thus computation of ρ_{new} must proceed in two steps: (1) calculation of $(\rho_1 + \rho_2)$; (2) calculation of $(\rho_1 - \rho_2)$. There is obviously no advantage in this procedure as compared with one calculation of the Patterson function and taking the minimum between it and its translated variation."

Paper 11

(Read by D. P. SHOEMAKER)

In reply to H. HAUPTMAN, SHOEMAKER explained that MIFR 1 could not be adapted to meshes finer than 1/120th of the cell edge, but that, when the program was re-written for IBM 709 and 7090, such a facility would be introduced.

J. L. KATZ gave $2\frac{1}{2}$ as an approximate factor for the gain in speed of a program written in machine code SAP over one in the interpretive scheme FORTRAN; but O. S. MILLS said that the corresponding ratio between PIG and AUTOCODE programs on MERCURY was lower—in the region of $1\cdot2:1\cdot0$.

M. WELLS said: " A method of carrying out a one-dimensional Fourier summation does not appear to be very well known. We require

$$A = \sum_0^{n-1} y_r \cos r\theta$$
$$B = \sum_0^{n-1} y_r \sin r\theta$$

Define a recurrence relation

$$t_r = 2t_{r+1} \cos\theta + y_r - t_{r+2}$$

and let

$$t_n = 0, t_{n-1} = y_{n-1}$$

Thus

$$A = t_0 - t_1 \cos\theta \text{ and } B = t_1 \sin\theta.$$

This method has the advantage of needing only the values of $\cos\theta$ and $\sin\theta$, rather than a series of values; it is also very economic of high-speed working space, and eliminates a multiplication for each term. This method is most useful in the second and third stages of a summation."

J. S. ROLLETT replied: " The method described by Dr. Wells is published by C. W. Clenshaw, in *Math. Tables and Aids to Computation*. I have considered it as a means of reducing the number of multiplications required, but rejected it because of the need to carry out operations for terms with zero amplitudes."

W. HOPPE mentioned the possibility of eliminating multiplications by using the same amplitudes for all Fourier terms, with the introduction of suitable phase-shifts, and stated that this system had been used in his small-scale analogue machine. " In principle, each Fourier wave will be replaced by two phase-shifted Fourier waves with constant amplitude. It is possible to translate this scheme into the language of a computer. The phase-shift means a shift in the table of the sine-function. It is necessary to choose a suitably fine mesh for the sine table. But—and this is the important point— the overall storage capacity needed for this table is smaller than for Beevers– Lipson table with two entries. Strong amplitudes can be broken up in a similar manner as in the MIFR 1 program. Another advantage is the continuous variability of grid spacing, which allows for direct plotting of contours in the paper output by the machine. There is one difficulty: the relation between phase-shift and amplitude is non-linear and it is difficult not to lose the advantage of eliminating multiplication because of the slow function-generating process. One possibility, of course, is the introduction of a table between phase and amplitude; but such a solution needs further storage capacity. This scheme can also be used for structure factor calculations, the sine functions being introduced in tabular form."

Papers 12 and 13

(Read by H. A. LEVY)

R. PEPINSKY asked for information about a program for preparing stereoscopic pictures of crystal structures, and LEVY replied: " This program, prepared by Dr. Busing, produces a stereoscopic pair of pictures of a crystal structure on the cathode ray tube output unit of the IBM 704. The input to the program includes a list of the independent atomic parameters (this may be taken from the output of a least squares cycle), the unit cell parameters, the symmetry relations, the number of unit cells desired, and the direction of view defined by three angles of rotation about mutually perpendicular axes. Perspective effects are included by shortening the more distant features and plotting them less densely. Atoms are portrayed by an array of dots on the surface of a sphere and thus appear somewhat transparent; the size of sphere and number of dots can be specified to distinguish atoms of different kinds. Provision has been made for outlining the unit cell and for supplying labels. The pair of pictures on 35 mm film may be mounted in a standard stereo frame and viewed with a stereo viewer, either directly or projected on a screen. We find that these pictures fulfil at least some of the functions of a model of the structure."

In answer to questions asked in discussion, LEVY added that this program was written for the 8192-word memory unit, and that specified atoms in the stereoscopic picture can be joined by bond-lines.

His reply to a question by R. A. SPARKS, about the relative effectivenesses of diagonal and full-matrix least squares refinement, was: " We have not ourselves carried out a refinement using the diagonal approximation, but we have had others report that one cycle of the complete matrix refinement would be roughly equivalent to three of the diagonal approximation, in cases in which the latter converged satisfactorily."

J. WUNDERLICH: " Cellobiose has 23 C and O atoms in the asymmetric unit and has been refined using both diagonal approximation and full-matrix least squares programs. In the former case over 20 cycles were computed with no end in sight. In the latter case only 4 cycles were required, though partially refined parameters were used as initial input."

D. FEIL asked whether the matrix of a preceding cycle had ever been used in refinement, and LEVY replied: " In one case we tried the normal equations matrix of the preceding cycle in combination with a newly computed vector, and compared the parameter changes thus given with those from a complete cycle. There was little resemblance. This was done in the early stage of the refinement."

J. S. ROLLETT said he has used the technique of using the same normal matrix in successive cycles with the block diagonal program for MERCURY. It was done at the end of the refinement to reduce the shifts from 0·01 Å to a negligible value, and the result was quite successful, saving one-third of the computer time.

J. D. DUNITZ pointed out that the full-matrix method was essential in dealing with disordered structures; for such cases, which are not uncommon, full-matrix programs ought therefore to be available.

Paper 14

(Read by D. H. TEMPLETON)

H. J. MILLEDGE asked whether crystal energies might be derivable by adding a suitable routine to a program designed for calculating interatomic distances. TEMPLETON agreed that it might be possible, but certainly difficult in the general case.

K. DORNBERGER-SCHIFF drew attention to the work of Emersleben. " He obtained closed mathematical expressions and found that crystal energies contain different terms: one proportional to the volume, containing Madelung sums, a second term proportional to the surface but depending on the planes *hkl* limiting the crystal, a third term proportional to the length of the edges of the crystal, and finally an absolute term. As a matter of fact, we are always faced with finite crystals and I wonder whether it would be more appropriate to consider these expressions in which the difficulties of the convergence of the infinite series do not occur, rather than the infinite series corresponding to the first term only." TEMPLETON replied: " The earliest paper I know of concerning the calculation of surface energy is by Born and Stern, whose calculation is in the spirit of the work described by Prof. Dornberger-Schiff. It is well known that in CsCl, one can get convergence to one limit if one sums for one ion in a space terminated in a cube with cations on the surface and to another limit if anions are on the surface. Thus it is possible to get quite wrong answers. On the other hand, one can get good accuracy by going only a few unit cells if a unit of structure can be chosen with very high symmetry." E. F. BERTAUT added that Templeton's calculations were valid for the ideal infinite crystal, in which the crystallographer is generally interested. The surface terms mentioned by Dornberger-Schiff depended on the size of the crystal, and were of interest only to the physicist concerned with crystal growth, surface reactivity, etc.

In reply to G. A. JEFFREY, TEMPLETON explained that the Madelung constants quoted in the literature for simple cubic structures (without variable atomic parameters) are reliable, but that many others are in error.

D. ROGERS said that he had recently used ZEBRA to estimate the aggregate dipole–dipole energy for 6: 6-nylon. He chose to include all dipoles within a sphere of radius 40 Å. A plot of energy against radius reached approximate constancy at about 25 Å, though oscillations of about 5% amplitude were still evident at 40 Å.

Papers 15 and 16

(Read by R. PEPINSKY and A. NIGGLI)

V. VAND explained that the Fourier programs were designed to display functions in thousandths of the cell edge; this could be conveniently achieved by calculating the function at hundredths of the cell edge and doing one cubic and one linear interpolation.

R. E. DICKERSON: (a) Would not the convergence of the optimal shift method be faster if, instead of using as the shift in each atomic parameter that value indicated by the reflection of maximum weight, one were to use a weighted average of the shift over all reflections in the subset? (b) How sensitive is this method to the particular choice of subset? NIGGLI: (a) This might be faster to calculate, but the convergence would be slower, as the spoiling by the other shifts would not be taken into account. (b) Very sensitive—if the sequence of the *hkl* to be handled is not chosen according to an appropriate weight, the convergence has proved to be much worse; e.g. if an important low-order *hkl* is corrected too late, it will spoil all the corrections previously made for higher orders.

M. M. WOOLFSON asked what were the advantages of this method compared with an examination of the $(F_o - F_c)$ map as suggested by Cochran, and added: " As a student I often tried to determine structures by moving trial molecules about a unit cell to get good fit for the axial reflections. This often gave brilliant agreement for completely incorrect structures and I feel that the same may very often be true even when a more random small selection of structure factors is chosen for refinement."

NIGGLI: " (a) This is correct, but the optimal shift method was designed specially in context with the random method Dr. Vand will talk about; and there it is essential that a computer can roughly refine and test a huge number of trial structures in a short time. (b) Of course, good agreement may be attained for a number of false structures; but it is up to the crystallographer to judge the choice of structure models offered by the computer, and later on to include more structure factors."

H. J. MILLEDGE commented that ordinary least squares methods, if protected by a provision to prevent doubtful signs from interfering with rapid convergence, seemed as effective, in the early stages of refinement, as examining one reflection at a time; to which NIGGLI replied: " The method as well as the program is devised for three-dimensional work. There is another reason for that: the shifts perpendicular to the *hkl*-plane are much more interrelated than two-dimensional shifts perpendicular to *hk*-lines, therefore a better convergence towards the right solution may be expected."

I. OLOVSSON suggested the use of the weighting system,

$$w = \Delta F / \{\sigma(F) \sin \theta\},$$

to avoid undue influence from terms likely to have large errors.

J. D. DUNITZ: " I think that it is proper, at some time during these proceedings, to raise the question of the comparative use (and usefulness) of computers and human brains. It is clearly of importance to program computers for the tasks to which they are best suited and not to burden them with problems which we can solve more efficiently ourselves.

We are particularly good at problems involving recognition of patterns out of the flux of impressions, even when these patterns do not correspond in detail to what we might have expected on the basis of our past experience. All of us here can recognize Professor Pepinsky without knowing exactly how tall he is, or how heavy, or the colour of his shirt. For all I know, it might be possible to program a computer to recognize Professor Pepinsky and thus to distinguish him from the hundred or so people in this audience, according to some set of specified criteria. Yet I am sure that Professor Pepinsky has the ingenuity to deceive our hypothetical computer, by wearing a false moustache, or dark glasses, or a bowler hat, or Dr. Cruickshanks' conference badge, or some combination of these. He would deceive the computer, but we should recognize him at once through his disguise.

I believe that the early stages of structure analysis depend very largely on such processes of recognition of patterns. These processes, it seems to me, are based not entirely on specified, or even potentially specifiable sets of criteria but also on the totality of our experience in such matters—on intuition, if you like. I am still to be convinced that computers can do this sort of thing as well as we can.

Dr. Niggli's very interesting paper provides me with an excuse to raise this point which I should very much like to hear discussed by those more competent to do so than myself."

Papers 17 and 18

(Read by R. A. SPARKS)

J. S. ROLLETT: " The latent roots of symmetric matrices of the type

$$
\begin{bmatrix}
50 & \pm 1 & \pm 1 \dots \\
\pm 1 & 50 & \pm 1 \dots \\
\pm 1 & \pm 1 & 50 \dots \\
\dots\dots\dots\dots\dots \\
\dots\dots\dots\dots\dots
\end{bmatrix}
$$

where the off-diagonal terms are $+1$ or -1, equally frequently and distributed at random, have been determined for various orders, n. It is found that $\lambda_{max} - \lambda_{min}$ is proportional to $n^{\frac{3}{2}}$. Since the ratio between the size of the diagonal and off-diagonal terms tends to go as $n^{\frac{1}{2}}$ this suggests that convergence difficulties get worse as $n^{\frac{1}{2}}$.

For $n = 64$ and 700 observations, $\lambda_{max}/\bar{\lambda} = 1\cdot52$ and $\lambda_{min}/\bar{\lambda} = 0\cdot46$. This suggests that about half of the difficulty with anthracene comes from the random fluctuations of the cross terms about their expectation values. The other half of the difficulty with block diagonal approximations with good scale-factor adjustment appears to be due to deviations of the mean values of the interatomic cross terms from zero."

D. W. J. CRUICKSHANK congratulated Sparks on his fine analysis of the efficiency of the various least squares approximations. He had originally intended, not to couple the scale with the average isotropic vibration in a 2×2 matrix, but to couple the scale with the average anisotropic vibrations in a 7×7 matrix. The reasons for this were connected with the accidental absences and were analysed in a paper (Cruickshank, (1956) *Acta Cryst.* **9,** 747) on anisotropic refinement by differential syntheses. Sparks' results for anthracene suggested that the 2×2 method was almost perfect for dealing with the scale, but Cruickshank thought that the 7×7 method might be appreciably better with layer structures when the refinement first progressed from individual isotropy to individual anisotropy.

W. N. LIPSCOMB: " Dr. Sparks deserves a great deal of credit for presenting us with algorithms which derive the effects on convergence in various least squares methods. What he has said about the purely diagonal least squares, and the full matrix least squares does indeed correspond very well with our experience, and hence we may have confidence that these new proposals in which certain off-diagonal terms are included will converge as efficiently as he indicates.

We certainly agree that one must not terminate the purely diagonal approximation when the shifts are on the order of the standard deviations. In our experience, when the shifts are about 0.1 times the standard deviations, in usual cases, the diagonal refinement may be safely terminated; and hence Dr. Sparks' remark that one must continue until the shifts are much less must, as he has indicated, refer to unusually pessimistic situations.

Neglect of off-diagonal terms for temperature and distance parameters, and especially the use of a single overall temperature factor for all atoms does, however, not allow for the discovery of incorrectly placed atoms (especially light atoms in a structure also containing heavy atoms) at earlier stages of the least squares analysis. Hence, there may be some preference for separate temperature factors on each atom, in spite of the longer computing time required, in the event that there may be incorrectly placed atoms in the trial structure."

H. J. MILLEDGE: " It may be true that mathematically it is advisable to continue until the shifts from a diagonal least squares refinement are of the order of 0.003 of the standard deviation, but since the standard deviation itself may be of the order of 0.001 in fractional coordinates, is it likely that such small shifts make chemical sense? " SPARKS: " How small would you say that the last set of shifts should be? Let me emphasize that the values quoted in the table are for the *worst* possible cases. However, one never knows that a given situation is *not* such a case. Therefore, I think one should be extremely cautious in *every* situation." In reply to a comment from V. VAND, SPARKS added: "The gradient technique which very closely resembles that of Vand and Pepinsky can be shown geometrically to be shifts in the direction of the gradient of ϕ and which terminate at a point where the shift vector is orthogonal to a new gradient direction. If the trial solution happens to be in a very long and narrow valley (corresponding to minimum and maximum eigenvectors), successive shifts will be orthogonal to one another but convergence will still be slow. The conjugate-gradient method is difficult to visualize geometrically. However, it is guaranteed to converge in n iterations and in practice converges much more rapidly than this."

D. VAN DER HELM, relaying a comment of C. H. MacGillavry: "Is it allowed to leave out the second-order differential quotients from a least squares calculation? Or is the effect estimated? The problem occurs quite often with a structure containing one heavy atom where, for instance, because the heavy atom is near a special position, half of the reflections are weak and the other half quite strong. In that case the second order differential quotients of the latter half may be quite large." SPARKS: "I have not investigated the influence of higher orders; however, some indication of their effect is given in the results where a poor trial structure was used to obtain the B-matrix."

C. J. BROWN and O. S. MILLS: The following table gives the times, in minutes, taken by L.S. programs written for two commercial British computers, PEGASUS and MERCURY. The problem was one which involved a centrosymmetric space group, $P2_1/c$, containing 14 atoms of 3 types, all in general positions. There were 917 non-zero reflections.

Notes for following Table

(1) Only that part of the program which is necessary for forming the L.S. equations is input at this stage. Each reflection is read off tape as required.
(2) The complete program and all the reflection ($h\,k\,l\,F$) data are stored in the machine; the reflection data are read twice for checking purposes.
(3) The 40% increase in time arises not from the increased amount of arithmetic involved in the 5×5 matrices (which involve the 3 positional parameters, thermal parameter and overall scale factor, i.e. the Curtis–Mills method (see p. 121), but through the necessity of communication with the drum.
(4) Roughly one-half of this increase in time is spent in "waiting" for the drum after a writing transfer.
(5) Basically the same information is output in all the programs; in the examples listed above, however, the MERCURY programs utilized a tabular lay-out whereas the PEGASUS output was of the minimum number of characters.
(6) The PEGASUS time includes that needed to read in the remainder of the program required for solution of the normal equations. The output of this program includes a weighting-scheme analysis in addition to the usual shifts, etc., output by both programs.

(7) An anisotropic refinement on MERCURY for this problem (again coded in AUTOCODE, and with all drum transfers checked) takes 64 minutes running time.

Anisotropic refinement. The refinement of cellobiose (45 atoms in the space group $P2_1$, of which 23 were refined anisotropically) which involved 1116 planes took 363 minutes on Cruickshank's PEGASUS program and 110 minutes on Rollett's MERCURY program.

The figures given below indicate clearly two main points: (i) the degree by which a program is slowed down whenever drum access is required, and (ii) the success achieved by Cruickshank in his programs for PEGASUS which has a very small immediate access store. Unfortunately it has not been possible to obtain information to decide whether it is more economic to perform more cycles of diagonal least squares (with an appropriate damping factor) rather than fewer, though longer, cycles where some off-diagonal terms are taken into account.

ISOTROPIC REFINEMENT
(Times in minutes)

Operation	PEGASUS program (D.W.J.C.) (3 × 3 for positions; 1 × 1 for thermal B_i)	MERCURY programs coded in AUTOCODE (O.S.M.)		
		Diagonal approxima-tion	5 × 5 matrix	5 × 5 matrix with drum transfers checked digit by digit
Input of program and data	3·5[1]	5[2]	5	5
Calculation time without output[7]	81	18	26[3]	33[4]
Output time for structure factors, etc. during calculation	7·5	13[5]	13	13
Solution of L.S. equations and output of answers	5·8[6]	1·5	2	2

Papers 20 and 21

(Read by E. F. BERTAUT and H. HAUPTMAN)

H. N. SHRIVASTAVA asked BERTAUT if he would clarify the meaning of the term " structure factor of order p "—in particular as to its significance in direct space. BERTAUT explained that the pth order structure factor was defined as that obtained when the scattering factors of the atoms are raised to the pth power. W. COCHRAN added to this explanation the comment that it was as well to note that, in the centrosymmetric case, the sign of the structure factor of order p would probably be that of F itself but may be different. Only in the case of a structure containing equal atoms would the signs certainly be the same. This point is of importance in assessing the value of some sign determining formulae which actually determine the probable sign of some higher order structure factor.

H. J. MILLEDGE then asked whether the usefulness of equations involving higher powers of the structure factors suggests that there could be some advantage in calculating " Patterson functions " using higher powers of the structure factors. BERTAUT was non-committal but did point out that the formulae would only calculate the signs of invariant structure factors of order p. W. COCHRAN gave even less encouragement to the idea by quoting the example of the F^4 synthesis which would yield the " Patterson of the Patterson." He did not see how this could be of any use. However, M. M. WOOLFSON did recall that in a paper by McLachlan it was shown that, theoretically at any rate, the manipulation of the Patterson function and functions of higher powers of F could reveal the structure itself. J. M. COWLEY referred to some work of his own in this field which was published in the paper *Acta Cryst.* **9**, 397. This showed that if a power series in intensities, which approximates to the structure amplitudes, is used instead of the intensities the effect is to sharpen the Patterson function in a manner which differs from that of the usual sharpening procedures. The previously mentioned paper discussed the application of this type of function.

E. F. BERTAUT made three points in commenting on HAUPTMAN's paper. These were—(i) as far as moment calculations are concerned it is only necessary to consider the moment generating function. To perform the task via consideration of the joint distribution functions is an unnecessary complication. (ii) One may state simply that the main invariants correspond to polygons in reciprocal space described by

$$\sum_j \vec{H_j} = 0 \text{ and } \sum_j \phi_j(H_j) = \text{invariant}\{\phi_j(H_j) = \text{phase of } E(H_j)\}.$$

(iii) The equations given for $P1$ and $P\bar{1}$ by Hauptman are not valid without modification for other space groups. New terms come in which have the same order of magnitude as the old. References to two papers *Acta Cryst.* **12**, 541 and 570 were given here.

In his reply to Bertaut's first point HAUPTMAN asserted that there were cases where the mathematical procedures which he and Karle had used could give an answer where Bertaut's system would not. He gave an example— to find the moments of cos (E). BERTAUT, with the aid of the blackboard, defended his viewpoint, apparently with success. HAUPTMAN then made the

v

point, which was well taken, that the pioneers in any field often do things in ways which are improved by later workers.

In answer to Bertaut's third point HAUPTMAN said that he disagreed and that the terms which he ignored were of much smaller magnitude than suggested by Bertaut. Since Bertaut's paper was not available at the time it was agreed to cease discussion on that point. It was raised again, however.

M. M. WOOLFSON then stated that as time passed he found less and less to dispute with Karle and Hauptman. However, he did find more and more that he had to interpret their formulae and criteria in terms of functions related to electron density. Thus when these workers referred to the rational independence of atomic coordinates they are indirectly referring to a resolved Patterson function. The fact that E_{2h}^2 may be larger than unity, and thus require renormalization, can be explained in terms of $r_i - r_j$ vectors overlapping $2r_j$ vectors in the Patterson function.

Some further discussion ensued concerning one of Hauptman's equations for $P1$. W. COCHRAN said that he believed he had given a Patterson-function interpretation of the formula involving $| E_1 E_2 E_3 | \cos (\phi_1 + \phi_2 + \phi_3)$. This approach is useful in assessing the likely scope of such formulae.

W. N. LIPSCOMB asked for an account of the structures solved by sign-determining methods. HAUPTMAN mentioned some structures including dimethoxybenzophenone and spurrite. LIPSCOMB then asked if they understood why the formulae had failed in the case of cellobiose. HAUPTMAN said that cases sometimes occurred where the formulae available could not deal with the situation. However, he felt sure that, in time, better sign-determining formulae would be found to deal with such cases.

Papers 22 and 23

(Read by W. COCHRAN and M. M. WOOLFSON)

In reply to G. A. JEFFREY'S question about applying his method three-dimensionally, COCHRAN replied that such an extension was possible though it would require much machine-time. It would be desirable to supply some information about the molecular geometry so as to restrict the number of three-dimensional syntheses needing to be calculated and assessed.

D. F. GRANT described a successful three-dimensional application of sign-relations, this being programmed on PEGASUS; it led to 154 correct signs out of 158, for a structure already known.

In reply to a question by E. F. BERTAUT, COCHRAN explained that the extent to which Sayre's equation holds is calculated only after signs have been allocated to all possible unitary structure factors, except the smallest.

W. HOPPE mentioned a case where the phase problem was easily solvent in projection, despite heavy overlap of atoms, because the overlap was almost exact, so that the projected structure resembled one with fewer atoms.

K. DORNBERGER-SCHIFF pointed out that successful elucidation of a structure in one projection followed by failure in other projections might be due to some form of stacking-disorder or micro-twinning; sometimes such disorder does not produce diffuse scattering strong enough to be detected, but it may be recognized by anomalous systematic absences.

C. H. CARLISLE, commenting on the failure to recognize the correct projected structure of glutathione, pointed out that this structure was finally solved directly from three-dimensional Fourier syntheses, sulphur being used as heavy atom. Weighting methods, such as those described by Sim, would probably have led to a quicker solution.

Paper 24

(Read by G. A. SIM)

G. KARTHA stressed the potentialities of the isomorphous-replacement method, as compared with the heavy-atom, for solving non-centrosymmetric structures. SIM agreed but pointed out that it implies collecting and estimating twice as many intensity data. He added: " In the non-centrosymmetrical case of the isomorphous-replacement method the use of both phase angles $(\alpha_H \pm \phi)$ derived from only two derivatives is equivalent to a heavy-atom method with the structure amplitudes weighted by a factor $(\cos \phi)$, since

$$A = |F| \cos (\alpha_H + \phi) + |F| \cos (\alpha_H - \phi)$$
$$= 2 |F| \cos \phi \cos \alpha_H,$$
$$B = |F| \sin (\alpha_H + \phi) + |F| \sin (\alpha_H - \phi)$$
$$= 2 |F| \cos \phi \sin \alpha_H.\text{"}$$

W. HOPPE mentioned a development of the heavy-atom weighting function as a power series. Two points were of special note: (a) A Fourier series calculated with a weighting function is equivalent to a sum of image functions, the first term being the ordinary sum-function, and the other terms are sum-functions of higher-power Patterson functions.

(b) When the heavy atom serves only to define phases with low accuracy, the first term is predominant, so that the synthesis is a good approximation to the ordinary sum-function, which is well known not to be the best image-seeking function. (A note on this development is to appear in *Acta Cryst.* or in *Z. Krist.*)

Papers 25 and 26

(Read by R. E. DICKERSON and M. G. ROSSMANN)

D. M. BLOW: " The following remarks result from work jointly between M. G. Rossmann and myself. They serve to link together some of the ideas of Sim's paper with the last paper.

Dickerson's equation (9) can be rewritten, with the use of equation (8) and neglecting terms of order ϵ^2, in the form

$$P(\phi)d\phi \propto \exp\{c_j \cos(\phi - \alpha_j) - d_j \cos 2(\phi - \alpha_j)\}d\phi,$$

where

$$c_j = \frac{(F_{Hj}^2 - f_j^2 - F^2)Ff_j}{2F_{Hj}^2 E^2}; d_j = \frac{F^2 f_j^2}{4F_{Hj}^2 E^2},$$

and where the heavy atom contribution has magnitude f_j and phase α_j.

Sim's result for the heavy-atom method may be written

$$P(\phi)d\phi \propto \exp\{c_H \cos(\phi - \alpha_H)\}d\phi,$$

where $c_H = 2Ff_H/\Sigma f_L^2$, and the known part of the structure factor has magnitude f_H and phase α_H. This has the same form as the first term of the previous equation. The second term is needed to give a double peak in the probability distribution, corresponding to the familiar ambiguity of the isomorphous replacement method.

The combination of several isomorphous replacements, as expressed by Dickerson's equation (11), can be shown to lead to

$$P(\phi)d\phi \propto \exp\{C \cos(\phi - \alpha_I) - D \cos 2(\phi - \alpha_{II})\}d\phi,$$

where the vectors C and D with phases α_I and $2\alpha_{II}$ are obtained by vector addition of the vectors (c_j, α_j) and $(d_j, 2\alpha_j)$:

$$(C, \alpha_I) = \sum_j (c_j, \alpha_j); \quad (D, 2\alpha_{II}) = \sum_j (d_j, 2\alpha_j).$$

From the computing point of view, this is a convenient way of avoiding a lengthy numerical integration which begins by computing $\epsilon(\phi)_j$ for every compound at 5° intervals of ϕ. Instead, only the quantities C, D, $\alpha_I - \alpha_{II}$ are involved in the numerical integration, which can thus be evaluated much more rapidly or looked up in a three-dimensional table.

There are more important consequences which follow from having the isomorphous replacement results and the heavy atom method results in the same form. Consider the situation, which has actually now begun to arise in protein work, where a large number of atomic positions are known, but the structure has not been fully solved. In any refinement procedure, should one use the phases of the known part of the structure, as in the B12 refinement, or the phases derived from isomorphous replacement? The probability approach shows that one can do better than either of these by multiplying by the corresponding probability functions. This can be done by adding in a vector c_H with phase α_H into the summation for the vector (C, α_I) given above, leaving the result in just the same mathematical form. As refinement proceeds, and more of the structure is known, the vector c_H becomes larger, and finally dominates the summation."

M. M. WOOLFSON: " The choice of the weighted sum of two possible F's rather than the more probable one is governed by other factors than a desire to obtain a maximum peak height in the calculated function. Choosing the more probable one does in fact give peaks of the same height; but, because the terms going into the summation are of higher amplitude, the peaks appear against larger background fluctuations and are therefore less well defined."

H. N. SHRIVASTAVA: " Can we have some idea of the accuracy of the temperature-factor parameters of the heavy atom used in the initial (6 Å) work? I wonder whether the observation that the figure of merit behaves like an artificial temperature factor in its relationship with $\sin^2\theta$ is due to undetected errors in these heavy atom parameters." DICKERSON: " We have refined the heavy atom parameters in two independent ways: one by trial-and-error least squares refinement with a centric projection; the other by a three-dimensional least squares method developed by Rossmann, both summarized in the preprint. It was found that the temperature factors were in reasonably good agreement; disagreement arose with the effective atomic numbers, Z. As was mentioned in the preprint, Rossmann's Z's were around 10–20% greater than the ones which were in fact used. This may be the cause of the holes and diffraction ripples actually found on the 24° Fourier synthesis, and this is being worked on at the present time.

Therefore it is less likely that there are errors in heavy atom temperature factors than in Z's. Even if some error were present, one would still expect a radial fall-off of $<m>$ with $(2 \sin \theta)^2$ simply because of the greater errors and lesser reliability of the data farther out in reciprocal space."

R. E. DICKERSON: " It may be of interest to mention that the vector Fourier coefficients used by Rossmann and Blow in their haemoglobin synthesis based on only two compounds were the vectors to the centre of gravity of the probability distribution with its two-fold ambiguity. Since this centroid vector must lie along the heavy atom vector direction, this amounts to doing a weighted heavy atom synthesis, with the weight of each term being the cosine of the error in phase angle involved in assuming the phase of the entire molecule to be that of the heavy atom."

D. P. SHOEMAKER: " I should like to raise the question whether, with only *two* compounds (namely the parent compound and an isomorphous non-centric two-heavy-atom compound), one can dispense with the Harker procedure (i.e. *accept* the ambiguities) and, calculating figures of merit by the Dickerson procedure, get a result which is approximately as good as that obtained by Rossmann with the minimum function method." ROSSMANN replied that this had been tried and the answer was in the affirmative.

G. KARTHA: " I would like to mention that about five years back (Kartha, G. and Ramachandran, G. N. (1955) *Acta Cryst.* **8,** 195) we showed that, by superposition methods based on one isomorphous crystal, the original structure could be recovered from a Patterson map from which light atom interaction had been removed, provided one knew the position of the replaceable group. If there is only one replaceable atom in a general position in the asymmetric unit, then this can be done in all space groups, both centrosymmetric and non-centrosymmetric, except for the 11 non-centric space groups P_1, P_2, $P2_1$, C_2, Pm, Pc, Cm, Ce, P_4, I_4 and P_6. In these cases the structure, accompanied by its inverse, is also obtained. However, even this ambiguity for these space groups can be resolved if we have more than one replaceable atom per asymmetric unit, so that all replaceable atoms in the unit cell together form a non-centrosymmetric grouping of atoms. Recently I have shown how the same results could be arrived at by working in reciprocal space, as Dr. Dickerson does, instead of real space." ROSSMANN agreed that this method was effectively equivalent to what he and Blow had done.

Papers 27 and 28

(Read by V. VAND and Y. OKAYA)

VAND replied in the negative to a question from D. H. TEMPLETON whether the second atom was excluded from points too close to the first. H. J. MILLEDGE: " Is it necessary to generate a completely random set of atoms? Can one not make use of chemical information and insert primitive groups of atoms (pairs, triplets, tetrahedral groups, for example) to reduce the number of independent units to be randomly situated? " VAND replied that this had not yet been done.

D. M. BLOW: " The ambiguity referred to in the quadratic solution method is exactly analogous to the ambiguity which arises in the single isomorphous replacement method referred to earlier today, in the discussion of Rossmann's paper. If there is a non-centrosymmetric arrangement of anomalous scatterers, the partial solution of the phase problem offered by this method is sufficient to give a Fourier similar to the true Fourier, but containing a background of " noise " terms. This result has also been found independently by Dr. Kartha. I believe that this method is superior to $P_s(u)$ method in complicated structures where $P_s(u)$ becomes hard to de-convolute because of overlapping peaks."

G. KARTHA: " Clearly the use of the anomalous-scattering method is extremely powerful for the solution of non-centrosymmetric structures, and we owe a lot to Pepinsky and Okaya for pointing out its importance. However, it may be pointed out that, instead of going to the solution through the real space function $P_s(u)$ and de-convoluting it, exactly the same could be arrived at by using $\mid F_H \mid^2 - \mid F_{\bar{H}} \mid^2$ directly to determine the phases of the reflections. It is not necessary to have the reflections on an absolute scale if one is interested only in obtaining all the results that are derivable from $\mid F_H \mid^2 - \mid F_{\bar{H}} \mid^2$ or the $P_s(u)$ function."

H. J. MILLEDGE: " How many structures in which the anomalous dispersion effect is large enough to be useful could have been solved by using the phases of the heavy anomalous scatterer alone? " R. PEPINSKY replied that in general the heavy-atom method alone would not have been adequate.

LIST OF PARTICIPANTS

ABRAHAMS, Dr. S. C., Bell, Murray Hill
AHMED, Dr. F. R., Ottawa
ARNOTT, Dr. S., Glasgow
ÅKESON, Mr. A., Stockholm
ÅSBRINK, Mr. S., Stockholm
BÄHR, Dr. S., Berlin
BERTAUT, Dr. E. F., Grenoble
BEZJAK, Dr. A., Zagreb
BLAIR, Mr. J., Glasgow (Comp. Lab.)
BLAND, Dr. J. A., Welwyn
BLOW, Dr. D. M., Cambridge
BROWN, Dr. C. J., Blackley
BRUMBERGER, Dr. H., Syracuse
CARLISLE, Dr. C. H., London
CLUNIE, Mr. J. S., Glasgow
COCHRAN, Dr. W., Cambridge
COULTER, Dr. C. L., Cambridge
COWLEY, Dr. J. M., Melbourne
CRUICKSHANK, Dr. D. W. J., Leeds
DAVIE, Mr. A. W., Glasgow
DAWSON, Dr. B., Melbourne
DENNERY, Mr. A., Paris
DICKERSON, Dr. R. E., Illinois
DORNBERGER-SCHIFF, Prof. K., Berlin
DREVER, Mr. E. L., Glasgow
DUNITZ, Prof. J. D., Zürich
FEIL, Mr. D., Pittsburgh
FERGUSON, Mr. G., Glasgow
FULLER, Dr. W., London
GILLES, Dr. D. C., Glasgow (Comp. Lab.)
GOODWIN, Dr. T. H., Glasgow
GRANT, Dr. D. F., Cardiff
HAMOR, Dr. T. A., Glasgow
HAUPTMAN, Dr. H. A., Washington
VAN DER HELM, Dr. D., Amsterdam
HERBSTEIN, Dr. F. H., Pretoria
HOEHNE, Dr. E., Berlin
HOPPE, Prof. W., Munich
IBALL, Dr. J., Dundee
IITAKA, Dr. Y., Berne
JAGGI, Dr. H., Berne
JEFFREY, Prof. G. A., Pittsburgh
JENSEN, Dr. L. H., Seattle
KANDA, Dr. F., Syracuse
KARTHA, Dr. G., Buffalo
KATZ, Dr. J. L., London
KENDREW, Dr. J. C., Cambridge

KENNARD, Dr. O., Mill Hill
KING, Mr. G. S. D., Brussells
LADELL, Dr. J., Irvington-on-Hudson
LEECH, Mr. J., Glasgow (Comp. Lab.)
LEVY, Dr. H. A., Oak Ridge
LIMINGA, Mr. R., Uppsala
LIPSCOMB, Prof. W. N., Harvard
LÖFGREN, Mr. T., Uppsala
LOW, Miss A., Glasgow (Comp. Lab.)
McGAVIN, Dr. S., Dundee
McMULLAN, Dr. R. K., Pittsburgh
McPHAIL, Mr. A. T., Glasgow
MARVIN, Dr. D. A., London
MATKOVIĆ, Dr. B., Zagreb
MILLEDGE, Drs. D. and H. J., London
MILLS, Dr. O. S., Manchester
MUIRHEAD, Miss H., Cambridge
MURRAY, Mr. I., Glasgow
NIGGLI, Dr. A., Zürich
NITTA, Prof. I., Osaka
OKAYA, Prof. Y., Penn. State
OLOVSSON, Dr. I., Uppsala
OWSTON, Dr. P. G., Welwyn
PAUL, Mr. I. C., Glasgow
PAULING, Dr. P., London
PEPINSKY, Prof. R., Penn. State
PILLING, Miss D. E., Leeds
RICHARDS, Dr. B., Wilton
ROBERTSON, Prof. J. M., Glasgow
ROGERS, Dr. D., Cardiff
ROLLETT, Dr. J. S., Oxford
ROSSMANN, Dr. M. G., Cambridge
ROWE, Dr. J. M., Welwyn
RUNDLE, Dr. R. E., Iowa
SADANAGA, Prof. R., Tokyo
ŠĆAVNIČAR, Dr. S., Zagreb
SCHEMMEL, Mr. H., Berlin
SHEARER, Dr. H. M. M., Durham
SHOEMAKER, Prof. D. P., M.I.T.
SHRIVASTAVA, Dr. H. N., Glasgow
SIM, Dr. G. A., Glasgow
SIME, Dr. J. G., Glasgow
SIMPSON, Miss M. L., Glasgow (Comp. Lab.)
SÖRUM, Dr. H., Trondheim
SPARKS, Dr. R. A., Los Angeles
SPEAKMAN, Dr. J. C., Glasgow

320

STRANDBERG, Dr. B., Uppsala
SUTHERLAND, Miss S., Glasgow
SUTTON, Mr. P. W., Wisconsin
TEMPLETON, Dr. D. H., Berkeley
TOLLIN, Mr. P., Cambridge
TROTTER, Dr. J., Glasgow
VAND, Prof. V., Penn. State
WALKER, Dr. G., Leeds
WATSON, Dr. D. G., Glasgow
WELLS, Mr. M., Cambridge

WESTMAN, Mr. S., Stockholm
WILL, Dr. G., Munich
WILLIAMS, Mr. D. G., Glasgow (Comp. Lab.)
WILLIS, Dr. B. T. M., Harwell
WOOD, Mr. J. S., North Staffordshire
WOOLFSON, Dr. M. M., Manchester
WUNDERLICH, Dr. J., Harvard
WYLIE, Mr. T. S., Glasgow
ZALKIN, Dr. A., Lawrence Lab.

INDEX